Test Item File

Quantitative Analysis for Management

Test Item File

Quantitative Analysis for Management

Ninth Edition

Barry Render
Ralph M. Stair Jr.
Michael E. Hanna

John Large *University of South Florida*
Lee Revere *University of Houston*

Upper Saddle River, New Jersey 07458

VP/Editorial Director: Jeff Shelstad
Executive Editor: Mark Pfaltzgraff
Managing Editor: Alana Bradley
Supplements Coordinator : Audrey Regan Solarino
Senior Editorial Assistant : Jane Avery
Manufacturing Manager: Christy Mahon
Director of Manufacturing: Vincent Scelta
Production Editor & Buyer: Carol O'Rourke
Printer/Binder: Courier, Bookmart Press

10 9 8 7 6 5 4 3 2 1
ISBN 0-13-185192-6

BRIEF CONTENTS

CD-ROM Modules

CHAPTER 1
Introduction to Quantitative Analysis

TRUE/FALSE

1.1 Interviews, statistical sampling, and company reports provide input data for quantitative analysis models.

ANSWER: TRUE

1.2 In many cases, acquiring input data is one of the most important and most difficult steps in the scientific method.

ANSWER: TRUE

1.3 Managers do not need to be familiar with the limitations, assumptions, and/ or specific applicability of the quantitative analysis technique to use it for accurate decision making.

ANSWER: FALSE

1.4 The primary purpose of quantitative analysis should be to gain a greater understanding of the problem, not to automate decision making.

ANSWER: TRUE

1.5 The quantitative analysis approach always results in a single solution.

ANSWER: FALSE

1.6 A quantitative model can be a mathematical representation of a situation.

ANSWER: TRUE

1.7 A mathematical model shows the relationship between quantifiable and non-quantifiable information.

ANSWER: FALSE

1.8 Decision variables may also be called parameters.

ANSWER: FALSE

1.9 Model variables can be controllable or uncontrollable.

ANSWER: TRUE

1.10 A series of steps or procedures that are repeated is known as an algorithm.

ANSWER: TRUE

1.11 The process of repeating the steps of an algorithm is called *doubling*.

ANSWER: FALSE

1.12 The processing and manipulating of raw data into meaningful information is the heart of quantitative analysis.

ANSWER: TRUE

1.13 Quantitative analysis tools are sometimes helpful even when a problem appears to have only a single alternative.

ANSWER: TRUE

1.14 All problems can be solved by considering only the quantitative issues.

ANSWER: FALSE

1.15 A profit equation is an example of a schematic model.

ANSWER: FALSE

1.16 Testing the data and model should be done before the results have been analyzed.

ANSWER: TRUE

1.17 Sensitivity analysis helps us estimate the effect of known and unknown errors in our model.

ANSWER: TRUE

1.18 Models can help us analyze a problem and sell a decision to those who must implement it.

ANSWER: TRUE

1.19 A sensitivity analysis allows a manager to answer the "what if" questions.

ANSWER: TRUE

1.20 One problem in using a quantitative model is that the necessary data may be unavailable.

ANSWER: TRUE

MULTIPLE CHOICE

1.21 Which of the following are reasons that a quantitative analysis technique might fail to solve a problem?

(a) underestimating the total cost of developing the model
(b) defining specific and measurable problem objectives
(c) underestimating the total time required to implement the solution
(d) sensitivity analysis shows changes in the model parameters results in changes to the solution.
(e) all of the above
(f) none of the above

ANSWER: f

1.22 Who is credited with pioneering the principles of the scientific approach to management?

(a) Adam Smith
(b) Henri Fayol
(c) John R. Locke
(d) Frederick W. Taylor
(e) Charles Babbage

ANSWER: d

1.23 A(n) ____________ is an abstract representation of reality or of a real-life situation.

(a) objective
(b) model
(c) analysis
(d) algorithm
(e) none of the above

ANSWER: b

1.24 A measurable quantity that may vary, or is subject to change, and can be controlled, is known as a(n)

(a) decision variable.
(b) algorithm.
(c) parameter.
(d) solution.
(e) none of the above

ANSWER: a

1.25 A set of logical and mathematical operations performed in a specific sequence is called a(n)

(a) complete enumeration.
(b) diagnostic analysis.
(c) algorithm.
(d) objective.
(e) none of the above

ANSWER: c

1.26 The variability of a solution to changes in the model and input data is an important part of the analysis of the results. This type of analysis is called ___________ analysis.

(a) sensitivity
(b) implicit
(c) normal
(d) scale
(e) objective

ANSWER: a

1.27 Expressing profits through the relationship among unit price, fixed costs, and variable costs is an example of

(a) a sensitivity analysis model.
(b) a quantitative analysis model.
(c) a postoptimality relationship.
(d) a parameter specification model.
(e) none of the above

ANSWER: b

1.28 A decision support system

(a) replaces conventional decision making.
(b) supports managerial decision making.
(c) is exactly the same as an expert system.
(d) does not allow for "what-if" scenarios.
(e) none of the above

ANSWER: b

1.29 Which of the following statement(s) are true regarding the advantages of mathematical modeling:

(a) Models accurately represent reality.
(b) Models can help decision makers formulate problems.
(c) Models can save time.
(d) Models may be the only way to solve some large and complex problems in a timely manner.
(e) all of the above

ANSWER: e

1.30 Which of the following statement(s) are true regarding the disadvantages of mathematical modeling?

(a) Models down play the importance of non-quantitative information.
(b) Models do not allow for changes in the parameters.
(c) Models do not oversimplify the real world variables.
(d) Models allow managers to ask "what if" questions.
(e) none of the above

ANSWER: a

1.31Managers can use mathematical modeling to

(a) gain insight into the nature of business relationships.
(b) answer "what if" questions.
(c) simulate business scenarios without the expense of real world implementation.
(d) reduce and/or understand the uncertainty that surrounds business actions.
(e) all of the above

ANSWER: e

1.32 All of the following terms are interchangeable except

(a) quantitative analysis.
(b) operations research.
(c) management science.
(d) research management.
(e) none of the above

ANSWER: d

1.33 Models that do not involve risk or chance are

(a) probabilistic models.
(b) postoptimality models.
(c) deterministic models.
(d) MIS models.
(e) none of the above

ANSWER: c

1.34 Which of the following could be good source(s) of data for use in model development?

(a) a well developed management information system
(b) workers who have been performing the task of interest or making the necessary decision
(c) information from government sources
(d) consumer market surveys
(e) all of the above

ANSWER: e

1.35 Postoptimality analysis is most closely associated with

(a) collecting input data.
(b) developing a model.
(c) sensitivity analysis.
(d) writing a computer program.
(e) none of the above

ANSWER: c

1.36 The breakeven point is an example of a

(a) postoptimality model.
(b) quantitative analysis model.
(c) schematic model.
(d) sensitivity analysis model.
(e) none of the above

ANSWER: b

1.37 A controllable variable is also called a

(a) parameter.
(b) decision variable.
(c) mathematical model.
(d) measurable quantity.
(e) none of the above

ANSWER: b

1.38 Evaluating all possible values of a variable in a model is called

(a) trial and error.
(b) complete enumeration.
(c) an algorithm.
(d) variablization.
(e) none of the above

ANSWER: b

1.39 Most of the models discussed in this book are

(a) schematic.
(b) scale models.
(c) physical models.
(d) mathematical models.
(e) none of the above

ANSWER: d

1.40 The statement, "Houston faces extreme air pollution problems due to its large commuter population and lack of public railways" represents what step in quantitative analysis?

(a) defining the problem
(b) acquiring input data
(c) testing the solution
(d) developing the solution
(e) all of the above

ANSWER: a

1.41 The primary purpose of quantitative models is to

(a) generate specific numbers for decision making.
(b) help the decision-maker gain insight into the important relationships involved in the decision.
(c) force the problem solver to adequately define the problem.
(d) automate the decision-making process.
(e) none of the above

ANSWER: b

1.42 In developing a quantitative model, it is most important to

(a) be especially good at mathematics.
(b) be especially good at using computers.
(c) be directly working the "problem" area of the business.
(d) represent reality as accurately as possible.
(e) none of the above

ANSWER: d

1.43 As one attempts to develop a model, which of the following problems is she likely to encounter?

(a) The problem may not fit a textbook approach.
(b) There will be no data available to test the model.
(c) Not everyone will understand the problem in the same way.
(d) all of the above
(e) none of the above

ANSWER: d

1.44 When a solution is implemented,

(a) we can be reasonably certain that unknown errors in the model will cause the suggested solution to fail.
(b) feedback should be provided to the analyst so that she may improve the model.
(c) the analyst's job is complete.
(d) the analyst should assume that the solution provided by the model was accurate.
(e) all of the above

ANSWER: b

SHORT ANSWER/ESSAY

1.45 Quantitative analysis is ________.

ANSWER: the scientific approach to managerial decision-making

1.46 A proposed building mock-up, technical drawings of gears, schematic diagrams, and algorithms are examples of ________.

ANSWER: models

1.47 A controllable variable is also called a ________ variable.

ANSWER: decision

1.48 The cost of placing an order for additional inventory items is an example of a ________.

ANSWER: parameter

1.49 Data stored in a company's accounting information system is an example of ________ data.

ANSWER: quantitative or input

1.50 In making a decision, both ________ and quantitative factors must be considered.

ANSWER: qualitative

1.51 Inaccurate model input data leads to inaccurate model solutions. This phenomena is commonly referred to as ________.

ANSWER: garbage in, garbage out

1.52 The solution process of ________ implies that we look at all possible solutions.

ANSWER: complete enumeration

1.53 Once we have a solution, we should then perform ________ analysis.

ANSWER: sensitivity or postoptimality

1.54 ________ models do not involve risk or chance.

ANSWER: Deterministic

CHAPTER 2
Probability Concepts and Applications

TRUE/FALSE

2.1 Subjective probability implies that we can measure the relative frequency of the values of the random variable.

ANSWER: FALSE

2.2 The use of "expert opinion" is one way to approximate subjective probability values.

ANSWER: TRUE

2.3 Mutually exclusive events exist if only one of the events can occur on any one trial.

ANSWER: TRUE

2.4 Stating that two events are statistically independent means that the probability of one event occurring is independent of the probability of the other event having occurred.

ANSWER: TRUE

2.5 Saying that a set of events is collectively exhaustive implies that one of the events must occur.

ANSWER: TRUE

2.6 Saying that a set of events is mutually exclusive and collectively exhaustive implies that one and only one of the events can occur on any trial.

ANSWER: TRUE

2.7 A posterior probability is a revised probability.

ANSWER: TRUE

2.8 Bayes' rule enables us to calculate the probability that one event takes place knowing that a second event has or has not taken place.

ANSWER: TRUE

2.9 A probability density function is a mathematical way of describing Bayes' Theorem.

ANSWER: FALSE

2.10 The probability, P, of any event or state of nature occurring is greater than or equal to 0 and less than or equal to 1.

ANSWER: TRUE

2.11 The probability of the sum of two variables is the sum of the probability of the two variables.
ANSWER: FALSE

2.12 If two events are mutually exclusive, the probability of both events occurring is simply the sum of the individual probabilities.

ANSWER: FALSE

2.13 Given two statistically dependent events (A,B), the conditional probability of $p(A|B) = p(B)/p(AB)$.

ANSWER: FALSE

2.14 Given two statistically independent events (A,B), the joint probability of $P(AB) = P(A) + P(B)$.

ANSWER: FALSE

2.15 Given three statistically independent events (A,B,C), the joint probability of $P(ABC) = P(A)*P(B)*P(C)$.

ANSWER: TRUE

2.16 Given two statistically independent events (A,B), the conditional probability of $P(A|B) = P(A)$.

ANSWER: TRUE

2.17 Assume that you have a box containing five balls: two red and three white. You draw a ball four times, each time replacing the ball just drawn before drawing the next. The probability of drawing a white ball is 1.0.

ANSWER: FALSE

2.18 Assume that you have a box containing five balls: two red and three white. You draw a ball two times, each time replacing the ball just drawn before drawing the next. The probability of drawing only one white ball is 0.20.

ANSWER: FALSE

2.19 If we roll a single die twice, the probability that the sum of the pips showing on the two rolls is four (4), is 1/6.

ANSWER: FALSE

2.20 If we have a single deck of cards, the drawing of a spade and a club are considered collectively exhaustive events.

ANSWER: FALSE

2.21 If we flip a coin three times, the probability of getting three heads is 0.125.

ANSWER: TRUE

2.22 If a bucket has three black balls and seven green balls, the probability that the second ball drawn (without replacement) will be green is 0.7.

ANSWER: FALSE

2.23 If a bucket has three black balls and seven green balls, and we draw balls without replacement, the probability of drawing a green ball is independent of the number of balls previously drawn.

ANSWER: FALSE

2.24 Assume that you have an urn containing 10 balls of the following description:

4 are white (W) and lettered (L)
2 are white (W) and numbered (N)
3 are yellow (Y) and lettered (L)
1 is yellow (Y) and numbered (N)

If you draw a numbered ball (N), the probability that this ball is white (W) is 0.667.

ANSWER: TRUE

2.25 Assume that you have an urn containing 10 balls of the following description:

4 are white (W) and lettered (L)
2 are white (W) and numbered (N)
3 are yellow (Y) and lettered (L)
1 is yellow (Y) and numbered (N)

If you draw a numbered ball (N), the probability that this ball is white (W) is 0.60.

ANSWER: FALSE

2.26 Assume that you have an urn containing 10 balls of the following description:

4 are white (W) and lettered (L)
2 are white (W) and numbered (N)
3 are yellow (Y) and lettered (L)
1 is yellow (Y) and numbered (N)

If you draw a lettered ball (L), the probability that this ball is white (W) is 0.70.

ANSWER: FALSE

2.27 An example of a discrete random variable might be the amount of rainfall during a particular storm.

ANSWER: FALSE

2.28 The number of bad checks written at a local store is an example of a discrete random variable.

ANSWER: TRUE

2.29 Given the following distribution

Outcome	Value of Random Variable	Probability
A	1	.4
B	2	.3
C	3	.2
D	4	.1

The expected value is 3.

ANSWER: FALSE

2.30 A new young executive is perplexed at the number of interruptions that occur due to employee relations. She has decided to track the number of interruptions that occur during each hour of her day. Over the last month, she has determined that between 0 and 3 interruptions occur during any given hour of her day. The data is shown below.

Number of Interruptions in 1 hour	**Probability**
0 interruption	.5
1 interruptions	.3
2 interruptions	.1
3 interruptions	.1

On average, she should expect 1 interruption per hour.

ANSWER: FALSE

2.31 A new young executive is perplexed at the number of interruptions that occur due to employee relations. She has decided to track the number of interruptions that occur during each hour of her day. Over the last month, she has determined that between 0 and 3 interruptions occur during any given hour of her day. The data is shown below.

Number of Interruptions in 1 hour	**Probability**
0 interruption	.4
1 interruptions	.3
2 interruptions	.2
3 interruptions	.1

On average, she should expect 1.0 interruptions per hour.

ANSWER: TRUE

2.32 The *expected value* of a binomial distribution is expressed as *np* where n equals the number of trials and p equals the probability of success of any individual trial.

ANSWER: TRUE

2.33 A national banking chain is evaluating the need for person-to-person drive-thru services. They are considering replacing drive-thru bank tellers with ATM machines during mid-day hours. Studies show that 16 percent of all drive thru transactions cannot be done with ATM machines and require in-person teller interaction. This problem can be solved using binomial distribution.

ANSWER: TRUE

2.34 A national banking chain is evaluating the need for person-to-person drive-thru services. They are considering replacing drive-thru bank tellers with ATM machines during mid-day hours. Studies show that 16 percent of all drive-thru transactions cannot be done with ATM machines and require in-person teller interaction. From this information, we can determine the probability that the next car using drive thru banking services that will require in-person teller interaction is 0.32.

ANSWER: FALSE

2.35 A national banking chain is evaluating the need for person-to-person drive-thru services. They are considering replacing drive-thru bank tellers with ATM machines during mid-day hours. Studies show that 16 percent of all drive-thru transactions cannot be done with ATM machines and requires in-person teller interaction. From this information, we can determine the probability that the next car using drive-thru banking services that will require in-person teller interaction is 0.16.

ANSWER: TRUE

2.36 A national banking chain is evaluating the need for person-to-person drive-thru services. They are considering replacing drive-thru bank tellers with ATM machines during mid-day hours. Studies show that 16 percent of all drive-thru transactions cannot be done with ATM machines and require in-person teller interaction. From this information, we can determine that the probability that one of the next two cars using drive-thru banking services that will require in-person teller interaction is 0.50.

ANSWER: FALSE

2.37 A national banking chain is evaluating the need for person-to-person drive-thru services. They are considering replacing drive-thru bank tellers with ATM machines during mid-day hours. Studies show that 16 percent of all drive-thru transactions cannot be done with ATM machines and require in-person teller interaction. From this information, we can determine that the probability that one of the next two cars using the drive-thru banking services that will require in-person teller interaction is 0.269.

ANSWER: TRUE

2.38 In a Normal distribution the Z value represents the number of standard deviations away from the mean that the X value is.

ANSWER: TRUE

2.39 Assume you have a Normal distribution representing the likelihood of completion times. The mean of this distribution is 10, and the standard deviation is 3. The probability of completing the project in 8 or fewer days is the same as the probability of completing the project in 18 days or more.

ANSWER: FALSE

2.40 Assume you have a Normal distribution representing the likelihood of completion times. The mean of this distribution is 10, and the standard deviation is 3. The probability of completing the project in 7 or fewer days is the same as the probability of completing the project in 13 days or more.

ANSWER: TRUE

MULTIPLE CHOICE

2.41 The classical method of determining probability is

(a) subjective probability.
(b) marginal probability.
(c) objective probability.
(d) joint probability.
(e) conditional probability.

ANSWER: c

2.42 Subjective probability assessments depend on

(a) the total number of trials.
(b) logic and past history.
(c) the relative frequency of occurrence.
(d) the number of occurrences of the event.
(e) experience and judgment.

ANSWER: e

2.43 If two events are mutually exclusive, then

(a) their probabilities can be added.
(b) they may also be collectively exhaustive.
(c) they cannot have a joint probability.
(d) if one occurs, the other cannot occur.
(e) all of the above

ANSWER: e

2.44 Which of the following situations is both mutually exclusive and collectively exhaustive?

(a) draw a diamond and a heart
(b) draw a 10 and a spade
(c) draw a face card and a number card
(d) draw a king and queen
(e) draw a red card and a heart

ANSWER: c

2.45 A conditional probability P(B|A) is equal to its marginal probability P(B) if

(a) it is a joint probability.
(b) statistical dependence exists.
(c) statistical independence exists.
(d) the events are mutually exclusive.
(e) P(A) = P(B).

ANSWER: c

2.46 The equation P(A|B) = P(AB)/P(B) is

(a) the marginal probability.
(b) equal to P(A).
(c) the formula for a conditional probability.
(d) an independent formula.
(e) none of the above

ANSWER: c

2.47 The equation P(A|B) = P(B)/P(AB) is

(a) the marginal probability.
(b) equal to 1/P(A).
(c) the formula for a conditional probability.
(d) an independent formula.
(e) none of the above

ANSWER: e

2.48 Bayes' Theorem is used to calculate

(a) revised probabilities.
(b) joint probabilities.
(c) prior probabilities.
(d) subjective probabilities.
(e) marginal probabilities.

ANSWER: a

2.49 If the sale of ice cream and pizza are independent, then as ice cream sales decrease by 60 percent during the winter months, pizza sales will

(a) increase by 60 percent.
(b) increase by 40 percent.
(c) decrease by 60 percent.
(d) cannot tell from information provided
(e) none of the above

ANSWER: d

2.50 If P(A) = 0.3, P(B) = 0.2, P(A and B) = 0.0 , what can be said about events A and B?

(a) They are independent.
(b) They are mutually exclusive.
(c) They are posterior probabilities.
(d) none of the above
(e) all of the above

ANSWER: b

2.51 Suppose that for a 5-year-old automobile, the probability the engine will need repair in year 6 is 0.3, while the probability that the tires need replacing in year 6 is 0.8. The probability that both the engine will need repair and the tires will need replacing in year 6 is 0.2. What is the probability that the tires will need to be replaced and the engine will need repair?

(a) 0.20
(b) 0.24
(c) 0.16
(d) 0.90
(e) none of the above

ANSWER: a

2.52 Suppose that for a 5 year old automobile, the probability the engine will need repair in year 6 is 0.3, while the probability that the tires need replacing in year 6 is 0.8. The probability that both the engine will need repair and the tires will need replacing in year 6 is 0.2. What is the probability that either the engine needs repair or the tires need replacing?

(a) 0.24
(b) 1.10
(c) 0.90
(d) 0.86
(e) none of the above

ANSWER: c

2.53 Suppose that for a 5 year old automobile, the probability the engine will need repair in year 6 is 0.3, while the probability that the tires need replacing in year 6 is 0.8. The probability that both the engine will need repair and the tires will need replacing in year 6 is 0.2. If it is known that the tires will need replacing, what is the probability that the engine needs repair?

(a) 0.67
(b) 0.25
(c) 0.16
(d) 0.90
(e) none of the above

ANSWER: b

2.54 Suppose that for a 5 year old automobile, the probability the engine will need repair in year 6 is 0.3, while the probability that the tires need replacing in year 6 is 0.8. The probability that both the engine will need repair and the tires will need replacing in year 6 is 0.2. If it is known that the engine needs repair, what is the probability that the tires will need replacing?

(a) 0.67
(b) 0.25
(c) 0.16
(d) 0.90
(e) none of the above

ANSWER: a

2.55 Suppose that for a 5 year old automobile, the probability the engine will need repair in year 6 is 0.3, while the probability that the tires need replacing in year 6 is 0.8. The probability that both the engine will need repair and the tires will need replacing in year 6 is 0.2. If it is known that the engine was repaired, what is the probability that the tires were also replaced?

(a) 0.67
(b) 0.25
(c) 0.16
(d) 0.90
(e) none of the above

ANSWER: a

2.56 A consulting firm has received 2 Super Bowl playoff tickets from one of its clients. To be fair, the firm is randomly selecting two different employee names to 'win' the tickets. There are 6 secretaries, 5 consultants and 4 partners in the firm. Which of the following statements is <u>not</u> true?

(a) The probability of a secretary winning a ticket on the first draw is 6/15.
(b) The probability of a secretary winning a ticket on the second draw given a consultant won a ticket on the first draw is 6/15.
(c) The probability of a consultant winning a ticket on the first draw is 1/3.
(d) The probability of two secretaries winning both tickets is 1/7.
(e) none of the above

ANSWER: b

2.57 A consulting firm has received 2 Super Bowl playoff tickets from one of its clients. To be fair, the firm is randomly selecting two different employee names to 'win' the tickets. There are 6 secretaries, 5 consultants, and 4 partners in the firm. Which of the following statements is true?

(a) The probability of a partner winning on the second draw given a partner won on the first draw is 3/14.
(b) The probability of a secretary winning on the second draw given a secretary won on the first draw is 2/15.
(c) The probability of a consultant winning on the second draw given a consultant won on the first draw is 5/14.
(d) The probability of a partner winning on the second draw given a secretary won on the first draw is 8/30.
(e) none of the above

ANSWER: a

2.58 A consulting firm has received 2 Super Bowl playoff tickets from one of its clients. To be fair, the firm is randomly selecting two different employee names to 'win' the tickets. There are 6 secretaries, 5 consultants, and 4 partners in the firm. Which of the following statements is true?

(a) The probability of two secretaries winning is the same as the probability of a secretary winning on the second draw given a consultant won on the first draw.
(b) The probability of a secretary and a consultant winning is the same as the probability of a secretary and secretary winning.
(c) The probability of a secretary winning on the second draw given a consultant won on the first draw is the same as the probability of a consultant winning on the second draw given a secretary won on the first draw.
(d) The probability that both tickets will be won by partners is the same as the probability that a consultant and secretary will win.
(e) None of the above.

ANSWER: b

2.59 At a university with 1,000 business majors, there are 200 business students enrolled in an introductory statistics course. Of these 200 students, 50 are also enrolled in an introductory accounting course. There are an additional 250 business students enrolled in accounting but not enrolled in statistics. If a business student is selected at random, what is the probability that the student is either enrolled in accounting or statistics, but not both?

(a) 0.45
(b) 0.50
(c) 0.40
(d) 0.05
(e) none of the above

ANSWER: c

2.60 At a university with 1,000 business majors, there are 200 business students enrolled in an introductory statistics course. Of these 200 students, 50 are also enrolled in an introductory accounting course. There are an additional 250 business students enrolled in accounting but not enrolled in statistics. If a business student is selected at random, what is the probability that the student is enrolled in accounting?

(a) 0.20
(b) 0.25
(c) 0.30
(d) 0.50
(e) none of the above

ANSWER: c

2.61 At a university with 1,000 business majors, there are 200 business students enrolled in an introductory statistics course. Of these 200 students, 50 are also enrolled in an introductory accounting course. There are an additional 250 business students enrolled in accounting but not enrolled in statistics. If a business student is selected at random, what is the probability that the student is enrolled in statistics?

(a) 0.05
(b) 0.20
(c) 0.25
(d) 0.30
(e) none of the above

ANSWER: b

2.62 At a university with 1,000 business majors, there are 200 business students enrolled in an introductory statistics course. Of these 200 students, 50 are also enrolled in an introductory accounting course. There are an additional 250 business students enrolled in accounting but not enrolled in statistics. If a business student is selected at random, what is the probability that the student is enrolled in both statistics and accounting?

(a) 0.05
(b) 0.06
(c) 0.20
(d) 0.25
(e) none of the above

ANSWER: a

2.63 At a university with 1,000 business majors, there are 200 business students enrolled in an introductory statistics course. Of these 200 students, 50 are also enrolled in an introductory accounting course. There are an additional 250 business students enrolled in accounting but not enrolled in statistics. If a business student is selected at random and found to be enrolled in statistics, what is the probability that the student is also enrolled in accounting?

(a) 0.05
(b) 0.30
(c) 0.20
(d) 0.25
(e) none of the above

ANSWER: d

2.64 At a university with 1,000 business majors, there are 200 business students enrolled in an introductory statistics course. Of these 200 students, 50 are also enrolled in an introductory accounting course. There are an additional 250 business students enrolled in accounting but not enrolled in statistics. Are the events "being enrolled in accounting" and "being enrolled in statistics" independent?

(a) yes
(b) no
(c) cannot be determined without more information
(d) all of the above
(e) none of the above

ANSWER: b

2.65 At a university with 1,000 business majors, there are 200 business students enrolled in an introductory statistics course. Of these 200, 50 are also enrolled in an introductory accounting course. There are an additional 250 business students enrolled in accounting but not enrolled in statistics. Are the events "being enrolled in accounting" and "being enrolled in statistics" mutually exclusive?

(a) yes
(b) no
(c) cannot be determined without more information
(d) all of the above
(e) none of the above

ANSWER: b

2.66 At a university with 1,000 business majors, there are 200 business students enrolled in an introductory statistics course. Of these 200, 50 are also enrolled in an introductory accounting course. There are an additional 250 business students enrolled in accounting but not enrolled in statistics. If a business student is selected at random, what is the probability that the student is enrolled in neither accounting nor statistics?

(a) 0.45
(b) 0.50
(c) 0.55
(d) 0.05
(e) none of the above

ANSWER: c

2.67 At a university with 1,000 business majors, there are 200 business students enrolled in an introductory statistics course. Of these 200, 50 are also enrolled in an introductory accounting course. There are an additional 250 business students enrolled in accounting but not enrolled in statistics. If a business student is selected at random, what is the probability that the student is not enrolled in accounting?

(a) 0.20
(b) 0.25
(c) 0.30
(d) 0.50
(e) none of the above

ANSWER: e

2.68 At a university with 1,000 business majors, there are 200 business students enrolled in an introductory statistics course. Of these 200, 50 are also enrolled in an introductory accounting course. There are an additional 250 business students enrolled in accounting but not enrolled in statistics. If a business student is selected at random, what is the probability that the student is not enrolled in statistics?

(a) 0.05
(b) 0.20
(c) 0.25
(d) 0.80
(e) none of the above

ANSWER: d

2.69 A production process is known to produce a particular item in such a way that 5 percent of these are defective. If two items are randomly selected as they come off the production line, what is the probability that the second item will be defective?

(a) 0.05
(b) 0.005
(c) 0.18
(d) 0.20
(e) none of the above

ANSWER: a

2.70 A production process is known to produce a particular item in such a way that 5 percent of these are defective. If two items are randomly selected as they come off the production line, what is the probability that both are defective (assuming that they are independent)?

(a) 0.010
(b) 0.100
(c) 0.200
(d) 0.025
(e) none of the above

ANSWER: d

2.71 A production process is known to produce a particular item in such a way that 5 percent of these are defective. These items are inspected but only 80 percent of all defective items are discovered by this inspection. What is the probability that a randomly selected item is tested and found to be defective?

(a) 0.08
(b) 0.10
(c) 0.04
(d) 0.20
(e) none of the above

ANSWER: c

2.72 When personal computers were introduced to the market, the computer hard drive failed 10 percent of the time. Although the hard drives were inspected, only 80 percent of all defective drives were discovered by this inspection. What is the probability that a randomly selected hard drive was tested and found to be defective?

(a) 0.08
(b) 0.10
(c) 0.80
(d) 0.20
(e) none of the above

ANSWER: a

2.73 When personal computers were introduced to the market, the computer hard drive failed 10 percent of the time. Although the hard drives were inspected, only 80 percent of all defective drives were discovered by this inspection. If two hard drives were randomly selected as they came off the production line, what is the probability that both were defective (assuming that they are independent)?

(a) 0.01
(b) 0.10
(c) 0.20
(d) 0.08
(e) none of the above

ANSWER: a

2.74 When personal computers were introduced to the market, the computer hard drive failed 10 percent of the time. Although the hard drives were inspected, only 80 percent of all defective drives were discovered by this inspection. If two hard drives were randomly selected as they came off the production line, what was the probability that exactly one of these (either the first one or the second one, but not both) was defective (assuming that they are independent)?

(a) 0.01
(b) 0.10
(c) 0.18
(d) 0.20
(e) none of the above

ANSWER: c

2.75 A dry cleaning business offers a pick-up and delivery service for a 10 percent surcharge. Management believes 60 percent of customers will take advantage of this service. They are also considering offering customers the option of opening an account and receiving monthly bills. They believe 60 percent of their customers (regardless of whether or not they use the pick-up service) will use the account service. If the two services are introduced to the market, what is the probability a customer uses both services?

(a) 0.12
(b) 0.60
(c) 0.36
(d) 0.24
(e) none of the above

ANSWER: c

2.76 A dry cleaning business offers a pick-up and delivery service for a 10 percent surcharge. Management believes 60 percent of the existing customers will take advantage of this service. They are also considering offering customers the option of opening an account and receiving monthly bills. They believe 60 percent of customers (regardless of whether or not they use the pick-up service) will use the account service. If the two services are introduced to the market, what is the probability that a customer uses only one of these services?

(a) 0.40
(b) 0.60
(c) 0.48
(d) 0.24
(e) none of the above

ANSWER: c

2.77 A dry cleaning business offers a pick-up and delivery service for a 10 percent surcharge. Management believes 60 percent of the existing customers will take advantage of this service. They are also considering offering customers the option of opening an account and receiving monthly bills. They believe 60 percent of customers (regardless of whether or not they use the pick-up service) will use the account service. If the two services are introduced to the market, what is the probability a customer uses neither of these services?

(a) 0.16
(b) 0.24
(c) 0.80
(d) 0.36
(e) none of the above

ANSWER: a

2.78 A dry cleaning business offers a pick-up and delivery service for a 10 percent surcharge. Management believes 60 percent of the existing customers will take advantage of this service. They are also considering offering customers the option of opening an account and receiving monthly bills. They believe 60 percent of customers (regardless of whether or not they use the pick-up service) will use the account service. Market research may be used to revise these probabilities. Based on market research, services were predicted to be successful 90 percent of the time. However, for services that failed, the market research predicted these would be successes 20 percent of the time. If market research is performed for the new pick up and delivery service, what is the probability that the results indicate a successful market for the product and the product actually is successful?

(a) 0.90
(b) 0.54
(c) 0.60
(d) 0.08
(e) none of the above

ANSWER: b

2.79 A dry cleaning business offers a pick-up and delivery service for a 10 percent surcharge. Management believes 60 percent of customers will take advantage of this service. They are also considering offering customers the option of opening an account and receiving monthly bills. They believe 60 percent of customers (regardless of whether or not they use the pick-up service) will use the account service. Market research may be used to revise these probabilities. Based on market research, services were predicted to be successful 90 percent of the time. However, for services that failed, the market research predicted these would be successes 20 percent of the time. If market research is performed for the new pick up and delivery service and the results indicate a successful market for the service, what is the probability that the service will actually be successful?

(a) 0.60
(b) 0.90
(c) 0.54
(d) 0.87
(e) none of the above

ANSWER: d

2.80 A company is considering producing two new electronic games designed for the popular Gameboy toy. Based on market data, management believes there is a 60 percent chance that a 'cops and robbers' game will be successful, and a 40 percent chance that a 'let's play house' game will be successful. As these products are completely different, it may be assumed that the success of one is totally independent of the success of the other. If two products are introduced to the market, what is the probability that both are successful?

(a) 0.12
(b) 0.60
(c) 0.36
(d) 0.24
(e) none of the above

ANSWER: d

2.81 A company is considering producing two new electronic games designed for the popular Gameboy toy. Based on market data, management believes that there is a 60 percent chance that a 'cops and robbers' game will be successful, and a 40 percent chance that 'let's play house' game will be successful. As these products are completely different, it may be assumed that the success of one is totally independent of the success of the other. If two products are introduced to the market, what is the probability that both are failures?

(a) 0.16
(b) 0.24
(c) 0.80
(d) 0.36
(e) none of the above

ANSWER: b

2.82 A company is considering producing some new Gameboy electronic games. Based on past records, management believes that there is a 70 percent chance that each of these will be successful, and a 30 percent chance of failure. Market research may be used to revise these probabilities. In the past, the successful products were predicted to be successful based on market research 90 percent of the time. However, for products that failed, the market research predicted these would be successes 20 percent of the time. If market research is performed for a new product, what is the probability that the results indicate a successful market for the product and the product actually is successful?

(a) 0.90
(b) 0.54
(c) 0.60
(d) 0.63
(e) none of the above

ANSWER: d

2.83 The expected value of a probability distribution is

(a) the measure of the spread of the distribution.
(b) the variance of the distribution.
(c) the average value of the distribution.
(d) the probability density function.
(e) the range of continuous values from point A to point B, inclusive.

ANSWER: c

2.84 Which of the following is not true for discrete random variables?

(a) The expected value is the weighted average of the values.
(b) They can assume only a countable number of values.
(c) The area under the curve equals one.
(d) The probability values always sum up to one.
(e) none of the above

ANSWER: c

2.85 The number of phone calls coming into a switchboard in the next five minutes will either be 0, 1, or 2. The probabilities are the same for each of these (1/3). If X is the number of calls arriving in a five-minute time period, what is the mean of X?

(a) 1/3
(b) 2/3
(c) 1
(d) 4/3
(e) none of the above

ANSWER: c

2.86 The number of phone calls coming into a switchboard in the next five minutes will either be 0, 1, 2, 3, 4, 5, or 6. The probabilities are the same for each of these (1/7). If X is the number of calls arriving in a five-minute time period, what is the mean of X?

(a) 2
(b) 3
(c) 4
(d) 5
(e) none of the above

ANSWER: b

2.87 A discrete random variable has a mean of 400 and a variance of 64. What is the standard deviation?

(a) 64
(b) 8
(c) 20
(d) 400
(e) none of the above

ANSWER: b

2.88 Which of the following is not true about continuous random variables?

(a) They have an infinite set of values.
(b) The area under each of the curves represents probabilities.
(c) The entire area under each of the curves equals one.
(d) Some may be described by uniform distributions or exponential distributions.
(e) They are useful for describing a discrete probability distribution.

ANSWER: e

2.89 Properties of the normal distribution include

(a) a continuous bell-shaped distribution.
(b) a discrete probability distribution.
(c) the number of trials is known and is either 1, 2, 3, 4, 5, etc.
(d) the random variable can assume only a finite or limited set of values.
(e) use in queuing.

ANSWER: a

2.90 Which of the following characteristics is true for a normal probability distribution?

(a) The area under the curve is one.
(b) It is symmetrical.
(c) The midpoint is also the mean.
(d) Sixty-eight percent of the area under the curve lies within one standard deviation of the mean.
(e) All of the above are true.

ANSWER: e

2.91 The number of cell phone minutes used by high school seniors follows a normal distribution with a mean of 500 and a standard deviation of 50. What is the probability that a student uses fewer than 600 minutes?

(a) 0
(b) 0.023
(c) 0.841
(d) 0.977
(e) none of the above

ANSWER: d

2.92 The number of cell phone minutes used by high school seniors follows a normal distribution with a mean of 500 and a standard deviation of 50. What is the probability that a student uses fewer than 400 minutes?

(a) 0
(b) 0.023
(c) 0.159
(d) 0.977
(e) none of the above

ANSWER: b

2.93 The number of cell phone minutes used by high school seniors follows a normal distribution with a mean of 500 and a standard deviation of 50. What is the probability that a student uses more than 350 minutes?

(a) 0.001
(b) 0.999
(c) 0.618
(d) 0.382
(e) none of the above

ANSWER: b

2.94 The number of cell phone minutes used by high school seniors follows a normal distribution with a mean of 500 and a standard deviation of 50. What is the probability that a student uses more than 580 minutes?

(a) 0.152
(b) 0.0548
(c) 0.848
(d) 0.903
(e) none of the above

ANSWER: b

2.95 Data for a particular subdivision near downtown Houston indicates the average price per square foot for a home is \$100 with a standard deviation of \$5. What is the probability that the average price per square foot for a home is greater than \$110?

(a) 0
(b) 0.023
(c) 0.841
(d) 0.977
(e) none of the above

ANSWER: b

2.96 Data for a particular subdivision near downtown Houston indicates the average price per square foot for a home is $100 with a standard deviation of $5. What is the probability that the average price per square foot for a home is greater than $90?

(a) 0
(b) 0.023
(c) 0.159
(d) 0.977
(e) none of the above

ANSWER: d

2.97 Data for a particular subdivision near downtown Houston indicates the average price per square foot for a home is $100 with a standard deviation of $5. What is the probability that the average price per square foot for a home is less than $85?

(a) 0.001
(b) 0.999
(c) 0.618
(d) 0.382
(e) none of the above

ANSWER: a

2.98 Data for a particular subdivision near downtown Houston indicates the average price per square foot for a home is $100 with a standard deviation of $5. What is the probability that the average price per square foot for a home is less than $108?

(a) 0.152
(b) 0.097
(c) 0.848
(d) 0.9452
(e) none of the above

ANSWER: d

2.99 The time required to complete a project is normally distributed with a mean of 80 weeks and a standard deviation of 10 weeks. The construction company must pay a penalty if the project is not finished by the due date in the contract. If a construction company bidding on this contract puts in a due date of 80 weeks, what is the probability that they will have to pay a penalty?

(a) 0
(b) 1.000
(c) 0.500
(d) 1/8
(e) none of the above

ANSWER: c

2.100 The time required to complete a project is normally distributed with a mean of 80 weeks and a standard deviation of 10 weeks. The construction company must pay a penalty if the project is not finished by the due date in the contract. If a construction company bidding on this contract wishes to be 90 percent sure of finishing by the due date, what due date (project week #) should be negotiated?

(a) 81.28
(b) 92.8
(c) 81.82
(d) .81954
(e) none of the above

ANSWER: b

2.101 The time required to travel downtown at 10am on Monday morning is known to be normally distributed with a mean of 40 minutes and a standard deviation of 5 minutes. What is the probability that it will take less than 40 minutes?

(a) 0.50
(b) 0.20
(c) 0.80
(d) 1.00
(e) none of the above

ANSWER: a

2.102 The time required to travel downtown at 10am on Monday morning is known to be normally distributed with a mean of 40 minutes and a standard deviation of 5 minutes. What is the probability that it will take less than 35 minutes?

(a) 0.84134
(b) 0.15866
(c) 0.53983
(d) 0.46017
(e) none of the above

ANSWER: b

2.103 The time required to travel downtown at 10am on Monday morning is known to be normally distributed with a mean of 40 minutes and a standard deviation of 5 minutes. What is the probability that it will take more than 40 minutes?

(a) 0.2500
(b) 0.0625
(c) 1.000
(d) 0.5000
(e) none of the above

ANSWER: d

2.104 Queuing Theory makes use of the

(a) normal probability distribution.
(b) uniform probability distribution.
(c) binomial probability distribution.
(d) Poisson probability distribution.
(e) none of the above

ANSWER: d

2.105 The number of cars passing through an intersection in the next five minutes can usually be described by the

(a) normal distribution.
(b) uniform distribution.
(c) exponential distribution.
(d) Poisson distribution.
(e) none of the above

ANSWER: d

2.106 Arrivals at a fast-food restaurant follow a Poisson distribution with a mean arrival rate of 16 customers per hour. What is the probability that in the next hour there will be exactly 12 arrivals?

(a) 0.0000
(b) 0.0661
(c) 0.7500
(d) 0.1322
(e) none of the above

ANSWER: b

2.107 Arrivals at a fast-food restaurant follow a Poisson distribution with a mean arrival rate of 16 customers per hour. What is the probability that in the next hour there will be exactly 8 arrivals?

(a) 1.000
(b) 0.200
(c) 0.175
(d) 0.825
(e) none of the above

ANSWER: e

2.108 Which of the following characteristics is not true for the exponential distribution?

(a) It is discrete probability distribution.
(b) It is also called the negative exponential distribution.
(c) It is used in dealing with queuing problems.
(d) It is used to describe the times between customer arrivals.
(e) The variance is the square of the expected value.

ANSWER: a

2.109 The length of time that it takes the tollbooth attendant to service each driver can typically be described by the

(a) normal distribution.
(b) uniform distribution.
(c) exponential distribution.
(d) Poisson distribution.
(e) none of the above

ANSWER: c

PROBLEMS

2.110 An urn contains 7 blue and 3 yellow chips. If the drawing of chips is done with replacement, determine the probability of:

(a) drawing three yellow chips
(b) drawing a blue chip on the first draw and a yellow chip on the second draw
(c) drawing a blue chip on the second draw given that a yellow chip was drawn on the first draw
(d) drawing a yellow chip on the second draw given that a blue chip was drawn on the first draw
(e) drawing a yellow chip on the second draw given that a yellow chip was drawn on the first draw

ANSWER: (a) 0.027 (b) 0.210 (c) 0.700 (d) 0.300 (e) 0.300

2.111 A market research study is being conducted to determine if a product modification will be well received by the public. A total of 1,000 consumers are questioned regarding this product. The table below provides information regarding this sample.

	Positive Reaction	Neutral Reaction	Negative Reaction
Male	240	60	100
Female	260	220	120

(a) What is the probability that a randomly selected male would find this change unfavorable (negative)?
(b) What is the probability that a randomly selected person would be a female who had a positive reaction?
(c) If it is known that a person had a negative reaction to the study, what is the probability that the person is male?

ANSWER: (a) 100/400 = 0.25 (b) 260/1000 = 0.260 (c) 100/220

2.112 In a production run of 200 units, there are exactly 10 defective items and 190 good items.

(a) What is the probability that a randomly selected item is defective?
(b) If two items are sampled without replacement, what is the probability that both are good?
(c) If two items are randomly sampled without replacement, what is the probability that the first is good but the second is defective?

ANSWER: (a) 10/200 = 0.05 (b) (190/200)(189/199) = 0.902 (c) (190/200)(10/199) = 0.048

2.113 A new television program was viewed by 200 people (120 females and 80 males). Of the females, 60 liked the program and 60 did not. Of the males, 60 of the 80 liked the program.

(a) What is the probability that a randomly selected individual liked the program?
(b) If a male in this group is selected, what is the probability that he liked the program?
(c) What is the probability that a randomly selected individual is a female and liked the program?

ANSWER: (a) 120/200 = 0.60 (b) 60/80 = 0.75 (c) 60/200 = 0.30

2.114 Colonel Motors (an automobile company) has prepared a marketing campaign for its best selling car. The focus of the campaign is quality, and it is claimed that 98 percent of the purchasers of this car have no complaints in the first year. You and your brother Theodore have each purchased one of these cars.

(a) What is the probability that neither of you has a complaint about the car in the first year if the advertising claim is true?
(b) What is the probability that exactly one of you has a complaint about the car in the first year if the advertising claim is true?

ANSWER: (a) 0.98(0.98) = 0.9604 (b) 0.02(0.98) + 0.98(0.02) = 0.0392

2.115 A local "home TV repair service" company has two repairmen who make all of the home repairs. The company sends Repairman D on 70 percent of all jobs, because the likelihood of a "second follow-up call" within a week is only 0.08 compared to 0.20 for Repairman K. If you had a recent repair job that is going to require a second follow-up call, what is the probability that Repairman K did your initial repair work?

ANSWER: P(K|2nd) = 0.06/0.116 = 0.517

2.116 Our department store is having a sale on personal computers, of which three are in stock (no rain checks). There is a certain probability of selling none. The probability of selling one is twice as great as the probability of selling none. The probability of selling two is three times the probability of selling none. Finally, the probability of selling all the personal computers is four times as great as the probability of selling none. In a table, list the outcomes and their probabilities. Hint: Let the probability of selling none equal x.

ANSWER:

Outcome	Probability
Sell 0	0.1
Sell 1	0.2
Sell 2	0.3
Sell 3	0.4

2.117 ABC Manufacturing has 6 machines that perform a particular task. Breakdowns occur frequently for this machine. Past records indicate that the number of breakdowns that occur each day is described by the following probability distribution:

Number of Breakdowns	Probability
0	0.4
1	0.3
2	0.2
3	0.1
More than 3	0.0

(a) What is the expected number of breakdowns in any given day?
(b) What is the variance for this distribution?
(c) What is the probability that there will be at least 2 breakdowns in a day?

ANSWER: (a) expected value = 1.0 (b) variance = 1.0 (c) P(2 or more) = 0.2 + 0.1 = 0.3

2.118 Fast Service Store has maintained daily sales records on the various size "Cool Drink" sales. Assuming that past performance is a good indicator of future sales,

"Cool Drink" Price	Number Sold
$0.50	75
$0.75	120
$1.00	125
$1.25	80
Total	400

(a) what is the probability of a customer purchasing a $1.00 "Cool Drink?"
(b) what is the probability of a customer purchasing a $1.25 "Cool Drink?"
(c) what is the probability of a customer purchasing a "Cool Drink" that costs greater than or equal to $1.00?
(d) what is the expected value of a "Cool Drink" ?
(e) what is the variance of a "Cool Drink" ?

ANSWER: (a) 125/400 = 0.3125 (b) 80/400 = 0.20 (c) 205/400 = 0.5125
(d) .88125 (e) 0.064

2.119 A southwestern tourist city has records indicating that the average daily temperature in the summer is 82 degrees F, which is normally distributed with a standard deviation of 3 degrees F. Based on these records, determine:

(a) the probability of a daily temperature between 79 degrees F and 85 degrees F
(b) the probability that the daily temperature exceeds 90 degrees F
(c) the probability that the daily temperature is below 76 degrees F

ANSWER: (a) $P(79<X<85) = 0.68268$ (b) $P(X>90) = 0.00379$ (c) $P(X<76) = 0.02275$

2.120 Using the table for finding the areas under normal curves, find the area under a normal curve with a mean of 200 and a standard deviation of 10 between the values of:

(a) 200 to 205
(b) 195 to 205
(c) 200 to 215
(d) 195 to 215
(e) 186.5 to 217

ANSWER: (a) 0.19146 (b) 0.38292 (c) 0.43319 (d) 0.62465 (e) 0.86692

2.121 The time required to complete a project is known to be normally distributed with a mean of 46 weeks and a standard deviation of 4 weeks.

(a) What is the probability that the project is finished in 40 weeks or fewer?
(b) What is the probability that the project is finished in 52 weeks or fewer?
(c) There is an 80 percent chance that the project will be finished in fewer than how many weeks?

ANSWER: (a) 0.06881 (b) 0.93319 (c) $46 + 0.84(4) = 49.36$

2.122 Arrivals in a university advising office during the week of registration are known to follow a Poisson distribution with an average of 4 people arriving each hour.

(a) What is the probability that exactly 4 people will arrive in the next hour?
(b) What is the probability that exactly 5 people will arrive in the next hour?

ANSWER: (a) $P(X=4) = 0.1952$ (b) $P(X=5) = 0.1563$

SHORT ANSWER/ESSAY

2.123 Explain why event probabilities range from zero to one.

ANSWER: Zero represents no chance of occurrence, while one represents a 100 percent chance of occurrence. Any number between zero and one represents that particular event's chance of occurrence. Any negative number or number exceeding one has no meaning for an event probability.

2.124 Using a standard deck of 52 cards, explain why the situation of drawing a 7 and a club is not collectively exhaustive.

ANSWER: It is possible to draw other cards that are non-clubs and also not a 7.

2.125 Using a standard deck of 52 cards, explain why the situation of drawing a 7 and a club is not mutually exclusive.

ANSWER: Only one of the 7s is a club.

2.126 If two events (A,B) are mutually exclusive, what is the probability of event A or event B occurring?

ANSWER: p(A or B) = p(A) + p(B)

2.127 If two events (A,B) are not mutually exclusive, what is the probability of event A or event B occurring?

ANSWER: p(A or B) = p(A) + p(B) - p(A and B)

2.128 If two events (A,B) are independent, what is their joint probability?

ANSWER: p(AB) = p(A) p(B)

2.129 If two events (A,B) are dependent, what is the conditional probability of p(A|B)?

ANSWER: p(A|B) = p(AB)/p(B)

2.130 If two events (A,B) are independent, then the conditional probability of p(A|B) =

ANSWER: p(A)

2.131 Explain what a discrete random variable is.

ANSWER: The random variable can only assume a finite or limited set of values.

2.132 Explain what a continuous random variable is.

ANSWER: The continuous random variable has an infinite or unlimited set of values.

2.133 List the two parameters of the normal distribution.

ANSWER: mean (μ) and standard deviation (σ)

2.134 List the parameters of the exponential distribution.

ANSWER: μ

2.135 List the parameters of the Poisson distribution.

ANSWER: λ

CHAPTER 3
Decision Analysis

TRUE/FALSE

3.1 Expected Monetary Value (EMV) is the average or expected monetary outcome of a decision if it can be repeated a large number of times.

ANSWER: TRUE

3.2 Expected Monetary Value (EMV) is the payoff you should expect to occur when you choose a particular alternative.

ANSWER: FALSE

3.3 The decision-maker has little or no control over a state of nature.

ANSWER: TRUE

3.4 Decision-making under risk is a probabilistic decision situation.

ANSWER: TRUE

3.5 The difference in decision-making under risk and decision-making under uncertainty is that under risk, we think we know the probabilities of the states of nature, while under uncertainty we do not know the probabilities of the states of nature.

ANSWER: TRUE

3.6 EVPI (Expected Value of Perfect Information) is a measure of the maximum value of additional information.

ANSWER: TRUE

3.7 When using the EOL as a decision criterion, the best decision is the alternative with the least EOL value.

ANSWER: TRUE

3.8 To determine the effect of input changes on decision results, we should perform a sensitivity analysis.

ANSWER: TRUE

3.9 The maximax decision criterion is used by pessimistic decision makers and maximizes the maximum outcome for every alternative.

ANSWER: FALSE

3.10 The maximin decision criterion is used by pessimistic decision makers and minimizes the maximum outcome for every alternative.

ANSWER: FALSE

3.11 Marginal analysis is an aid to decision-making when there are a large number of alternatives and/or states of nature.

ANSWER: TRUE

3.12 The decision theory processes of maximizing Expected Monetary Value and minimizing Expected Opportunity Loss should lead us to choose the same alternatives.

ANSWER: TRUE

3.13 The several criteria (maximax, maximin, equally likely, criterion of realism, minimax) used for decision-making under uncertainty may lead to the choice of different alternatives.

ANSWER: TRUE

3.14 One advantage of using decision trees over decision tables when making sequential decisions is that the tree better depicts the sequential aspect of the decisions.

ANSWER: TRUE

3.15 The nodes on decision trees represent either decisions or states of nature.

ANSWER: TRUE

3.16 Any problem that can be presented in a decision table can also be graphically portrayed in a decision tree.

ANSWER: TRUE

3.17 Any problem that can be represented in a decision tree can be easily portrayed in a decision table.

ANSWER: FALSE

3.18 The expected value of sample information (EVSI) is equal to the expected value of the best decision with sample information (at no cost to gather) less the maximum expected monetary value (EMV).

ANSWER: TRUE

3.19 The EMV approach and Utility theory always result in the same choice of alternatives.

ANSWER: FALSE

3.20 Utility theory may help the decision-maker include the impact of qualitative factors that are difficult to include in the EMV model.

ANSWER: TRUE

3.21 In a decision problem where we wish to use Bayes' theorem to calculate posterior probabilities, we should always begin our analysis with the assumption that all states of nature are equally likely, and use the sample information to revise these probabilities to more realistic values.

ANSWER: FALSE

3.22 A utility curve that shows utility increasing at an increasing rate as the monetary value increases represents the utility curve of a risk seeker.

ANSWER: TRUE

3.23 A utility curve that shows utility increasing at a decreasing rate as the monetary value increases represents the utility curve of a risk seeker.

ANSWER: FALSE

3.24 If someone has a utility curve that increases linearly with increasing monetary value, we would call this person risk indifferent or risk neutral.

ANSWER: TRUE

3.25 Utility values range from -1 to +1.

ANSWER: FALSE

3.26 By studying a person's Utility Curve, one can determine whether the individual is a risk seeker, risk avoider, or is indifferent to risk.

ANSWER: TRUE

3.27 Rational people make decisions that maximize the expected utility.

ANSWER: TRUE

3.28 Utility theory provides a decision criterion that is superior to the EMV or EOL in that it may allow the decision maker to incorporate her own attitudes toward risk

ANSWER: TRUE

3.29 The assignment of a utility value of 1 to an alternative implies that alternative is preferred to all others.

ANSWER: TRUE

3.30 The assignment to a utility value of 0 to an alternative implies the alternative is preferred to all others.

ANSWER: FALSE

3.31 The following figure illustrates a utility curve for someone who is a risk seeker.

3.31 The following figure illustrates a utility curve for someone who is a risk seeker.

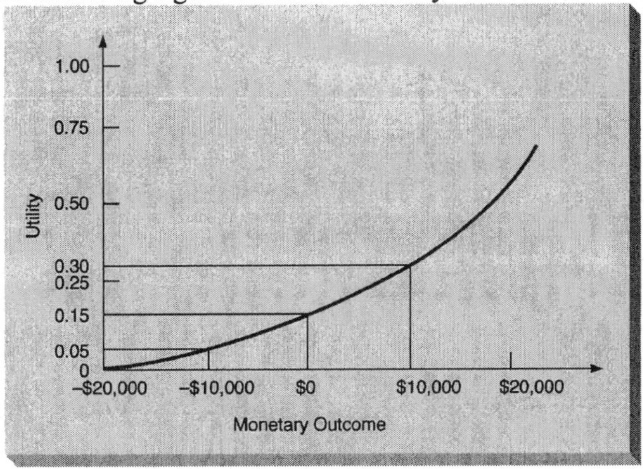

ANSWER: TRUE

MULTIPLE CHOICE

3.32 Expected monetary value (EMV) is

(a) the average or expected monetary outcome of a decision if it can be repeated a large number of times.
(b) the average or expected value of the decision, if you know what would happen ahead of time.
(c) the average or expected value of information if it were completely accurate.
(d) the amount you would lose by not picking the best alternative.
(e) a decision criterion that places an equal weight on all states of nature.

ANSWER: a

3.33 A pessimistic decision-making criterion is

(a) maximax.
(b) equally likely.
(c) maximin.
(d) decision-making under certainty.
(e) minimax.

ANSWER: c

3.34 Which of the following is true about the expected value of perfect information?

(a) It is the amount you would pay for any sample study.
(b) It is calculated as EMV minus EOL.
(c) It is calculated as expected value with perfect information minus maximum EMV.
(d) It is the amount charged for marketing research.
(e) none of the above

ANSWER: c

3.35 If product demand follows a normal distribution and we want to apply marginal analysis, we need to know

(a) the mean sales estimate.
(b) the standard deviation of the sales estimate.
(c) the marginal profit.
(d) the marginal loss.
(e) all of the above

ANSWER: e

3.36 The following is a payoff table giving profits for various situations.

	States of Nature		
Alternatives	A	B	C
Alternative 1	120	140	120
Alternative 2	200	100	50
Alternative 3	100	120	180
Do Nothing	0	0	0

What decision would an optimist make?

(a) Alternative 1
(b) Alternative 2
(c) Alternative 3
(d) Do Nothing
(e) none of the above

ANSWER: b

3.37 The following is a payoff table giving profits for various situations.

	States of Nature		
Alternatives	A	B	C
Alternative 1	120	140	120
Alternative 2	200	100	50
Alternative 3	100	120	180
Do Nothing	0	0	0

What decision would a pessimist make?

(a) Alternative 1
(b) Alternative 2
(c) Alternative 3
(d) Do Nothing
(e) none of the above

ANSWER: a

3.38 The following is an opportunity loss table.

	States of Nature		
Alternatives	A	B	C
Alternative 1	0	90	85
Alternative 2	50	0	110
Alternative 3	75	80	0

What decision should be made based on the minimax regret criterion?

(a) Alternative 1
(b) Alternative 2
(c) Alternative 3
(d) does not matter
(e) none of the above

ANSWER: c

3.39 The following is an opportunity loss table.

	States of Nature		
Alternatives	A	B	C
Alternative 1	30	0	10
Alternative 2	5	20	0
Alternative 3	0	20	25

What decision should be made based on the minimax regret criterion?

(a) Alternative 1
(b) Alternative 2
(c) Alternative 3
(d) State of Nature C
(e) none of the above

ANSWER: b

3.40 The following is an opportunity-loss table.

	State of Nature		
Alternatives	A	B	C
Alternative 1	20	100	0
Alternative 2	100	0	25
Alternative 3	0	40	90

The probabilities for the states of nature A, B, and C are 0.3, 0.5, and 0.2, respectively. If a person were to use the expected opportunity loss criterion, what decision would be made?

(a) Alternative 1
(b) Alternative 2
(c) Alternative 3
(d) State of Nature C
(e) none of the above

ANSWER: b

3.41 The following is a payoff table giving profits for various situations.

	States of Nature		
Alternatives	A	B	C
Alternative 1	100	120	180
Alternative 2	120	140	120
Alternative 3	200	100	50
Do Nothing	0	0	0

The probabilities for states of nature A, B, and C are 0.3, 0.5, and 0.2, respectively. If a person selected Alternative 1, what would the expected profit be?

(a) 120
(b) 133.33
(c) 126
(d) 180
(e) none of the above

ANSWER: c

3.42 Dr. Mac, a surgeon, must decide what mode of treatment to use on Mr. Samuels. There are three modes of treatment, Mode A, B, and C; and three possible states of nature: 1.Treatment succeeds and patient leads a normal life, 2. Patient survives treatment but is permanently disabled, and 3. Patient fails to survive treatment. Dr. Mac has prepared the decision table below. What mode of treatment maximizes the expected value?

Treatment Mode	Outcome		
	Normal Life	Disability	Non-Survival
A	$1,000,000	-$2,000,000	-$500,000
P(outcome)	.5	.2	.3
B	$3,000,000	-$2,500,000	-$500,000
P(outcome)	.5	.3	.2
C	$10,000,000	-$5,000,000	-$600,000
P(outcome)	.4	.4	.2

(a) Mode A
(b) Mode B
(c) Mode C
(d) All three treatments are equally desirable.
(e) none of the above

ANSWER: c

3.43 Consider the following payoff table.

	States of Nature	
Alternatives	A	B
Alternative 1	100	150
Alternative 2	200	100
Probability	0.4	0.6

Based upon these probabilities, a person would select Alternative 2. Suppose there is concern about the accuracy of these probabilities. It can be stated that Alternative 2 will remain the best alternative as long as the probability of A is at least

(a) 0.33.
(b) 0.50.
(c) 0.40.
(d) 0.60.
(e) none of the above

ANSWER: a

3.44 Consider the following payoff table.

	States of Nature	
Alternatives	A	B
Alternative 1	100	150
Alternative 2	200	100
Probability	0.4	0.6

How much should be paid for a perfect forecast of the state of nature?

(a) 170
(b) 30
(c) 10
(d) 100
(e) none of the above

ANSWER: b

3.45 The following is a payoff table giving profits for various situations.

	States of Nature		
Alternatives	A	B	C
Alternative 1	100	120	180
Alternative 2	200	100	50
Alternative 3	120	140	120
Do Nothing	0	0	0

The probabilities for states of nature A, B, and C are 0.3, 0.5, and 0.2, respectively. If a perfect forecast of the future were available, what is the expected value with this perfect information?

(a) 130
(b) 160
(c) 166
(d) 36
(e) none of the above

ANSWER: c

3.46 The following is a payoff table giving profits for various situations.

	States of Nature		
Alternatives	A	B	C
Alternative 1	100	120	180
Alternative 2	200	100	50
Alternative 3	120	140	120
Do Nothing	0	0	0

The probabilities for states of nature A, B, and C are 0.3, 0.5, and 0.2, respectively. If a perfect forecast of the future were available, what is the expected value of perfect information (EVPI)?

(a) 166
(b) 0
(c) 36
(d) 40
(e) none of the above

ANSWER: c

3.47 Nick has plans to open some pizza restaurants, but he is not sure how many to open. He has prepared a payoff table to help analyze the situation.

	States of Nature		
Alternatives	Good Market	Fair Market	Poor Market
Open 1	380,000	70,000	- 400,000
Open 2	200,000	80,000	- 200,000
Do Nothing	0	0	0

As Nick does not know how his product will be received, he assumes that all three states of nature are equally likely to occur. If he uses the equally likely criterion, what decision would he make?

(a) open 1
(b) open 2
(c) good market
(d) fair market
(e) poor market

ANSWER: b

3.48 Nick has plans to open some pizza restaurants, but he is not sure how many to open. He has prepared a payoff table to help analyze the situation.

	States of Nature		
Alternatives	Good Market	Fair Market	Poor Market
Open 1	380,000	70,000	-400,000
Open 2	200,000	80,000	-200,000
Do Nothing	0	0	0

Nick believes there is a 40 percent chance that the market will be good, a 30 percent chance that it will be fair, and a 30 percent chance that it will be poor. A market research firm will analyze market conditions and will provide a perfect forecast (they provide a money back guarantee). What is the most that should be paid for this forecast?

(a) $ 44,000
(b) $ 53,000
(c) $123,000
(d) $176,000
(e) none of the above

ANSWER: c

3.49 Daily sales for a perishable food product are known to be 8, 9, 10, or 11 cases with probabilities 0.2, 0.3, 0.4, and 0.1, respectively. Cases not sold during the day are worthless, but cases can only be produced in the morning before the store opens. The cost of producing one of these is $4 while the selling price is $7. If you choose to produce 10 cases in the morning to sell, what is the probability that you will be able to meet today's demand?

(a) 0.20
(b) 0.30
(c) 0.40
(d) 0.10
(e) 0.90

ANSWER: e

3.50 Daily sales for a perishable food product are known to be 8, 9, 10, or 11 cases with probabilities 0.2, 0.3, 0.4, and 0.1, respectively. Cases not sold during the day are worthless, but cases can only be produced in the morning before the store opens. The cost of producing one of these is $4 while the selling price is $7. How many cases should you produce to maximize profit?

(a) 8
(b) 9
(c) 10
(d) 11
(e) none of the above

ANSWER: b

3.51 Joel Turner sells donuts at the student service building. Daily sales of donuts are approximately normally distributed with a mean of 500 and a standard deviation of 40. Joel's cost of purchasing each donut is 15 cents, and they are sold for 35 cents each. Joel plans to use a marginal analysis based on the normal distribution to make a decision. How many donuts should Joel purchase each day?

(a) 500.0
(b) 520.8
(c) 507.2
(d) 524.7
(e) none of the above

ANSWER: c

3.52 Mickey sells newspapers on a corner every day. He pays 10 cents for each paper and sells it for 25 cents. He knows the demand is always for 30, 40, or 50 papers, but he doesn't know ahead of time which of these will occur. Papers left at the end of the day are sold to a paper company for 2 cents each. If he decides to purchase 40 papers but demand is only for 30, what would his profits be?

(a) 3.50
(b) 3.70
(c) 7.50
(d) 4.00
(e) none of the above

ANSWER: b

3.53 Daily sales for submarine sandwiches are known to be 28, 29, 30, or 31 sandwiches with probabilities of 0.2, 0.3, 0.4, and 0.1, respectively. Sandwiches not sold during the day are worthless, and sandwiches can only be produced in the morning before the store opens. The cost of producing one sandwich is $2, while the selling price is $3.50. If you wish to maximize expected profit, how many sandwiches should be produced each day?

(a) 31
(b) 30
(c) 29
(d) 28
(e) none of the above

ANSWER: c

3.54 Daily sales for submarine sandwiches are known to be 28, 29, 30, or 31 sandwiches with probabilities of 0.2, 0.3, 0.4, and 0.1, respectively. Sandwiches not sold during the day are worthless, and sandwiches can only be produced in the morning before the store opens. The cost of producing one sandwich is $2, while the selling price is $3.50. If you choose to produce 29 sandwiches in the morning to sell, what is the probability that you will have sandwiches left over when the store closes?

(a) 0.20
(b) 0.30
(c) 0.40
(d) 0.50
(e) 0.90

ANSWER: a

3.55 Daily sales of submarine sandwiches are known to be 28, 29, 30, or 31 sandwiches with probabilities of 0.1, 0.3, 0.4, and 0.2, respectively. The cost of producing one sandwich is $2, while the selling price is $3.50. Sandwiches not sold during the day are given to a local homeless shelter, and you believe that you will receive $0.40 in "goodwill" for each sandwich given to the shelter. Sandwiches can only be produced in the morning before the store opens. If you wish to maximize expected profit, how many sandwiches should be produced each day?

(a) 28
(b) 29
(c) 30
(d) 31
(e) none of the above

ANSWER: c

3.56 Mickey sells newspapers on a corner every day. He pays 10 cents for each paper and sells them for 25 cents. He knows that the demand is always for 30, 40, or 50 papers, but he doesn't know ahead of time which of these will occur. Papers left at the end of the day are worthless. He purchased 40 of the papers, and at the end of the day finds that he has made a profit of $3.50. What was demand?

(a) 30
(b) 40
(c) 50
(d) There is insufficient information to solve this problem.
(e) none of the above

ANSWER: a

3.57 Mickey sells newspapers on a corner every day. He pays 10 cents for each paper and sells them for 25 cents. He knows that the demand is always for 30, 40, or 50 papers, but he doesn't know ahead of time which of these will occur. Papers left at the end of the day are sold to a paper company. If he decides to purchase 40 papers but demand is only for 30, at what price must he sell the remaining papers to the paper company to earn a profit of $3.70?

(a) $0.05
(b) $0.04
(c) $0.03
(d) $0.02
(e) none of the above

ANSWER: d

3.58 Katie Hammond is paying her way through college by working at various odd jobs. She contracted with the school to produce and sell programs at football games. The cost of producing the programs is 50 cents each and they sell for $1.25 each. Programs not sold at the game are worthless. Demand for programs at each game is normally distributed with a mean of 2,500 and a standard deviation of 200. How many should Katie produce for the upcoming game (round off to the nearest unit)?

(a) 2,550
(b) 2,580
(c) 2,500
(d) 2,700
(e) none of the above

ANSWER: a

3.59 J. Tom Ball has developed plans for a therapy clinic for stressed-out chemical plant workers. He has estimated that demand for services (measured in hours) will be normally distributed with a mean of 120 hours (per month) and a standard deviation of 20. J. Tom foresees fixed monthly expenses of $3,000. He plans to contract the work to unemployed Ph.D.s in psychology. He will pay them $50 per hour for their time, and this is his variable cost of providing service. He will charge $80 per hour to his clients. If J. Tom is to break even on this venture, how many hours per month of therapy time must be demanded?

(a) 100
(b) 600
(c) 1,200
(d) 60
(e) none of the above

ANSWER: a

3.60 J. Tom Ball has developed plans for a therapy clinic for stressed-out chemical plant workers. He has estimated that demand for services (measured in hours) will be normally distributed with a mean of 120 hours (per month) and a standard deviation of 20. J. Tom foresees fixed monthly expenses of $3,000. He will charge $80 per hour to his clients. He plans to contract the work to unemployed Ph.D.s in psychology. What must he pay them per hour if he wants the break-even point to be 100 hours per month?

(a) $40/hr
(b) $50/hr
(c) $60/hr
(d) $70/hr
(e) none of the above

ANSWER: b

3.61 Decision trees are particularly useful when

(a) perfect information is available.
(b) formulating a conditional values table.
(c) the opportunity loss table is available.
(d) a sequence of decisions must be made.
(e) all possible outcomes and alternatives are not known.

ANSWER: d

3.62 The expected value of sample information (EVSI) can be used to

(a) establish a maximum amount to spend on additional information.
(b) calculate conditional probabilities.
(c) establish risk avoidance.
(d) provide points on a utility curve.
(e) none of the above

ANSWER: a

3.63 A market research survey is available for $10,000. Using a decision tree analysis, it is found that the expected monetary value with no survey is $62,000. If the expected value of sample information is -$7,000, what is the expected monetary value with the survey?

(a) $45,000
(b) $62,000
(c) -$17,000
(d) $55,000
(e) none of the above

ANSWER: a

3.64 A market research survey is available for $10,000. Using a decision tree analysis, it is found that the expected monetary value with the survey is $75,000. The expected monetary value with no survey is $62,000. What is the expected value of sample information?

(a) -$7,000
(b) $3,000
(c) $7,000
(d) $13,000
(e) none of the above

ANSWER: d

3.65 Bayes' Theorem enables decision-makers to revise probabilities based on

(a) perfect information.
(b) knowing, ahead of time, the actual outcome of the decision.
(c) additional information.
(d) measurements of utility.
(e) none of the above
ANSWER: c

3.66 A company is considering producing a new children's bar soap. A market research firm has told the company that if they perform a survey the successful production of a favorable market occurs 65 percent of the time. That is, P(positive survey | favorable market) = 0.65. Similarly, 40 percent of the time the survey falsely predicts a favorable market; thus, P(positive survey | unfavorable market) = 0.40. These statistics indicate the accuracy of the survey. Prior to contacting the market research firm, the company's best estimate of a favorable market was 50 percent. So, P(favorable market) = 0.50 and P(unfavorable market) = 0.50. Using Bayes' theorem, determine the probability of a favorable market given a favorable survey.

(a) 0.62
(b) 0.38
(c) 0.53
(d) 0.65
(e) none of the above
ANSWER: a

3.67 The following table provides information regarding probabilities for survey results for two states of nature.

Survey Results	Favorable Market (FM)	Unfavorable Market (UM)
Positive	0.65	0.40
Negative	0.35	0.60

(e.g., P(positive survey|FM)=0.65; P(positive survey|UM)=0.40)

The prior probability of a favorable market is 0.70, and an unfavorable market 0.30.

Determine the probability that the survey will predict a favorable market.

(a) 0.65
(b) 0.40
(c) 0.575
(d) 0.657
(e) none of the above

ANSWER: c

3.68 The following table provides information regarding probabilities for survey results for two states of nature.

Survey Results	Favorable Market (FM)	Unfavorable Market (UM)
Positive	0.65	0.40
Negative	0.35	0.60

(e.g., P(positive survey|FM)=0.65; P(positive survey|UM)=0.40)

What is the probability that if a favorable market occurs, the survey will have been positive?

(a) 0.40
(b) 0.65
(c) 0.35
(d) 0.60
(e) none of the above

ANSWER: b

3.69 Utilization of Bayes' Theorem requires the use of all but

(a) prior probabilities.
(b) marginal probabilities.
(c) conditional probabilities.
(d) posterior probabilities.
(e) expected monetary values (EMV).

ANSWER: e

3.70 A risk avoider is a person for whom the utility of an outcome

(a) decreases as the monetary value increases.
(b) stays the same as monetary value increases.
(c) increases as the monetary value increases.
(d) increases at a decreasing rate as monetary value increases.
(e) none of the above

ANSWER: d

3.71 A utility curve showing utility increasing at an increasing rate as the monetary value increases represents

(a) a risk avoider.
(b) utility assessment.
(c) a risk seeker.
(d) conditional values.
(e) expected utilities.

ANSWER: c

3.72 In constructing a utility curve,

(a) a comparison is made with the different amounts of money at different times.
(b) the certainty of a certain amount is compared with the willingness to gamble that amount on a larger amount.
(c) one takes the risk out of gambling.
(d) inflation plays a critical part in the evaluation.
(e) none of the above

ANSWER: b

3.73 Utility values range from

(a) -1 to 1
(b) 1 to 10
(c) 0 to 1
(d) 1 to 100
(e) none of the above

ANSWER: c

3.74 A rational decision maker must choose between two alternatives. Alternative 1 has a higher EMV than Alternative 2, but the decision-maker chooses Alternative 2. What might explain why this occurs?

(a) Alternative 2 may have a higher expected utility.
(b) Alternative 1 may have a lower expected opportunity loss.
(c) The probabilities are not known.
(d) A rational decision maker could not possibly choose alternative 2.
(e) none of the above

ANSWER: a

3.75 Robert Weed is considering purchasing life insurance. He must pay a $180 premium for a $100,000 life insurance policy. If he dies this year, his beneficiary will receive $100,000. If he does not die this year, the insurance company pays nothing and Robert must consider paying another premium next year. Based on actuarial tables, there is a 0.001 probability that Robert will die this year. If Robert wishes to maximize his EMV, he would not buy the policy if the EMV were negative for him. He has determined that the EMV is, indeed negative for him, but decides to purchase the insurance anyway. Why?

(a) He believes that the actual likelihood of his death occurring in the next twelve months is really much greater than the actuarial estimate.
(b) While the EMV is negative, the utility gained from purchasing the insurance is positive, and high.
(c) Mr. Weed is not rational.
(d) (a) or (c)
(e) none of the above

ANSWER: b

3.76 If one's utility curve is not a straight line (i.e., risk indifferent), then one's utility can, over a particular range of EMV,

(a) increase at an increasing rate as the monetary value increases.
(b) increase at an increasing rate as the monetary value decreases.
(c) increase at a decreasing rate as the monetary value increases.
(d) increase at a decreasing rate as the monetary value decreases.
(e) any of the above

ANSWER: e

3.77 It is sometimes said that "Those who gamble the most are the ones who can least afford to lose." These people gamble because

(a) the EMV is positive.
(b) the EMV is negative.
(c) the gambler has no family to consider if he/she dies.
(d) there is utility other than monetary to consider.
(e) none of the above

ANSWER: d

PROBLEMS

3.78 A concessionaire for the local ballpark has developed a table of conditional values for the various alternatives (stocking decision) and states of nature (size of crowd).

	STATES OF NATURE (size of crowd)		
Alternatives	Large	Average	Small
Large Inventory	$22,000	$12,000	- $2,000
Average Inventory	$15,000	$12,000	$6,000
Small Inventory	$ 9,000	$ 6,000	$5,000

If the probabilities associated with the states of nature are 0.30 for a large crowd, 0.50 for an average crowd, and 0.20 for a small crowd, determine:

(a) the alternative that provides the greatest expected monetary value (EMV)
(b) the expected value of perfect information (EVPI)

ANSWERS:
(a) For large inventory alternative maximum EMV = $12,200
(b) EVPI = 13800 – 12200 = 1,600

3.79 A concessionaire for the local ballpark has developed a table of conditional values for the various alternatives (stocking decision) and states of nature (size of crowd).

	States of Nature (size of crowd)		
Alternatives	Large	Average	Small
Large Inventory	$22,000	$12,000	- $2,000
Average Inventory	$15,000	$12,000	$6,000
Small Inventory	$ 9,000	$ 6,000	$5,000

If the probabilities associated with the states of nature are 0.30 for a large crowd, 0.50 for an average crowd, and 0.20 for a small crowd, determine:

(a) the opportunity loss table
(b) minimum expected opportunity loss (EOL)

ANSWERS:

(a) Opportunity Loss Table

	States of Nature		
Alternatives	Large	Average	Small
Large	0	0	8,000
Average	7,000	0	0
Small	13,000	6,000	1,000

(b) minimum EOL = $1,600

3.80 The ABC Co. is considering a new consumer product. They believe there is a probability of 0.4 that the XYZ Co. will come out with a competitive product. If ABC adds an assembly line for the product and XYZ does not follow with a competitive product, their expected profit is $40,000; if they add an assembly line and XYZ does follow, they still expect a $10,000 profit. If ABC adds a new plant addition and XYZ does not produce a competitive product, they expect a profit of $600,000; if XYZ does compete for this market, ABC expects a loss of $100,000.

(a) determine the EMV of each decision
(b) determine the EOL of each decision
(c) compare the results of a and b
(d) calculate the EVPI

ANSWERS:

(a)

Decision	EMV
add assembly line	$28,000
plant addition	$320,000
do nothing	$0

(b)

Decision	EOL
add assembly line	$336,000
plant addition	$44,000
do nothing	$364,000

(c) The plant addition is best for both models. The maximum EMV alternative is always the same as the minimum EOL alternative.

(d) EVPI = 44,000

3.81 The ABC Co. is considering a new consumer product. They have no idea whether or not the XYZ Co. will come out with a competitive product. If ABC adds an assembly line for the product and XYZ does not follow with a competitive product, their expected profit is $40,000; if they add an assembly line and XYZ does follow, they still expect a $10,000 profit. If ABC adds a new plant addition and XYZ does not produce a competitive product, they expect a profit of $600,000; if XYZ does compete for this market, ABC expects a loss of $100,000.
Calculate Hurwicz's criterion of realism using α's of 0.7, 0.3, and 0.1.

ANSWERS:

	Criterion of Realism		
Decision	$\alpha = 0.7$	$\alpha = 0.3$	$\alpha = 0.1$
add assembly line	$31,000	$19,000	$13,000
plant addition	$390,000	$110,000	- $30,000
do nothing	$0	$0	$0

3.82 Barbour Electric is considering the introduction of a new product. This product can be produced in one of several ways: (a) using the present assembly line at a cost of $25 per unit, (b) using the current assembly line after it has been overhauled (at a cost of $10,000) with a cost of $22 per unit; and (c) on an entirely new assembly line (costing $30,000) designed especially for the new product with a per unit cost of $20. Barbour is worried, however, about the impact of competition. If no competition occurs, they expect to sell 15,000 units the first year. With competition, the number of units sold is expected to drop to 9,000. At the moment, their best estimate is that there is a 40% chance of competition. They have decided to make their decision based on the first year sales.

(a) develop the decision table (EMV)
(b) develop a decision table (EOL)
(c) what should they do?

ANSWERS:

(a)

Alternative	No Competition	Competition	EMV
	P = 0.60	P = 0.40	
(a) Present line	$375,000	$225,000	$315,000
(b) Overhauled line	$340,000	$208,000	$287,000
(c) New line	$330,000	$210,000	$282,000

(b)

Alternative	No Competition	Competition	EMV
	P = 0.60	P = 0.40	
(a) Present line	$45,000	$17,000	$33,800
(b) Overhauled line	$10,000	$0	$6000
(c) New line	$0	$2,000	$800

(c) They should build the new line.

3.83 The following payoff table provides profits based on various possible decision alternatives and various levels of demand.

	States of Nature		
	Demand		
Alternatives	Low	Medium	High
Alternative 1	80	120	140
Alternative 2	90	90	90
Alternative 3	50	70	150

The probability of a low demand is 0.4, while the probability of a medium and high demand is each 0.3.

(a) What decision would an optimist make?
(b) What decision would a pessimist make?
(c) What is the highest possible expected monetary value?
(d) Calculate the expected value of perfect information for this situation.

ANSWER:
(a) Alternative 3
(b) Alternative 2
(c) maximum EMV = 110
(d) EVPI = 117- 110 = 7

3.84 The ABC Co. is considering a new consumer product. They believe that the XYZ Co. may come out with a competing product. If ABC adds an assembly line for the product and XYZ does not follow with a competitive product, their expected profit is $40,000; if they add an assembly line and XYZ does follow, they still expect a $10,000 profit. If ABC adds a new plant addition and XYZ does not produce a competitive product, they expect a profit of $600,000; if XYZ does compete for this market, ABC expects a loss of $100,000. For what value of probability that XYZ will offer a competing product will ABC be indifferent between the alternatives?
ANSWER:
Let X = probability XYZ offers a competing product. Then:

EMV(assembly line) = $10,000*X + $40,000*(1-X)
EMV(addition) = -$100,000*X + $600,000*(1-X) or:

$10,000*X + $40,000 * (1-X) = -$100,000*X + $600,000*(1-X) or:

$10,000*X - $40,000*X + $40,000 = -$100,000*X -$600,000*X + $600,000

-$30,000*X + $700,000 *X = $600,000 - $40,000

$670,000*X = $560,000

X = $560,000/$670,000 = 0.836

If the probability that XYZ will offer a competing product is estimated to be 0.836, then ABC will be indifferent between the two alternatives. If the probability that XYZ will offer a competing product is estimated to be less than 0.836, then ABC should invest in the addition.

3.85 A company is considering expansion of its current facility to meet increasing demand. A major expansion would cost $500,000, while a minor expansion would cost $200,000. If demand is high in the future, the major expansion would result in an additional profit of $800,000, but if demand is low, then there would be a loss of $500,000. If demand is high, the minor expansion will result in an increase in profits of $200,000, but if demand is low, then there is a loss of $100,000. The company has the option of not expanding. For what probability of a high demand will the company be indifferent between the two expansion alternatives?

ANSWER:

	States of Nature	
Alternatives	Demand is high	Demand is low
Major expansion	$800,000 - $500,000	-$500,000 - $500,000
Minor expansion	$200,000 - $200,000	-$100,000 - $200,000
Do nothing	$0	$0

	States of Nature	
Alternatives	Demand is high	Demand is low
Major expansion	$300,000	-$1,000,000
Minor expansion	$0	-$300,000
Do nothing	$0	$0

If we define X = probability of High Demand, then:

$300,000*X - $1,000,000*(1-X) = $0*X - $300,000*(1-X)

X = 0.7

For a probability of High Demand equal to 0.7, the decision-maker would be indifferent between the two expansion alternatives.

3.86 Orders for clothing from a particular manufacturer for this year's Christmas shopping season must be placed in February. The cost per unit for a particular dress is $20 while the anticipated selling price is $50. Demand is projected to be 50, 60, or 70 units. There is a 40 percent chance that demand will be 50 units, a 50 percent chance that demand will be 60 units, and a 10 percent chance that demand will be 70 units. The company believes they can sell any leftover goods to a discount store, but they are uncertain as to the price the discount store will pay. For what price to be paid by the discount store would they order 70 cases of dresses in February?

ANSWER:

Let X = price to be paid by the discount store; then:

Payoff Table:

	States of Nature Demand (units)		
Alternatives	50	60	70
Order 50	1500	1500	1500
Order 60	1300 + 10X	1800	1800
Order 70	1100 + 20X	1600 + 10X	2100
Probabilities:	0.4	0. 5	0.1

And, the company would order 70 units when EMV(70) = EMV(60).

$(1300 + 10X) *0.4 + 1800*0.5 + 1800*0.1 =$
$(1100+20X)*0.4 + (1600+10X)*0.5 + 2100*0.1$

$520+ 4X + 900 +180 = 440 + 8X +800 + 5X +210$

$9X = 150$

$X = 150/9 = 16.67$

Therefore, if the company could get at least $16.67 per dress from the discount store, the appropriate decision would be to order 70 units.

3.87 Norman L. Flowers holds the exclusive university contract for donut sales. The demand (based on historical records) appears to follow the following distribution:

Daily Demand (Dozens)	Probability
4	0.15
5	0.25
6	0.30
7	0.25
8	0.05

The cost of producing these is $1.20 per dozen while the selling price is $4.20 per dozen. Based on a marginal analysis of this situation, how many donuts should Norman produce each day?

ANSWER: P > 1.20/4.20 = 0.286. Therefore, Norman should produce seven dozen.

3.88 David N. Goliath is planning to open a sporting goods store. However, the initial investment is $100,000. He currently has this money in a certificate of deposit earning 15 percent. He may leave it there if he decides not to open the store. If he opens the store and it is successful he will generate a profit of $40,000. If it is not successful, he will lose $80,000. What would the probability of a successful store have to be for David to prefer this to investing in a CD?

ANSWER: p(40000) +(1-p)-(80000) > 0.15(100000), therefore p > 0.79

3.89 You are considering adding a new food product to your store for resale. You are certain that, in a month, minimum demand for the product will be 6 units, while maximum demand will be 8 units. (Unfortunately, the new product has a one-month shelf life and is considered to be waste at the end of the month.) You will pay $60/unit for this new product while you plan to sell the product at a $40/unit profit. The estimated demand for this new product in any given month is 6 units(p=0.1), 7 units(p=0.4), and 8 units(p=0.5). Using EMV analysis, how many units of the new product should be purchased for resale?

ANSWER:

EMV(purchase 6 for resale) = 6(40)(0.1) + 6(40)(0.4) + 6(40)(0.5) = 240

EMV(purchase 7 for resale) = [6(40)-60](0.1) + 7(40)(0.4) + 7(40)(0.5) = 270

EMV(purchase 8 for resale) = [6(40)-2(60)](0.1) + [7(40)-60](0.4) + 8(40)(0.5) = 260

Choose to purchase seven units for resale (largest EMV)

3.90 Mark M. Upp has just been fired as the university bookstore manager for setting prices too low (only 20 percent above suggested retail). He is considering opening a competing bookstore near the campus, and he has begun an analysis of the situation. There are two possible sites under consideration. One is relatively small, while the other is large. If he opens at Site 1 and demand is good, he will generate a profit of $50,000. If demand is low, he will lose $10,000. If he opens at Site 2 and demand is high, he will generate a profit of $80,000, but he will lose $30,000 if demand is low. He also has the option of not opening at either site. He believes that there is a 50 percent chance that demand will be high. A market research study will cost $5,000. The probability of a good demand given a favorable study is 0.8. The probability of a good demand given an unfavorable study is 0.1. There is a 60 percent chance that the study will be favorable.

(a) Should Mark use the study? Why?
(b) If the study is done and the results are favorable, what would Mark's expected profit be?

ANSWER:

(a) Yes, he should use the study. His EMV with the study is $29,800 while the highest EMV without the study is $25,000.

(b) Given a favorable survey result, Mark would select Site 2 and have an EMV of $53,000.

3.91 Mark M. Upp has just been fired as the university bookstore manager for setting prices too low (only 20 percent above suggested retail). He is considering opening a competing bookstore near the campus, and he has begun an analysis of the situation. There are two possible sites under consideration. One is relatively small, while the other is large. If he opens at Site 1 and demand is good, he will generate a profit of $50,000. If demand is low, he will lose $10,000. If he opens at Site 2 and demand is high, he will generate a profit of $80,000, but he will lose $30,000 if demand is low. He also has the option of not opening either. He believes that there is a 50 percent chance that demand will be high. Mark can purchase a market research study. The probability of a good demand given a favorable study is 0.8. The probability of a good demand given an unfavorable study is 0.1. There is a 60 percent chance that the study will be favorable. Should Mark use the study? Why? What is the maximum amount Mark should be willing to pay for this study? What is the maximum amount he should pay for any study?

ANSWER:

Yes, he should use the study. His EMV with the study is $34,800 while the highest EMV without the study is $25,000. He should pay no more than $9,800 for this study. He should pay no more than $10,000 for a "perfect" study.

3.92 Before a marketing research study was done, John Colorado believed there was a 50/50 chance that his music store would be a success. The research team determined that there is a 0.9 probability that the marketing research will be favorable given a successful music store. There is also a 0.8 probability that the marketing research will be unfavorable given an unsuccessful music store.

(a) If the marketing research is favorable, what is the revised probability of a successful music store?
(b) If the marketing research is unfavorable, what is the revised probability of a successful music store?

ANSWER:

(a) 0.82
(b) 0.11

3.93 Before a market survey is done, there is a 50/50 chance that a new soccer supply store would be a success. The people doing the survey have determined that there is a 0.8 probability that the survey will be favorable given a successful store. There is also a 0.7 probability that the survey will be unfavorable given an unsuccessful store. What is the probability that the survey will be unfavorable?

ANSWER: 0.45

3.94 Before a marketing research study was done, John Colorado believed there was a 50/50 chance that his music store would be a success. The research team determined that there is a 0.9 probability that the marketing research will be favorable given a successful music store. There is also a 0.8 probability that the marketing research will be unfavorable given an unsuccessful music store.

(a) If the marketing research is favorable, what is the revised probability of an unsuccessful music store?
(b) If the marketing research is unfavorable, what is the revised probability of an unsuccessful music store?

ANSWER:

(a) 0.18
(b) 0.89

3.95 Mark M. Upp has just been fired as the university bookstore manager for setting prices too low (only 20 percent above suggested retail). He is considering opening a competing bookstore near the campus, and he has begun an analysis of the situation. There are two possible sites under consideration. One is relatively small while the other is large. If he opens at Site 1 and demand is good, he will generate a profit of $50,000. If demand is low, he will lose $10,000. If he opens at Site 2 and demand is high he will generate a profit of $80,000, but he will lose $30,000 if demand is low. He also has decided that he will open at one of these sites. He believes that there is a 50 percent chance that demand will be high. He assigns the following utilities to the different profits:

U(50,000) = 0.72 U(-10,000) = 0.22
U(80,000) = 1 U(-30,000) = 0

Using expected utility theory, what should Mark do?

ANSWER:

Expected utility (Site 1) = 0.5(0.72) + 0.5(0.22) = 0.47

Expected utility (Site 2) = 0.5(1.00) + 0.5(0.00) = 0.50

Therefore he should open at Site 2.

3.96 Mark M. Upp has just been fired as the university book store manager for setting prices too low (only 20 percent above suggested retail). He is considering opening a competing bookstore near the campus, and he has begun an analysis of the situation. There are two possible sites under consideration. One is relatively small, while the other is large. If he opens at Site 1 and demand is good, he will generate a profit of $50,000. If demand is low, he will lose $10,000. If he opens at Site 2 and demand is high he will generate a profit of $80,000, but he will lose $30,000 if demand is low. He also has decided that he will open at one of these sites. He believes that there is a 50 percent chance that demand will be high. He assigns the following utilities to the different profits:

U(50000) = ? U(-10000) = 0.22
U(80000) = 1 U(-30000) = 0

For what value of utility for $50,000, U(50000), will Mark be indifferent between the two alternatives?

ANSWER:

Expected utility (Site 1) = 0.5X + 0.5(0.22)
Expected utility (Site 2) = 0.5(1) + 0.5(0) = 0.50

Therefore: 0.5X + 0.5(0.22) = 0.50
or: 0.5X = 0.50 - 0.11 = 0.39
And: X = 0.39/0.5 = 0.78

Therefore, if Mark has U(50,000) = 0.78 he will be indifferent between the two alternatives.

3.97 Pat Lucky would like a utility curve constructed for his monetary preference from $0 to $10,000. Pat is willing to risk a sure $7,000 on a 50/50 chance of making $10,000 or losing all his money. Similarly, Pat would be willing to risk a sure $5000 for a 40 percent chance of making $10,000 (60 percent chance of losing it all). Finally, he would be willing to risk $3,000 on a 10 percent chance of making $10,000 (90 percent chance of losing it all). Pat also plays dogs, ponies, and state lotteries – he received a severe concussion when dropped on his head when young. Is Pat a risk avoider or risk seeker?

ANSWER: Pat is a risk avoider.

SHORT ANSWER/ESSAY

3.98 Briefly describe decision-making under certainty.

ANSWER: decision-making with certain knowledge of the consequence of every outcome

3.99 Briefly describe decision-making under risk.

ANSWER: decision-making with knowledge of the probability of occurrence of every outcome

3.100 Biefly describe decision-making under uncertainty.

ANSWER: decision-making without knowledge of the probability of occurrence of every outcome

3.101 In general terms, describe a decision node.

ANSWER: a node from which one of several alternatives may be chosen

3.102 In general terms, describe a state of nature node.

ANSWER: a node out of which one state will occur

3.103 Briefly describe decision tree analysis.

ANSWER: define the problem, draw the tree, assign the probabilities to the states of nature, estimate payoffs for each alternative, compute EMV

3.104 Briefly describe EVSI.

ANSWER: EVSI = EV (best decision with sample information) – EV (of best decision without sample information)

3.105 Describe the utility curve of a risk seeker.

ANSWER: utility increasing at an increasing rate as the monetary value increases

3.106 Describe the utility curve of a risk avoider.

ANSWER: utility increasing at a decreasing rate as the monetary value increases

3.107 Describe utility assessment.

ANSWER: Assign the worst outcome a utility of 0 and the best outcome a utility of 1. Assign all other outcomes a utility value other than the best or worst outcome.

CHAPTER 4
Regression Models

TRUE/FALSE

4.1 Cost estimation models are an example of regression models.

ANSWER: TRUE

4.2 One purpose of regression is to understand the relationship between variables.

ANSWER: TRUE

4.3 One purpose of regression is to predict the value of one variable based on the other variable.

ANSWER: TRUE

4.4 The variable to be predicted is the independent variable.

ANSWER: FALSE

4.5 The dependent variable is also called the explanatory variable.

ANSWER: FALSE

4.6 A scatter diagram is a graphical depiction of the relationship between the dependent and independent variables.

ANSWER: TRUE

4.7 In a scatter diagram, the independent variable is typically plotted on the horizontal axis.

ANSWER: TRUE

4.8 There is no relationship between variables unless the data points lie in a straight line.

ANSWER: FALSE

4.9 In any regression model, there is an implicit assumption that a relationship exists between the variables.

ANSWER: TRUE

4.10 In regression, there is random error that can be predicted.

ANSWER: FALSE

4.11 Estimates of the slope, intercept, and error are found from sample data.

ANSWER: FALSE

4.12 Error is the difference in the actual values and the predicted values.

ANSWER: TRUE

4.13 The regression line minimizes the sum of the squared errors.

ANSWER: TRUE

4.14 Errors are positive values that indicate the accuracy of the regression line.

ANSWER: FALSE

4.15 Summing the error values is misleading because negative errors cancel out positive errors.

ANSWER: TRUE

4.16 The SST measures the total variability in the dependent variable about the mean.

ANSWER: TRUE

4.17 The SSE measures the total variability in the independent variable about the regression line.

ANSWER: FALSE

4.18 The SSR indicates how much of the total variability in the dependent variable is explained by the regression model.

ANSWER: TRUE

4.19 The coefficient of determination takes on values between -1 and + 1.

ANSWER: FALSE

4.20 The coefficient of determination gives the proportion of the variability in the dependent variable that is explained by the regression equation.

ANSWER: TRUE

4.21 The correlation coefficient has values between 0 and +1.

ANSWER: FALSE

4.22 Errors are also called residuals.

ANSWER: TRUE

4.23 The regression model assumes the error terms are dependent.

ANSWER: FALSE

4.24 The regression model assumes the errors are not normally distributed.

ANSWER: FALSE

4.25 The errors have a mean of zero.

ANSWER: TRUE

4.26 The errors do not have a constant variance.

ANSWER: FALSE

4.27 If the assumptions of regression have been met, errors plotted against the independent variable will typically show patterns.

ANSWER: FALSE

4.28 Often, a plot of the residuals will highlight any glaring violations of the assumptions.

ANSWER: TRUE

4.29 The error standard deviation is estimated by MSE.

ANSWER: FALSE

4.30 The standard error of the estimate is also called the variance of the regression.

ANSWER: FALSE

4.31 An F-test is used to determine if there is a relationship between the dependent and independent variables.

ANSWER: TRUE

4.32 The null hypothesis in the F-test is that there is a linear relationship between the X and Y variables.

ANSWER: FALSE

4.33 If the significance level for the F-test is high, there is a relationship between the dependent and independent variables.

ANSWER: FALSE

4.34 When the significance level is small in the F-test, we can reject the null hypothesis that there is no linear relationship.

ANSWER: TRUE

4.35 Just because there is a relationship between two variables it does not mean there is a strong relationship.

ANSWER: TRUE

4.36 For statistical tests of significance about the coefficients, the null hypothesis is that the slope is 1.

ANSWER: FALSE

4.37 In a simple linear regression model, the significance test of the regression coefficient gives essentially the same information as the F-test.

ANSWER: TRUE

4.38 The multiple regression model includes several dependent variables.

ANSWER: FALSE

4.39 A dummy variable is another method for coding quantitative data.

ANSWER: FALSE

4.40 Another name for a dummy variable is a binary variable.

ANSWER: TRUE

4.41 The best model is a statistically significant model with a high r-square and few variables.

ANSWER: TRUE

4.42 The adjusted r-square will always increase as additional variables are added to the model.

ANSWER: FALSE

4.43 The value of r-squared can never decrease when more variables are added to the model.

ANSWER: TRUE

4.44 A variable should be added to the model regardless of the impact (increase or decrease) on the adjusted r-square value.

ANSWER: FALSE

4.45 Multicollinearity exists when a variable is correlated to other variables.

ANSWER: TRUE

4.46 If multicollinearity exists, then individual interpretation of the variables is questionable, but the overall model is still good for prediction purposes.

ANSWER: TRUE

4.47 Transformations may be used when nonlinear relationships exist between variables.

ANSWER: TRUE

4.48 A high correlation always implies that one variable is causing a change in the other variable.

ANSWER: FALSE

4.49 Using an F-test and concluding a linear regression model is helpful in predicting the dependent variable implies it is the best model.

ANSWER: FALSE

MULTIPLE CHOICE

4.50 Which of the following statements is true regarding a scatter diagram?

(a) It provides very little information about the relationship between the regression variables.
(b) It is a plot of the independent and dependent variables.
(c) It is a line chart of the independent and dependent variables.
(d) It has a value between –1 and +1
(e) It gives the percent of variation in the dependent variable that is explained by the independent variable.

ANSWER: b

4.51 The random error in a regression equation:

(a) is the predicted error.
(b) includes both positive and negative terms.
(c) will sum to a large positive number.
(d) is used the estimate the accuracy of the slope.
(e) is maximized in a least squares regression model.

ANSWER: b

4.52 Which of the following statements (are) is not true about regression models?

(a) Estimates of the slope are found from sample data.
(b) The regression line minimizes the sum of the squared errors.
(c) The error is found by subtracting the actual data value from the predicted data value.
(d) The dependent variable is the explanatory variable.
(e) The intercept coefficient is not typically interpreted.

ANSWER: d

4.53 Which of the following equalities is correct?

(a) SST = SSR + SSE
(b) SSR = SST + SSE
(c) SSE = SSR + SST
(d) SST = SSC + SSR
(e) SSE = Actual Value – Predicted Value

ANSWER: a

4.54 The sum of squared error (SSE) is

(a) a measure of the total variation in Y about the mean.
(b) a measure of the total variation in X about the mean.
(c) a measure in the variation of Y about the regression line.
(d) a measure in the variation of X about the regression line.
(e) none of the above

ANSWER: c

4.55 If computing a causal linear regression model of Y = a + bX and the resultant r^2 is very near zero, then one would be able to conclude that

(a) Y = a + bX is a good forecasting method.
(b) Y = a + bX is not a good forecasting method.
(c) a multiple linear regression model is a good forecasting method for the data.
(d) a multiple linear regression model is not a good forecasting method for the data.
(e) none of the above

ANSWER: b

4.56 Which of the following statements is true about r^2 ?

(a) It is also called the coefficient of correlation.
(b) It is also called the coefficient of variation.
(c) It represents the percent of variation in X that is explained by Y.
(d) It represents the percent of variation in the error that is explained by Y.
(e) It ranges in value from –1 to + 1.

ANSWER: b

4.57 The coefficient of determination resulting from a particular regression analysis was 0.85. What was the slope of the regression line?

(a) 0.85
(b) -0.85
(c) 0.922
(d) There is insufficient information to answer the question.
(e) none of the above

ANSWER: d

4.58 The diagram below illustrates data with a

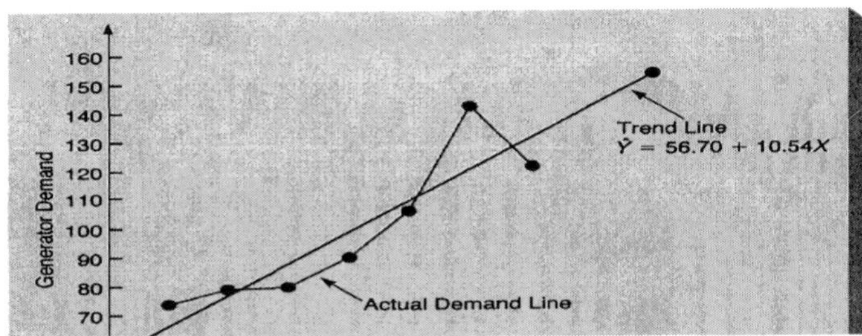

(a) negative correlation coefficient.
(b) zero correlation coefficient.
(c) positive correlation coefficient.
(d) correlation coefficient equal to +1.
(e) none of the above

ANSWER: c

4.59 The correlation coefficient resulting from a particular regression analysis was 0.25. What was the coefficient of determination?

(a) 0.5
(b) -0.5
(c) 0.0625
(d) There is insufficient information to answer the question.
(e) none of the above

ANSWER: c

4.60 The coefficient of determination resulting from a particular regression analysis was 0.85. What was the correlation coefficient?

(a) 0.5
(b) -0.5
(c) 0.922
(d) There is insufficient information to answer the question.
(e) none of the above

ANSWER: c

4.61 Which of the following is an assumption of the regression model?

(e) none of the above

ANSWER: c

4.61 Which of the following is an assumption of the regression model?

(a) The errors are independent.
(b) The errors are not normally distributed.
(c) The errors have a standard deviation of zero.
(d) The errors have an irregular variance.
(e) The errors follow a cone pattern.

ANSWER: a

4.62 In a good regression model the residual plot shows

(a) a cone pattern.
(b) an arched pattern.
(c) a random pattern.
(d) an increasing pattern.
(e) a decreasing pattern.

ANSWER: c

4.63 The mean square error (MSE) is

(a) denoted by s.
(b) denoted by k.
(c) the SSE divided by the number of observations.
(d) the SSE divided by the degrees of freedom.
(e) none of the above

ANSWER: d

4.64 In simple linear regression which of the following is true regarding significance testing?

(a) the significance level for the overall model will be the same as the significance level for the hypothesis test about the slope.
(b) an F-test is used to test the hypothesis that the slope is equal to zero.
(c) the significance test for the intercept tests the hypothesis that the intercept is equal to zero.
(d) a high level of significance implies the model is a good prediction equation.
(e) a low level of significance implies the Y variable is a good predictor of the X variable.

ANSWER: a

4.65 A prediction equation for starting salaries (in $1,000's) and SAT scores was performed using simple linear regression. In the regression printout shown below, what can be said about the level of significance for the overall model?

SUMMARY OUTPUT

Regression Statistics	
Multiple R	0.935018123
R Square	0.87425889
Adjusted R Square	0.860287655
Standard Error	3.307295949
Observations	11

ANOVA

	df	*SS*	*MS*	*F*	*Significance F*
Regression	1	684.4652324	684.4652	62.57564	2.42144E-05
Residual	9	98.44385847	10.93821		
Total	10	782.9090909			

	Coefficients	*Standard Error*	*t Stat*	*P-value*	*Lower 95%*
Intercept	-29.14060468	8.660080997	-3.36493	0.008324	-48.73108387
SAT	0.065443841	0.008273059	7.910476	2.42E-05	0.046728866

(a) SAT is not a good predictor for starting salary.
(b) Overall the model does not provide a good prediction equation.
(c) The significance level for SAT indicates the slope is not equal to zero.
(d) The significance level for SAT indicates the slope is equal to zero.
(f) The significance level for the intercept indicates the model is not valid.

ANSWER: c

4.66 A healthcare executive is using regression to predict total revenues. She has decided to include both patient length of stay and insurance type in her model. Insurance type can be grouped into the following categories: Medicare, Medicaid, Managed Care, Self-Pay, and Charity. Which of the following is not true?

(a) Insurance type requires the use of dummy variables.
(b) Insurance type requires the use of binary variables.
(c) Insurance type will be represented in the regression model by five dummy variables.
(d) Insurance type will be represented in the regression model by four binary variables.

ANSWER: d

4.67 A healthcare executive is using regression to predict total revenues. She has decided to include both patient length of stay and insurance type in her model. Insurance type can be grouped into three categories: Government-Funded, Private-Pay, and 'Other'. Her model is

(a) Y = bo.
(b) Y = bo + b1X1.
(c) Y = bo + b1X1 + b2X2.
(d) Y = bo + b1X1 + b2X2 + b3X3.
(e) Y = bo + b1X1 + b2X2 + b3X3 +b4X4.

ANSWER: d

4.68 A healthcare executive is using regression to predict total revenues. She is deciding whether or not to include both patient length of stay and insurance type in her model. Her first regression model only included patient length of stay. The resulting r^2 was .83, with an adjusted r^2 of .82 and her level of significance was .003. In the second model, she included both patient length of stay and insurance type. The r^2 was .84 and the adjusted r^2 was .80 for the second model and the level of significance did not change. Which of the following statements is true?

(a) The second model is a better model.
(b) The first model is a better model.
(c) The r^2 increased when additional variables were added because these variables significantly contribute to the prediction of total revenues.
(d) The adjusted r^2 always increases when additional variables are added to the model.
(f) None of the above statements are true.

ANSWER: b

4.69 Which of the following statements is not true?

(a) The value of r^2 can never decrease as more variables are added to the model.
(b) The value of r^2 always increases as more variables are added to the model.
(c) The value of adjusted r^2 can never decrease as more variables are added to the model.
(d) The value of adjusted r^2 is contingent upon the number of variables in the model.
(e) All of the above statements are true.

ANSWER: c

4.70 Which of the following statements provides the best guidance for model building?
(a) If the value of r^2 increases as more variables are added to the model, the variables should always remain in the model, regardless of the magnitude of increase.
(b) If the value of the adjusted r^2 increases as more variables are added to the model, the variables should always remain in the model.
(c) If the value of r^2 increases as more variables are added to the model, the variables should never remain in the model, regardless of the magnitude of the increase.
(d) If the value of the adjusted r^2 increases as more variables are added to the model, the variables should never remain in the model.
(e) None of the statements provide accurate guidance.

ANSWER: b

4.71 Which of the following is not a common pitfall of regression?

(a) If the assumptions are not met, the statistical tests may not be valid.
(b) Two variables may be highly correlated to one another but one is not causing the other to change.
(c) Using a regression equation beyond the range of X is very questionable.
(d) Being concerned about the t-test for the coefficients of the independent variables.
(e) Concluding a statistically significant relationship implies practical value.

ANSWER: d

4.72 Which of the following is true regarding a regression model with multicollinearity, a high r^2 value and a low F-test significance level.

(a) The model is not a good prediction model.
(b) The high value of r^2 is due to the multicollinearity.
(c) The interpretation of the coefficients is valuable.
(d) The significance level tests for the coefficients are not valid.
(e) The significance level for the F-test is not valid.

ANSWER: d

PROBLEMS

4.73 A air conditioning and heating repair firm conducted a study to determine if the outside temperature could be used to predict the cost of an electric bill for homes during the winter months in Houston, Texas. The resulting regression equation was:

$Y = 227.19 - 1.45X$, where Y = monthly cost, X = outside air temperature

(a) If the temperature averaged 45 degrees during December, what is the forecasted cost of December's electric bill?

(b) If the temperature averaged 40 degrees during January, what is the forecasted cost of January's electric bill?

(c) Suppose that December's average temperature was 45 degrees and the actual bill was \$176.54, while January's average temperature was 40 and the actual bill was \$183.69. Calculate the mean absolute deviation for this.

ANSWER:

(a) 227.19 - 1.45(45) = 161.94

(b) 227.19 -1.45(40) = 169.19

(c) MAD = (14.6 + 14.5)/2 = 14.55

4.74 A large school district is reevaluating its teachers' salaries. They have decided to use regression analysis to predict mean teachers' salaries at each elementary school. The researcher uses years of experience to predict salary. The resulting equation was:

Y = 19389.21 + 1330.12X, where Y = salary and X = years of experience

(a) If a teacher has 10 years of experience, what is the forecasted salary?

(b) If a teacher has 5 years of experience, what is the forecasted salary?

(c) Based on this equation, for every additional year of service, a teacher could expect her salary to increase by how much?

ANSWER:

(a) $19,389.21 + 1330.12(10) = $32,690.41

(b) $19,389.21 + 1330.12(5) = $26,039.81

(c) $1,330.12

4.75 A air conditioning and heating repair firm conducted a study to determine if the outside temperature, thickness of the insulation, and age of the equipment could be used to predict the electric bill for a home during the winter months in Houston, Texas. The resulting regression equation was:

Y = 256.89 – 1.45X1 –11.26X2 +6.10X3,
where Y = monthly cost, X1 = temperature, X2 = insulation thickness, X3 = age of equipment

(a) If December has an average temperature of 45 degrees and the heater is 2 years old with insulation that is 6 inches thick, what is the forecasted monthly electric bill?

(b) If January has an average temperature of 40 degrees and the heater is 12 years old with insulation that is 2 inches thick, what is the forecasted monthly electric bill?

(c) Suppose that December's average temperature was 45 degrees and the actual bill was $276.54, while January's average temperature was 40 and the actual bill was $305.69. Calculate the mean absolute deviation for this.

ANSWER:

(a) $256.89 – 1.45(45) –11.26(6) +6.10(2) = $271.40
(b) $256.89 – 1.45(40)–11.26(2) +6.10(12) = $294.61

(c) MAD = (5.14 + 11.08)/2 = 8.11

4.76 A large school district is reevaluating its teachers' salaries. They have decided to use regression analysis to predict mean teacher salaries at each elementary school. The researcher uses years of experience to predict salary. The raw data is given in the table below. The resulting equation was:

Y = 19389.21 + 1330.12X, where Y = salary and X = years of experience

Salary	Yrs Exp
$24,265.00	8
$27,140.00	5
$22,195.00	2
$37,950.00	15
$32,890.00	11
$40,250.00	14
$36,800.00	9
$30,820.00	6
$44,390.00	21
$24,955.00	2
$18,055.00	1
$23,690.00	7
$48,070.00	20
$42,205.00	16

(a) Develop a scatter diagram.

(b) What is the MAD?

(c) What is the correlation coefficient?

(d) What is the coefficient of determination?

(e) What is the MSE?

ANSWERS:

(a)

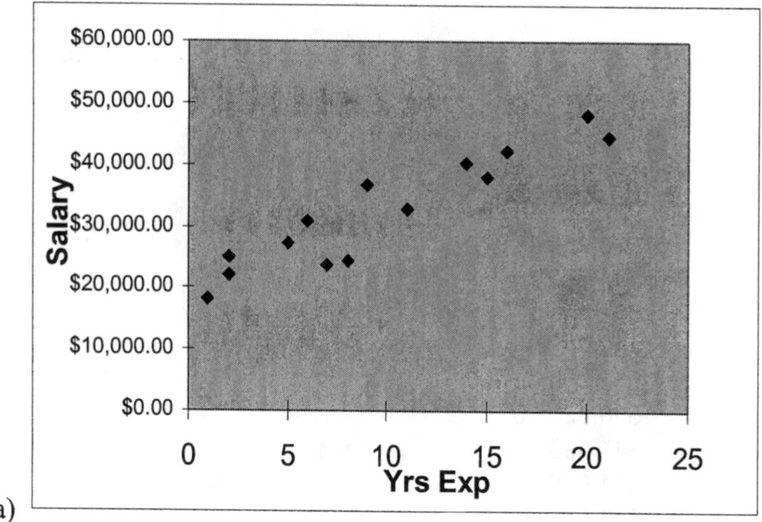

(b) 2698.95

(c) .936

(d) .877

(e) 11674818

4.77 A large international sales organization has collected data on the number of employees and the annual gross sales during the last 7 years. Determine

(a) a scatter diagram.
(b) the correlation coefficient.
(c) the coefficient of determination.
(d) the least squares trend line.
(d) the predicted value of sales for 2100 employees.
(e) the MAD.
(f) the MSE.

# of employees	sales (in $000's)
1975	100
2010	110
2005	122
2020	130
2030	139
2031	152
2050	164
2100	?

ANSWER:

(a)

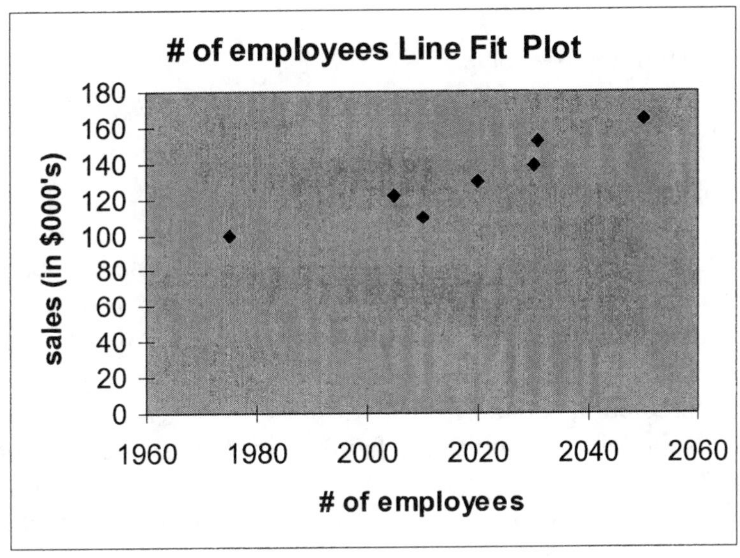

(b) .937

(c) .878

(d) Y = -1663.03 + .889X1

(e) 203.87 or $203,870

(f) 6.069

(g) 74.74

4.78 A large department store has collected the following monthly data on lost sales revenue due to theft and the number of security guard hours on duty:

Lost Sales Revenue ($000's)	Total Security Guard hours	Lost Sales Revenue ($000's)	Total Security Guard hours
1.0	600	1.8	950
1.4	630	2.1	1300
1.9	1000	2.3	1350
2.0	1200		

(a) Determine the least squares regression equation.
(b) Using the results of part (a), find the estimated lost sales revenues if the total number of security guard hours is 800.
(c) Calculate the coefficient of correlation.
(d) Calculate the coefficient of determination.

ANSWER:

(a) least squares equation $Y = .3780 + .0014X$

(b) $Y = .3780 + 0.0014(800) = 1.498$

(c) coefficient of correlation = 0.955

(d) coefficient of determination = 0.9121

4.79 Bob White is conducting research on monthly expenses for medical care, including over-the-counter medicine. His dependent variable is monthly expenses for medical care while his independent variable is number of family members. Below is his Excel output.

(a) What is the prediction equation?
(b) Based on his model, each additional family member increases the predicted costs by how much?
(c) Based on the significance F-test, is this model a good prediction equation?
(d) What percent of the variation in medical expenses is explained by the size of the family?
(e) Can the null hypothesis that the slope is zero be rejected? Why or why not?
(f) What is the value of the correlation coefficient?

SUMMARY OUTPUT

Regression Statistics	
Multiple R	0.695
R Square	0.483
Adjusted R Square	0.474
Standard Error	55.278
Observations	21

ANOVA

	df	*SS*	*MS*	*F*	*Significance F*
Regression	1	99929.47	99929.47	32.70311	0.00016
Residual	19	58057.48	3055.657		
Total	20	157987			

	Coefficients	*Standard Error*	*t Stat*	*P-value*
Intercept	110.47	35.53407	3.109087	0.0057
X	16.83	0.819024	5.718663	0.00016

ANSWERS:

(a) Y = 110.48 + 16.83X

(b) $16.83

(c) Yes, because the p value for the F-test is low

(d) 48.3% of the variation in medical expenses is explained by family size.

(e) The null hypothesis can be rejected, the slope is not equal to zero based on the low p value.

(f) 0.695

4.80 A large school district is reevaluating its teachers' salaries. They have decided to use regression analysis to predict mean teacher salaries at each high school. The researcher uses years of experience and subject matter (Math, Science, English, Other) to predict salary. The raw data is given in the table below. The resulting equation was

Y = 19389.21 + 1330.12X1 + X2, where Y = salary, X1 = years of experience, X2 = math, X3 = science, X4 = English.

Salary	Yrs Exp	Subject
$24,265.00	8	English
$27,140.00	5	English
$22,195.00	2	math
$37,950.00	15	science
$32,890.00	11	other
$40,250.00	14	math
$36,800.00	9	math
$30,820.00	6	science
$44,390.00	21	math
$24,955.00	2	science
$18,055.00	1	English
$23,690.00	7	English
$48,070.00	20	science
$42,205.00	16	math
$24,265.00	6	other
$27,140.00	8	other
$36,875.00	7	math
$37,950.00	9	math
$32,890.00	1	English
$40,250.00	4	science

(a) What is the prediction equation?

(b) What is the correlation coefficient?

(c) What is the coefficient of determination?

(d) What is the MAD?

(e) What is the MSE?

ANSWERS:

(a) Y = 20747.1 + 882.15X1 + 6661.11X2 + 7369.71X3 + 579.45X4

(b) 0.852

(c) 0.726

(d) 3395.89

(e) 24516052

4.81 Bob White is conducting research on monthly expenses for medical care, including over the counter medicine. His dependent variable is monthly expenses for medical care while his independent variables are number of family members and insurance type (government funded, private insurance and other). He has coded insurance type as the following:

X2 = 1 if government funded, X3 = 1 if private insurance

Below is his Excel output.

(a) What is the prediction equation?
(b) Based on the significance F-test, is this model a good prediction equation?
(c) What percent of the variation in medical expenses is explained by the independent variables?
(d) Based on his model, what are the predicted monthly expenses for a family of four with private insurance?
(e) Based on his model, what are the predicted monthly expenses for a family of two with government funded insurance?
(f) Based on his model, what are the predicted monthly expenses for a family of five with no insurance?

Regression Statistics	
Multiple R	0.8590
R Square	0.7379
Adjusted R Square	0.7182
Standard Error	952.3605
Observations	18

ANOVA	*df*	*SS*	*MS*	*F*	*Significance F*
Regression	3	1.32E+08	43977657	48.48745	1.21E-0'
Residual	14	12697866	906990.4		
Total	17	1.45E+08			

	Coefficients	*Standard Error*	*t Stat*	*P-value*
Intercept	144.91	1025.911	0.141246	0.889688
X1	11.63	1.247247	9.330762	2.19E-07
X2	-13.70	8.786907	-1.55916	0.141272
X3	-9.11	1.166068	7.810781	1.81E-06

ANSWERS:

(a) Y = 144.91 + 11.63X1 – 13.70 X2 – 9.11X3

(b) The model is a good prediction equation because the significance level for the F-test is low.

(c) 73.79 percent of the variation in medical expenses is explained by family size and insurance type.

(d) $182.32

(e) $154.47

(f) $203.06

SHORT ANSWER/ESSAY

4.82 The variable to be predicted is called the _____________ variable.

ANSWER: dependent or response

4.83 Explain the purpose of regression models.

ANSWER: To understand the relationship between variables and to predict the value of one variable using the value of another variable.

4.84 What is the purpose of a scatter diagram?

ANSWER: To investigate the relationship between variables.

4.85 The X variable is known as the _____________ variable.

ANSWER: independent or explanatory or predictor.

4.86 Estimates of the slope and intercept are found from __________ data.

ANSWER: sample

4.87 The actual value minus the predicted value yields ___________.

ANSWER: error

4.88 The regression line minimizes the sum of the ______________ _________.

ANSWER: squared errors

4.89 The _______ measures the total variability in Y about the mean.

ANSWER: SST or sum of squares total

4.90 The ________ measures the variability in Y about the regression line.

ANSWER: SSE or sum of squares error

4.91 The __________ indicates how much total variability in Y is explained by the regression model.

ANSWER: SSR or sum of squares due to regression or r-squared

4.92 SST = SSR + _______.

ANSWER: SSE or sum of squares error

4.93 Explain what r-squared is.

ANSWER: It is a value between 0 and +1 and measures the amount of variability in Y that is explained by the regression equation.

4.94 What can be said about a r-squared value of 0.96?

ANSWER: This indicates that 96% of the variation in the dependent variable is being explained by the regression equation and there is a strong correlation between the variables.

4.95 Explain what the correlation coefficient is.

ANSWER: It is a value between -1 and +1 that measures the strength of the linear relationship between the X and Y variables.

4.96 What can be said about a correlation coefficient of -1?

ANSWER: This is a perfect positive correlation where all of the values lie in a straight line. The negative value indicates that as X increases in value, Y decreases in value.

4.97 What can be said about a correlation coefficient of +1?

ANSWER: This is a perfect positive correlation where all of the values lie in a straight line. The positive value indicates that as X increases in value, so does Y.

4.98 Another name for the Multiple R that is given in Excel is

ANSWER: correlation coefficient or coefficient of correlation.

4.99 Describe a residual plot.

ANSWER: A residual plot is a plot of the error terms against the independent variable. Residual plots that show patterns often indicate violations in the assumptions of the regression model.

4.100 The standard deviation of the regression is also called _______________.

ANSWER: the standard error of the estimate

4.101 When the significance level of a statistical test is ________, we can reject the null hypothesis.

ANSWER: low

4.102 What is the difference in simple linear regression models and multiple regression models?

ANSWER: multiple regression models have more than one independent variable

4.103 To include qualitative data in regression analysis, you must first create a ___________variable.

ANSWER: dummy or binary or indicator

4.104 The number of dummy variables must equal ___________ the number of categories of a qualitative variable.

ANSWER: one less than

4.105 As more variables are added to the model, what happens to the r-square value?

ANSWER: It goes up.

4.106 Discuss the relationship between r-square and adjusted r-square.

ANSWER: The value of r-square can never decrease when more variables are added to the model; however, the adjusted r-square may decrease when more variables are added to the model.

4.107 When the independent variables are correlated with each other ___________ is said to exist.

ANSWER: multicollinearity or collinearity

4.108 With a nonlinear relationship, a ______________ is necessary to turn a nonlinear model into a linear model.

ANSWER: transformation

4.109 List four pitfalls of regression.

ANSWER: If the assumptions are not met, the statistical test may not be valid. Correlation does not necessarily mean causation. If multicollinearity is present, the model is still good for prediction but interpretation of the individual coefficients is questionable. Interpretation outside of the range of X values is questionable. The regression equation should not be used to predict a value of Y when X is zero. Using the F-test and concluding a linear relationship is helpful in predicting Y does not mean that this is the best relationship. A statistically significant relationship does not mean practical value.

CHAPTER 5
Forecasting

TRUE/FALSE

5.1 To make a forecast which is accurate over time requires historical data.

ANSWER: TRUE

5.2 No single forecasting method is superior to another.

ANSWER: TRUE

5.3 The three categories of forecasting models are time series, quantitative, and qualitative.

ANSWER: FALSE

5.4 Time-series models attempt to predict the future by using historical data.

ANSWER: TRUE

5.5 Time-series models rely on judgment in an attempt to incorporate qualitative or subjective factors into the forecasting model.

ANSWER: FALSE

5.6 A moving average forecasting method is a causal forecasting method.

ANSWER: FALSE

5.7 An exponential forecasting method is a time-series forecasting method.

ANSWER: TRUE

5.8 A trend-projection forecasting method is a causal forecasting method.

ANSWER: FALSE

5.9 Qualitative models produce forecasts that are little better than simple guesses or coin tosses.

ANSWER: FALSE

5.10 One of the most popular qualitative forecasting methods is the Delphi technique.

ANSWER: TRUE

5.11 A disadvantage of the Delphi technique is that results are obtained slowly.

ANSWER: TRUE

5.12 A scatter diagram is useful to determine if a relationship exists between two variables.

ANSWER: TRUE

5.13 When one plots a scatter diagram, the independent variable (X) is always *time*.

ANSWER: FALSE

5.14 The naive forecast for the next period is the actual value observed in the current period.

ANSWER: TRUE

5.15 Mean absolute deviation (MAD) is simply the sum of forecast errors.

ANSWER: FALSE

5.16 Time-series models enable the forecaster to include specific representations of various qualitative and quantitative factors.

ANSWER: FALSE

5.17 Four components of time series are trend, moving average, exponential smoothing, and seasonality.

ANSWER: FALSE

5.18 The fewer the periods over which one takes a moving average, the more accurately the resulting forecast mirrors the actual data of the most recent time periods.

ANSWER: TRUE

5.19 In a weighted moving average, the weights assigned must sum to 1.

ANSWER: FALSE

5.20 As a causal method, moving averages are preferable to exponential smoothing.

ANSWER: FALSE

5.21 An advantage of exponential smoothing over a simple moving average is that the exponential smoothing model can be extended to include a trend term.

ANSWER: TRUE

5.22 Exponential smoothing cannot be used for data with a trend.

ANSWER: FALSE

5.23 In a second order exponential smoothing, a low β gives less weight to more recent trends

ANSWER: TRUE

5.24 An advantage of exponential smoothing over a simple moving average is that exponential smoothing requires one to retain less data.

ANSWER: TRUE

5.25 Often, a variety of variables may be successfully used in a trend projection forecast of a single independent variable.

ANSWER: FALSE

5.26 A seasonal index must be between –1 and +1.

ANSWER: FALSE

5.27 A seasonal index of 1 means that the season is average.

ANSWER: TRUE

5.28 The process of isolating linear trend and seasonal factors to develop a more accurate forecast is called regression.

ANSWER: FALSE

5.29 The purpose of a tracking *signal* is to help us estimate the forecast error at each data point.

ANSWER: FALSE

5.30 Adaptive smoothing is analogous to exponential smoothing where the coefficients α and β are periodically updated to improve the forecast.

ANSWER: TRUE

5.31 Bias is the average error of a forecast model.

ANSWER: TRUE

MULTIPLE CHOICE

5.32 Which of the following is not classified as a qualitative forecasting model?

(a) exponential smoothing
(b) Delphi
(c) executive opinion
(d) sales force composite
(e) consumer market survey

ANSWER: a

5.33 A graphical plot with sales on the Y axis and time on the X axis is a

(a) scatter diagram.
(b) trend projection.
(c) radar chart.
(d) line graph.
(e) bar chart.

ANSWER: a

5.34 Which of the following statements about scatter diagrams is true?

(a) Time is always plotted on the Y axis.
(b) It can depict the relationship among three variables simultaneously.
(c) It is helpful when forecasting with qualitative data.
(d) The variable to be forecasted is placed on the Y axis.
(e) It is not a good tool for understanding time-series data.

ANSWER: d

5.35 Which of the following is a technique used to determine forecasting accuracy?

(a) Mean deviation
(b) Squared Average Error
(c) Mean Absolute Percent Error
(d) Delphi Method
(e) none of the above

ANSWER: c

5.36 Given that the MAD for the following forecast is 2.5, what is the actual value in period 2?

Period	Forecast	Actual
1	100	95
2	110	
3	120	123
4	130	130

(a) 120
(b) 98
(c) 108
(d) 115
(e) none of the above

ANSWER: c

5.37 Given the MAD for the following forecast is 4.0 what is the forecast value in period 4?

Period	Forecast	Actual
1	15	11
2	20	13
3	25	21
4		23

(a) 24
(b) 30
(c) 23
(d) 33
(e) none of the above

ANSWER: a

5.38 Enrollment in a particular class for the last four semesters has been 120, 126, 110, and 130. Suppose a one-semester moving average was used to forecast enrollment (this is sometimes referred to as a naive forecast). Thus, the forecast for the second semester would be 120, for the third semester it would be 126, and for the last semester it would be 110. What would the MSE be for this situation?

(a) 196.00
(b) 230.67
(c) 100.00
(d) 42.00
(e) none of the above

ANSWER: b

5.39 Given that the MSE for the following forecast is 9.5, what is the forecast value in period 3?

Period	Forecast	Actual
1	100	95
2	110	108
3		123
4	130	130

(a) 108
(b) 118
(c) 128
(d) 115
(e) none of the above

ANSWER: e

5.40 Assume that you have tried three different forecasting models. For the first, the MAD = 2.5, for the second, the MSE = 10.5, and for the third, the MAPE = 2.7. We can then say:

(a) the third method is the best.
(b) the second method is the best.
(c) methods one and three are preferable to method two.
(d) method two is least preferred.
(e) none of the above

ANSWER: e

5.41 Given that the MSE for the following forecast is 37.5, what is the actual value for period 1?

Period	Forecast	Actual
1	15	
2	20	13
3	25	21
4	30	23

(a) 15
(b) 16
(c) 11
(d) 10
(e) none of the above

ANSWER: e

5.42 Daily demand for newspapers for the last 10 days has been as follows: 12, 13, 16, 15, 12, 18, 14, 12, 13, 15. Forecast sales for the next day using a two-day moving average.

(a) 14
(b) 13
(c) 15
(d) 28
(e) none of the above

ANSWER: a

5.43 As one increases the number of periods used in the calculation of a moving average,

(a) greater emphasis is placed on more recent data.
(b) less emphasis is placed on more recent data.
(c) the emphasis placed on more recent data remains the same.
(d) it requires a computer to automate the calculations.
(e) one is usually looking for a long-term prediction.

ANSWER: b

5.44 Enrollment in a particular class for the last four semesters has been 120, 126, 110, and 135. The best forecast of enrollment next semester, based on a three-semester moving average, would be

(a) 126.
(b) 135.
(c) 120.
(d) 123.
(e) 125.

ANSWER: d

5.45 Which of the following is not a problem with moving average models?

(a) Larger number of periods may smooth out real changes.
(b) They take a considerable period of time to construct.
(c) They don't pick up trends in time to react to the trends.
(d) They require that lots of past data be kept.
(e) none of the above

ANSWER: b

5.46 Daily demand for newspapers for the last 10 days has been as follows: 12, 13, 16, 15, 12, 18, 14, 12, 13, 15. Forecast sales for the next day using a three-day weighted moving average where the weights are 3, 1, and 1 (the highest weight is for the most recent number).

(a) 12.8
(b) 13.0
(c) 70.0
(d) 14.0
(e) none of the above

ANSWER: d

5.47 A weighted moving average having the early periods more heavily weighted

(a) is more responsive to recent demand changes.
(b) is less responsive to recent demand.
(c) places emphasis on the past demand data.
(d) is always the most effective weighting scheme.
(e) is not a time-series model.

ANSWER: b

5.48 An exponential smoothing model having a large α

(a) is more responsive to recent demand changes.
(b) is less responsive to recent demand.
(c) places emphasis on the past demand data.
(d) is always the most effective weighting scheme.
(e) is not a time-series model.

ANSWER: a

5.49 Enrollment in a particular class for the last four semesters has been 120, 126, 110, and 130. Develop a forecast of enrollment next semester using exponential smoothing with an alpha = 0.2. Assume that an initial forecast for the first semester was 120 (so the forecast and the actual were the same).

(a) 118.96
(b) 121.17
(c) 130
(d) 120
(e) none of the above

ANSWER: b

5.50 In picking the smoothing constant for an exponential smoothing model, we should look for a value which

(a) produces a nice-looking curve.
(b) produces the values you would like to see.
(c) produces values which compare well with actual values based on a standard measure of error.
(d) cause the least computational effort.
(e) none of the above

ANSWER: c

5.51 In the exponential smoothing forecasting method, β is the

(a) slope of the trend line.
(b) new forecast.
(c) Y-axis intercept.
(d) independent variable.
(e) trend smoothing constant.

ANSWER: e

5.52 The computer monitoring of tracking signals and self adjustment is referred to as

(a) exponential smoothing.
(b) adaptive smoothing.
(c) trend projections
(d) tracking signals
(e) running sum of forecast errors (RFSE)

ANSWER: b

5.53 Which of the following is not a characteristic of trend projections?

(a) The variable being predicted is the Y variable.
(b) Time is the X variable
(c) It is useful for predicting the value of one variable based on time trend.
(d) It is helpful for determining if time is causing the dependent variable.
(e) none of the above

ANSWER: d

5.54 When both trend and seasonal components are present in time series, which of the following is most appropriate?

(a) the use of moving averages
(b) the use of centered moving averages
(c) the use of exponential smoothing
(d) the use of weighted moving averages
(e) none of the above

ANSWER: b

5.55 A tracking signal was calculated for a particular set of demand forecasts. This tracking signal was positive. This would indicate that

(a) demand is greater than the forecast.
(b) demand is less than the forecast.
(c) demand is equal to the forecast.
(d) the MAD is negative.
(e) none of the above

ANSWER: a

5.56 A tracking signal was calculated for a particular set of demand forecasts. This tracking signal was negative. This would indicate that

(a) the trend portion of the model was inappropriate.
(b) the nontrend portion of the model was inappropriate.
(c) the EMSE is negative.
(d) the MAD is negative.
(e) none of the above

ANSWER: a

PROBLEMS

5.57 Demand for a particular type of battery fluctuates from one week to the next. A study of the last 6 weeks provides the following demands (in dozens): 4, 5, 3, 6, 7, 8 (last week).

(a) Forecast demand for the next week using a 2-week moving average.
(b) Forecast demand for the next week using a 3-week moving average.

ANSWER:

(a) (7+8)/2 = 7.5
(b) (6+7+8)/3 = 7

5.58 Daily high temperatures in the city of Houston for the last week have been: 93, 94, 93, 95, 96, 88, 90 (yesterday).

(a) Forecast the high temperature today using a 3-day moving average.
(b) Forecast the high temperature today using a 2-day moving average.
(c) Calculate the mean absolute deviation based on a 2-day moving average.

ANSWER:

(a) (96+88+90)/3 = 91.3
(b) (88+90)/2 = 89
(c) MAD = 13.5/5 = 2.7

5.59 For the data below

Month	Automobile Battery Sales	Month	Automobile Battery Sales
January	20	July	17
February	21	August	18
March	15	September	20
April	14	October	20
May	13	November	21
June	16	December	23

(a) Develop a scatter diagram.
(b) Develop a three-month moving average.
(c) Compute MAD.

ANSWER:
(a) Scatter diagram

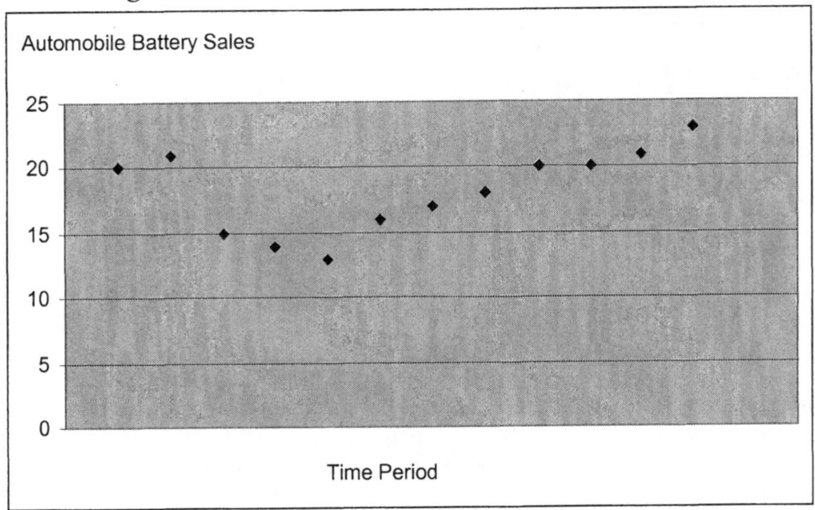

(b)

Month	Automobile Battery Sales	3-Month Moving Avg.	Absolute Deviation
January	20	-	-
February	21	-	-
March	15	-	-
April	14	18.67	4.67
May	13	16.67	3.67
June	16	14	2
July	17	14.33	2.67
August	18	15.33	3.67
September	20	17	3
October	20	18.33	1.67
November	21	19.33	1.67
December	23	20.33	2.67
January	-	21.33	-

(c) MAD = 2.74

5.60 For the data below

Month	Automobile Tire Sales	Month	Automobile Tire Sales
January	80	July	68
February	84	August	100
March	60	September	80
April	56	October	80
May	52	November	84
June	64	December	92

(a) Develop a scatter diagram.
(b) Compute a three-month moving average.
(c) Compute the MSE.

ANSWER:

(a) scatter diagram

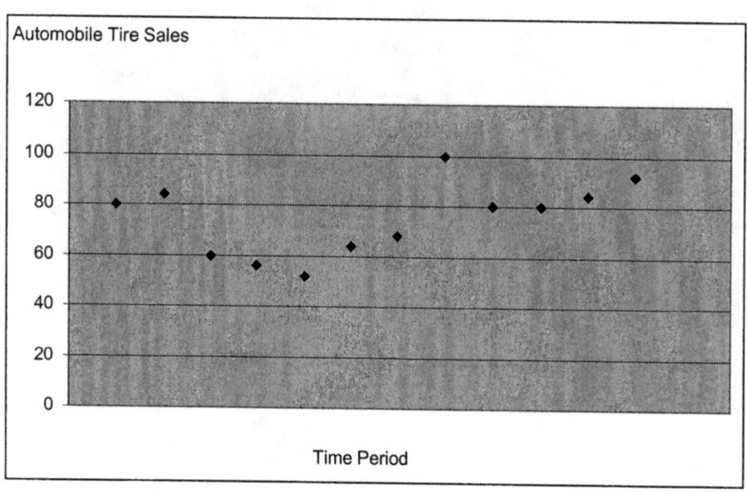

(b)

Month	Automobile Tire Sales	3-Month Tire Avg.	Squared Error
January	80	-	-
February	84	-	-
March	60	-	-
April	56	74.7	349.69
May	52	66.7	216.09
June	64	56.0	64
July	68	57.3	114.49
August	100	61.3	1497.69
September	80	77.3	7.29
October	80	82.7	7.29
November	84	86.7	7.29
December	92	81.3	114.49
January	-	85.33	

(c) MSE = 264.26

5.61 For the data below

Year	Automobile Sales	Year	Automobile Sales
1990	116	1977	119
1991	105	1998	34
1992	29	1999	34
1993	59	2000	48
1994	108	2001	53
1995	94	2002	65
1996	27	2003	111

(a) Develop a scatter diagram.
(b) Develop a six-year moving average forecast.
(c) Find MAPE.

ANSWERS:

(a) scatter diagram

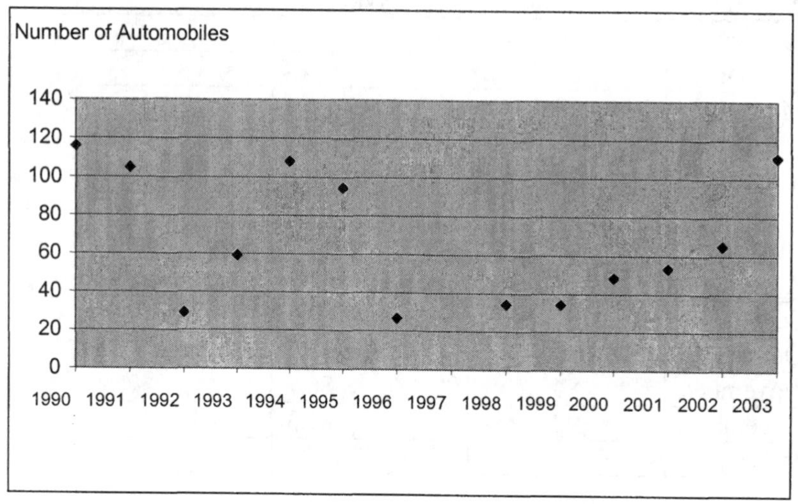

(b)

Year	Number of Automobiles	Forecast	Error	|Error / Actual|
1990	116	X		
1991	105	X		
1992	29	X		
1993	59	X		
1994	108	X		
1995	94	X		
1996	27	85.2	-58.2	2.15
1977	119	70.3	48.7	0.41
1998	34	72.7	-38.7	1.14
1999	34	73.5	-39.5	1.16
2000	48	69.3	-21.3	0.44
2001	53	59.3	-6.3	0.12
2002	65	52.5	12.5	0.19
2003	111	58.8	52.2	0.47

(c) MAPE = .76 * 100% = 76%

5.62 Use exponential smoothing with $\alpha = 0.2$ to forecast battery sales. Assume the forecast for January was 22 batteries.

Month	Automobile Battery Sales
January	20
February	21
March	15
April	14

ANSWER: Forecasts for January to April are: 22, 21.6, 21.48, 20.184.

5.63 Average starting salaries for students using a placement service at a university have been steadily increasing. A study of the last four graduating classes indicates the following average salaries: \$20,000, \$22,000, \$23,000, and \$25,000 (last graduating class). Predict the starting salary for the next graduating class using an exponential smoothing model with $\alpha = 0.2$. Assume that the initial forecast was \$20,000 (so that the forecast and the actual were the same).

ANSWER: Forecast for next period = 21,736.00

5.64 Use exponential smoothing with $\alpha = 0.3$ to forecast the battery sales. Assume the forecast for January was 22 batteries.

Month	Automobile Tire Sales
January	20
February	21
March	15
April	14

ANSWER:

Month	Automobile Tire Sales	Forecasts
January	20	22.00
February	21	21.4
March	15	21.28
April	14	19.40

5.65 Given the following data, if MAD = 1.25, determine what the actual demand must have been in period 2 (A_2).

Time Period	Actual (A)	Forecast (F)	|A-F|
1	2	3	1
2	A_2 = ?	4	-
3	6	5	1
4	4	6	2

ANSWER:

$A_2 = 3$ or $A_2 = 5$

5.66 Calculate (a) MAD, (b) MSE, and (c) MAPE for the following forecast versus actual sales figures.

Forecast	Actual
100	95
110	108
120	123
130	130

ANSWER:

(a) MAD = 10/4 = 2.5
(b) MSE = 38/4 = 9.5
(c) MAPE = (0.0956/4)100 = 2.39%

5.67 Use the sales data given below to determine

(a) the least squares trend line.
(b) the predicted value for 2002 sales.
(c) the MAD.
(d) the unadjusted forecasting MSE.

Year	Sales (units)	Year	Sales (units)
1995	130	1999	169
1996	140	2000	182
1997	152	2001	194
1998	160	2002	?

ANSWER:

(a) $\hat{y} = 119.14 + 10.46X$
(b) 119.14 + 10.46(8) = 202.82
(c) MAD = 1.01
(d) MSE = 1.71

5.68 For the data below

Year	Automobile Sales	Year	Automobile Sales
1990	116	1977	119
1991	105	1998	34
1992	29	1999	34
1993	59	2000	48
1994	108	2001	53
1995	94	2002	65
1996	27	2003	111

(a) Determine the least squares regression line.
(b) Determine the predicted value for 2004.
(c) Determine the MAD.
(d) Determine the unadjusted forecasting MSE.

ANSWER:

(a) $\hat{y} = 85.15 - 1.8X1$
(b) $85.15 - 1.8\ (15) = 58.15$
(c) MAD = 30.09
(d) MSE = 1,121.66

5.69 Given the following gasoline data

Quarter	Year 1	Year 2
1	150	156
2	140	148
3	185	201
4	160	174

(a) Compute the seasonal index for each quarter.
(b) Suppose we expect year 3 to have annual demand of 800, what is the forecast value for each quarter in year 3?

ANSWER:

(a)

Quarter	Year 1	Year 2	Average two-year demand	Quarterly demand	Average seasonal index
1	150	156	153	164.25	.93
2	140	148	144	164.25	.88
3	185	201	193	164.25	1.18
4	160	174	167	164.25	1.02

(b)

Quarter	Forecast
1	200 * .93 = 186.30
2	200 * .88 = 175.34
3	200 * 1.18 = 235.01
4	200 * 1.02 = 203.35

5.70 Given the following data and seasonal index

Month	Sales	
	Year 1	Year 2
Jan	8	8
Feb	7	9
Mar	5	6
Apr	10	11
May	9	12
June	12	16
July	15	20
Aug	20	25
Sept	4	4
Oct	3	2
Nov	8	7
Dec	9	9

(a) Compute the seasonal index using only year 1 data.
(b) Determine the deseasonalized demand values using year 2 data.
(c) Determine the trend line on year 2's deseasonalized data.
(d) Forecast the sales for the first 3 months of year 3, adjusting for seasonality.

ANSWER:

(a) and (b)

Month	Year 1		Year 2	
	Sales	Seasonal index	Sales	Deseasonalized data
Jan	8	.87	8	6.98
Feb	7	.76	9	6.87
Mar	5	.55	6	3.27
Apr	10	1.09	11	12.00
May	9	.98	12	11.78
June	12	1.31	16	20.94
July	15	1.64	20	32.73
Aug	20	2.18	25	54.54
Sept	4	.44	4	1.75
Oct	3	.33	2	0.65
Nov	8	.87	7	6.11
Dec	9	.98	9	8.84

(c) $y = 11.96 + .29\ X$

(d) Jan = [11.96 + .29 (13)] *.87 = 13.69
Feb = [11.96 + .29 (14)] *.67 = 12.18
Mar = [11.96 + .29 (15)] *.55 = 8.97

SHORT ANSWER/ESSAY

5.71 In what way might it be said that all forecasting models are subjective?

ANSWER: The forecaster always make a choice as to which variables to include, what data is acceptable, and which measurements appropriate.

5.72 In general terms, describe what causal forecasting models are.

ANSWER: Causal forecasting models incorporate variables or factors that might influence the quantity being forecasted.

5.73 In general terms, describe what qualitative forecasting models are.

ANSWER: Qualitative forecasting models attempt to incorporate judgmental or subjective factors into the model.

5.74 Briefly describe the Delphi forecasting method.

ANSWER: the Delphi forecasting method is an iterative group process that allows for individuals, at various locations, to make a qualitative forecast.

5.75 Briefly describe the executive opinion forecasting method.

ANSWER: The executive opinion forecasting model uses the opinions of a small group of high-level managers and makes a group estimate of demand.

5.76 Briefly describe the consumer market survey forecasting method.

ANSWER: It is a forecasting method that solicits input from customers or potential customers regarding their future purchasing plans.

5.77 Explain, briefly, why the Delphi forecasting approach is probably the most useful of those discussed when attempting to forecast 50 to 100 years into the future.

ANSWER: (a) There is little or no useful quantitative data available; (b) the knowledge of several, perhaps many, disciplines will be required; (c) you wish to be able to weight each of the sources about equally.

5.78 Briefly describe why the scatter diagram is helpful.

ANSWER: Scatter diagrams show the relationships between model variables.

5.79 Explain, briefly, why most forecasting error measures use either the absolute or the square of the error.

ANSWER: A deviation is equally important whether it is above or below the actual. This also prevents negative errors from canceling positive errors that would understate the true size of the errors.

5.80 List four measures of historical forecasting errors.

ANSWER: MAD, MSE, MAPE, Bias

5.81 In general terms, describe what time-series forecasting models are.

ANSWER: forecasting models that make use of historical data

5.82 List the possible components of time-series data.

ANSWER: trend, seasonality, cycles, random variations, or noise

5.83 Explain, briefly, why the larger number of periods included in a moving average forecast, the less well the forecast identifies rapid changes in the variable of interest.

ANSWER: The larger the number of periods included in the moving average forecast, the less the average is changed by the addition or deletion of a single number.

5.84 State the mathematical expression for weighted moving average.

ANSWER: $F_t = F_{t-1} + \alpha(Y_{t-1} - F_{t-1})$

5.85 Explain, briefly, why, in the exponential smoothing forecasting method, the larger the value of the smoothing constant, α, the better the forecast will be in allowing the user to see rapid changes in the variable of interest.

ANSWER: The larger the value of α, the greater is the weight placed on the most recent occurrences.

5.86 In exponential smoothing, discuss the difference between α and β.

ANSWER: α is a weight applied to adjust for the difference between last period actual and forecasted value. β is a trend smooth constant.

5.87 In general terms, describe the difference between a regression model and trend projection.

ANSWER: In trend projections, the independent variable is always time.

5.88 In general terms, describe a centered moving average.

ANSWER: Centered moving averages are used to compute seasonal indexes when there is a trend.

5.89 The decomposition approach to forecasting (using trend and seasonal components) may be helpful when attempting to forecast a time-series. Could an analogous approach be used in multiple regression analysis? Explain briefly.

ANSWER: An analogous approach would be possible using time as one independent variable and using a set of dummy variables to represent the seasons.

5.90 What is one advantage of using causal models over time-series or qualitative models?

ANSWER: Use of the causal model requires that the forecaster gain an understanding of the causes, not merely the frequency of variation;, i.e., the forecaster gains a greater understanding of the problem than the other methods.

5.91 Discuss the use of a tracking signal.

ANSWER: A tracking signal measures how well predictions fit actual data. By setting tracking limits, a manager is signaled to reevaluate the forecasting method.

CHAPTER 6
Inventory Control Models

TRUE/FALSE

6.1 Inventory is such an expensive asset that it may account for as much as 40 percent of a firm's invested capital.

ANSWER: TRUE

6.2 The objective of inventory control is to minimize customer dissatisfaction due to inventory control outages, called stockouts.

ANSWER: FALSE

6.3 In the decoupling function, some inventory may be stored between each production process to act as a buffer.

ANSWER: TRUE

6.4 Service level is the chance, measured in percent, that there will be a stockout.

ANSWER: FALSE

6.5 A stockout is a situation that occurs when there is no inventory on hand.

ANSWER: TRUE

6.6 The concept of inventory is applicable to both manufacturing and service organizations.

ANSWER: TRUE

6.7 One reason inventory is required is the uneven flow of resources through a company.

ANSWER: TRUE

6.8 Generally, supply and demand will be constant for a product.

ANSWER: FALSE

6.9 Economic order quantity (EOQ) analysis has recently become practical as a consequence of high-speed computers.

ANSWER: FALSE

6.10 As the amount of inventory rises, the total cost to the firm also rises.

ANSWER: FALSE

6.11 The purpose of the EOQ model is to achieve a balance between the cost of holding inventory and the cost of stockouts.

ANSWER: FALSE

6.12 Under the assumptions made to develop the EOQ model, average inventory is one half the maximum inventory.

ANSWER: TRUE

6.13 The EOQ model is relatively insensitive to minor violations of the basic assumptions.

ANSWER: TRUE

6.14 The production run model is useful when a firm purchases inventory that is delivered over a period of time.

ANSWER: TRUE

6.15 We can develop an EOQ model for any situation for which we can define an "ordering" cost (order, setup, etc.) and a holding cost.

ANSWER: TRUE

6.16 The economic order quantity helps one estimate the optimal number of units to purchase with each order.

ANSWER: TRUE

6.17 The reorder point occurs during a stockout.

ANSWER: FALSE

6.18 Safety stock is ignored when computing the reorder point.

ANSWER: FALSE

6.19 In a quantity discount model, the production cost must be included in the total cost calculation.

ANSWER: TRUE

6.20 In a quantity discount model, the ordering cost will exceed the holding cost if the discount level is ordered.

ANSWER: FALSE

6.21 Safety stock can be used to "compensate" for variation in delivery lead times.

ANSWER: TRUE

6.22 We can usually determine an appropriate safety stock even if we are unable to accurately assess the actual cost of a stockout.

ANSWER: TRUE

6.23 A lower level of inventory saves costs in two ways: It costs less to acquire and store the inventory, and it decreases the effort required to avoid stockouts.

ANSWER: FALSE

6.24 ABC analysis places inventory into 26 categories for computer analysis.

ANSWER: FALSE

6.25 In ABC inventory analysis, items in the "A" group should have the lowest dollar value to the firm.

ANSWER: FALSE

6.26 The costs involved in a typical inventory model are order costs, management costs, and holding costs.

ANSWER: FALSE

6.27 Understanding the inventory control process is a significant part of the problem of inventory model building.

ANSWER: TRUE

MULTIPLE CHOICE

6.28 Inventory

(a) is any stored resource used to satisfy current or future need.
(b) includes raw materials, work-in-process, and finished goods.
(c) levels for finished goods are a direct function of demand.
(d) needs from raw materials through finished goods can be reasonably determined, once finished goods demand is determined.
(e) all of the above

ANSWER: e

6.29 Which of the following is not a use of inventory?

(a) the decoupling function
(b) the translucent function
(c) an inflation hedge
(d) allows for quantity discounts
(e) to avoid stockouts and shortages
ANSWER: b

6.30 In making inventory decisions, the purpose of the basic model is to

(a) minimize customer dissatisfaction.
(b) minimize stock on hand.
(c) minimize carrying costs.
(d) minimize ordering costs.
(e) minimize the sum of carrying costs and ordering costs.

ANSWER: e

6.31 Which of the following factors is (are) not included in ordering cost?

(a) bill paying
(b) obsolescence
(c) purchasing department overhead costs
(d) inspecting incoming inventory
(e) developing and sending purchase orders

ANSWER: b

6.32 Which of the following factors is (are) not included in carrying cost?

(a) spoilage
(b) obsolescence
(c) cost of capital
(d) inspecting incoming inventory
(e) warehousing overhead costs

ANSWER: d

6.33 Mark Achin sells 3,600 electric motors each year. The cost of these is $200 each, and demand is constant throughout the year. The cost of placing an order is $40, while the holding cost is $20 per unit per year. There are 360 working days per year and the lead-time is 5 days. If Mark orders 200 units each time he places an order, what would his total ordering cost be for the year?

(a) $2,000
(b) $2,720
(c) $200
(d) $720
(e) none of the above

ANSWER: d

6.34 The annual demand for a product has been projected at 2,000 units. This demand is assumed to be constant throughout the year. The ordering cost is $20 per order, and the holding cost is 20 percent of the purchase cost. The purchase cost is $40 per unit. There are 250 working days per year. Currently, the company is ordering 500 units each time an order is placed. Assuming the company uses a safety stock of 20 units resulting in a reorder point of 60 units, what is the expected lead-time for delivery?

(a) 4 days
(b) 5 days
(c) 6 days
(d) 7 days
(e) none of the above

ANSWER: b

6.35 Andre Candess manages an office supply store. One product in the store is computer paper. Andre knows that 10,000 boxes will be sold this year at a constant rate throughout the year. There are 250 working days per year and the lead-time is 3 days. The holding cost is $15 per box per year. Andre orders 500 boxes each time he orders from his supplier. If his total relevant inventory cost (holding cost plus ordering cost) is $4,350, what is his cost for each order?

(a) $50/order
(b) $40/order
(c) $30/order
(d) $20/0rder
(e) none of the above

ANSWER: c

6.36 As the service level increases,

(a) carrying cost increases at an increasing rate.
(b) carrying cost increases at a decreasing rate.
(c) carrying cost decreases at a decreasing rate.
(d) carrying cost decreases at an increasing rate.
(e) none of the above

ANSWER: a

6.37 R.C. Barker makes purchasing decisions for his company. One product that he buys costs $50 per unit when the order quantity is less than 500. When the quantity ordered is 500 or more, the price per unit drops to $48. The ordering cost is $30 per order and the annual demand is 7,500 units. The holding cost is 10 percent of the purchase cost. If R.C. orders 500 units each time he places an order, what would the total annual holding cost be?
(a) $450
(b) $1,200
(c) $1,250
(d) $2,400
(e) none of the above
ANSWER: b

6.38 Which of the following is not an assumption for the basic EOQ model?

(a) Only an integer number of orders can be made each year.
(b) Quantity discounts are not possible.
(c) Inventory receipt is instantaneous (all at once).
(d) With orders placed at the correct time, there will be no shortages.
(e) Demand is known.

ANSWER: a

6.39 For the basic EOQ model, which of the following relationships is not true?

(a) The optimal number of orders per year equals annual demand divided by the EOQ.
(b) The reorder point equals daily demand times the lead-time in days.
(c) The average dollar level of inventory equals unit price times order quantity.
(d) Average inventory level equals one-half the order size.
(e) At EOQ, ordering cost equals carrying cost.

ANSWER: c

6.40 The EOQ model without the instantaneous receipt assumption is commonly called the

(a) quantity discount model.
(b) safety stock model.
(c) planned shortage model.
(d) production run model.
(e) none of the above

ANSWER: d

6.41 In the production run model of EOQ, the ordering cost of the basic model is replaced by the

(a) setup cost.
(b) stockout cost.
(c) carrying cost.
(d) material cost.
(e) none of the above

ANSWER: a

6.42 Sensitivity analysis of EOQ refers to

(a) the attitude of top management toward the use of the EOQ model.
(b) an assessment of the impact of obsolescence upon the EOQ.
(c) analysis of how much the EOQ will change when other variables change.
(d) a study of the impact of storing incompatible products in the same warehouse.
(e) analysis of the impact of stock shortages on customers or on production.

ANSWER: c

6.43 Consider an inventory situation in which all the EOQ assumptions are met except there are quantity discounts. When a person orders more than the EOQ so that the discount price can be had, which of the following is true?

(a) Total ordering cost usually decreases relative to EOQ cost.
(b) Total purchase cost usually increases relative to EOQ cost.
(c) Total holding cost usually decreases relative to EOQ cost.
(d) Holding cost per unit usually increases relative to EOQ cost.
(e) none of the above

ANSWER: a

6.44 The annual demand for a product has been projected at 2,000 units. This demand is assumed to be constant throughout the year. The ordering cost is $20 per order, and the holding cost is 20 percent of the purchase cost. Currently, the purchase cost is $40 per unit. There are 250 working days per year. Whenever an order is placed, it is known that the entire order will arrive on a truck in 6 days. Currently, the company is ordering 500 units each time an order is placed. What is the total holding cost for the year using this policy?

(a) $400
(b) $2,000
(c) $4,000
(d) $8,000
(e) none of the above
Answer b

ANSWER: b

6.45 Mark Achin sells 3,600 electric motors each year. The cost of these is $200 each, and demand is constant throughout the year. The cost of placing an order is $40, while the holding cost is $20 per unit per year. There are 360 working days per year and the lead-time is 5 days. If Mark orders 200 units each time he places an order, what would his average inventory be (in units)?

(a) 100
(b) 200
(c) 60
(d) 120
(e) none of the above

ANSWER: a

6.46 Andre Candess manages an office supply store. One product in the store is computer paper. Andre knows that 10,000 boxes will be sold this year at a constant rate throughout the year. There are 250 working days per year and the lead-time is 3 days. The cost of placing an order is $30, while the holding cost is $15 per box per year. How many units should Andre order each time to minimize his annual inventory cost?

(a) 200
(b) 400
(c) 500
(d) 100
(e) none of the above

ANSWER: a

6.47 Daniel Trumpe has computed the EOQ for a product he sells to be 400 units. However, due to recent events he has a cash flow problem. Therefore, he orders only 100 units each time he places an order. Which of the following is true for this situation?

(a) Total ordering cost will be higher than total holding cost.
(b) Total ordering cost will be lower than total holding cost.
(c) Total ordering cost will equal total holding cost.
(d) Nothing can be determined without more information.
(e) none of the above

ANSWER: a

6.48 The EOQ is particularly sensitive to which of the following?

(a) yearly demand
(b) order cost
(c) holding cost
(d) production cost
(e) none of the above

ANSWER: e

6.49 To evaluate quantity discounts, one uses the EOQ model, and modifies the model so that

(a) holding cost is considered as a percentage of unit cost rather than a separable dollar cost.
(b) the EOQ is calculated to lie within one of the cost corridors.
(c) holding cost is calculated on an "average basis" across the discounts.
(d) any one of the above approaches could be used
(e) none of the above

ANSWER: a

6.50 Which of the following does not have an impact on EOQ?

(a) safety stock
(b) demand per unit time
(c) order cost
(d) all of the above
(e) none of the above

ANSWER: a

6.51 Demand for a product is constant, but the lead time fluctuates. The demand during the lead time is normally distributed with a mean of 40 and a standard deviation of 4. If they have calculated a reorder point of 45.12 units, what service level are they assuming?

(a) 85 percent
(b) 90 percent
(c) 95 percent
(d) 97.5 percent
(e) none of the above

ANSWER: b

6.52 Judith Thompson is the manager of the student center cafeteria. She is introducing pizza as a menu item. The pizza is ordered frozen from a local pizza establishment and baked at the cafeteria. Judith anticipates a weekly demand of 10 pizzas. The cafeteria is open 45 weeks a year, 5 days a week. The ordering cost is $15 and the holding cost is $0.40 per pizza per year. What is the optimal number of pizzas Judith should order?

(a) 184 pizzas
(b) 9 pizzas
(c) 5 pizzas
(d) 28 pizzas
(e) none of the above

ANSWER: a

6.53 If Judith Thompson (in the previous problem) decides to round up her calculated optimal order quantity so as to have a whole number of pizzas to order, what will be the difference between the holding cost and ordering cost?

(a) $0, both costs are equal
(b) holding costs will be larger than ordering costs
(c) ordering costs will be larger than holding costs
(d) the outcome is uncertain until calculated
(e) none of the above

ANSWER: b

6.54 R.C. Barker makes purchasing decisions for his company. One product that he buys costs $50 per unit when the order quantity is less than 500. When the quantity ordered is 500 or more, the price per unit drops to $48. The ordering cost is $30 per order and the annual demand is 7,500 units. The holding cost is 10 percent of the purchase cost. If R.C. wishes to minimize his total annual inventory costs, he must evaluate the total cost for two possible order quantities. What are these two possible quantities? (Round answer to nearest unit.)

(a) 300 and 306
(b) 300 and 500
(c) 306 and 50
(d) 200 and 306
(e) none of the above

ANSWER: b

6.55 The annual demand for a product is 1,000 units. The company orders 200 units each time an order is placed. The lead-time is 6 days, and the company has determined that 20 units should be held as a safety stock. There are 250 working days per year. What is the reorder point?

(a) 20
(b) 24
(c) 44
(d) 120
(e) none of the above

ANSWER: c

6.56 The annual demand for a product has been projected at 2,000 units. This demand is assumed to be constant throughout the year. The ordering cost is $20 per order, and the holding cost is 20 percent of the purchase cost. Currently, the purchase cost is $40 per unit. There are 250 working days per year. Whenever an order is placed, it is known that the entire order will arrive on a truck in 6 days. Currently, the company is ordering 500 units each time an order is placed. What is the reorder point under the current policy?

(a) 48
(b) 100
(c) 6
(d) 24
(e) none of the above

ANSWER: a

6.57 Andre Candess manages an office supply store. One product in the store is computer paper. Andre knows that 10,000 boxes will be sold this year at a constant rate throughout the year. There are 250 working days per year and the lead-time is 3 days. The cost of placing an order is \$30, while the holding cost is \$15 per box per year. If Andre orders 500 boxes each time he orders from his supplier, what would his total relevant inventory cost be (holding cost plus ordering cost)?

(a) \$3,000
(b) \$4,350
(c) \$3,075
(d) \$3,750
(e) none of the above

ANSWER: b

6.58 Rolf Steps is the production manager for a local manufacturing firm. This company produces staplers and other items. The holding cost is \$2 per unit per year. The cost of setting up the production line for this is \$25. There are 200 working days per year. The production rate for this product is 80 per day. If the production order quantity is 200 units, what was the daily demand (rounded to the nearest whole unit)?

(a) 6 units
(b) 7 units
(c) 8 units
(d) 9 units
(e) none of the above

ANSWER: b

6.59 The "point at which to reorder" depends directly on which of the following?

(a) lead time
(b) ordering cost
(c) EOQ.
(d) storage costs
(e) none of the above

ANSWER: a

6.60 Judith Thompson, the manager of the student center cafeteria, has added pizza to the menu. The pizza is ordered frozen from a local pizza establishment and baked at the cafeteria. Judith anticipates a weekly demand of 10 pizzas. The cafeteria is open 45 weeks a year, 5 days a week. The ordering cost if $15 and the holding cost is $0.40 per pizza per year. The pizza vendor has a 4-day lead-time and Judith wants to maintain 1 pizza for safety stock. What is the optimal reorder point?

(a) 10
(b) 8
(c) 4
(d) 9
(e) none of the above

ANSWER: d

6.61 R.C. Barker makes purchasing decisions for his company. One product that he buys costs $50 per unit when the order quantity is less than 500. When the quantity ordered is 500 or more, the price per unit drops to $48. The ordering cost is $30 per order and the annual demand is 7,500 units. The holding cost is 10 percent of the purchase cost. How many units should R.C. order to minimize his total annual inventory cost? (Round answer to nearest unit.)

(a) 300
(b) 306
(c) 500
(d) 200
(e) none of the above

ANSWER: c

6.62 The annual demand for a product has been projected at 2,000 units. This demand is assumed to be constant throughout the year. The ordering cost is $20 per order, and the holding cost is 20 percent of the purchase cost. Currently, the purchase cost is $40 per unit. There are 250 working days per year. Whenever an order is placed, it is known that the entire order will arrive on a truck in 6 days. How many units should the company order each time an order is placed if the company wishes to minimize total inventory cost?

(a) 100
(b) 200
(c) 250
(d) 500
(e) none of the above

ANSWER: a

6.63 Judith Thompson, the student cafeteria manager, has decided to keep pizza as a permanent menu item after 3 successful months. She has entered discussions with the local pizza supplier to obtain a quantity discount. Currently, each pizza costs $4.75; however, if Judith purchases at least 225 pizzas at a time, their cost is $4.25 each. How much money can Judith save by ordering 225 pizzas at a time?

(a) Judith will not save any money
(b) $258.48
(c) $223.48
(d) $260.00
(e) none of the above

ANSWER: c

6.64 Extra inventory that is used to avoid stockouts is known as

(a) planned shortages.
(b) quantity discounts.
(c) safety stock.
(d) service level.
(e) ABC analysis.

ANSWER: c

6.65 As the service level increases,

(a) safety stock increases at a decreasing rate.
(b) safety stock increases at an increasing rate.
(c) safety stock decreases at an increasing rate.
(d) safety stock decreases at a decreasing rate.
(e) none of the above

ANSWER: b

6.66 A person is using the normal distribution to determine the safety stock for a product. What "z" value would be associated with a 90 percent service level?

(a) 0.90
(b) 1.28
(c) 0.53
(d) –0.90
(e) none of the above

ANSWER: b

6.67 Demand for a product is constant, but the lead-time fluctuates. The demand during the lead-time is normally distributed with a mean of 40 and a standard deviation of 4. If the company wishes to maintain a 90 percent service level, how much safety stock should be held?

(a) 45.12
(b) 41.28
(c) 1.28
(d) 5.12
(e) none of the above

ANSWER: d

6.68 The annual demand for a product is 1,000 units. The company orders 200 units each time an order is placed. The lead-time is 6 days. There are 250 working days per year. If the reorder point is 50, what safety stock are they using?

(a) 22
(b) 4
(c) 26
(d) 28
(e) none of the above

ANSWER: c

6.69 The annual demand for a product has been projected at 2,000 units. This demand is assumed to be constant throughout the year. The ordering cost is $20 per order, and the holding cost is 20 percent of the purchase cost. The purchase cost is $40 per unit. There are 250 working days per year. Whenever an order is placed, it is known that the entire order will arrive on a truck in 6 days. Currently, the company is ordering 500 units each time an order is placed. What level of safety stock would give a reorder point of 60 units?

(a) 10
(b) 14
(c) 18
(d) 22
(e) none of the above

ANSWER: e

6.70 A person is using the normal distribution to determine the safety stock for a product. The "z" value of 1.65 would be associated with what service level?

(a) 90 percent
(b) 95 percent
(c) 100 percent
(d) 92.5 percent
(e) none of the above

ANSWER: b

6.71 A person is using the normal distribution to determine the safety stock for a product. The "z" value of 2.32 would be associated with what service level?

(a) 95 percent
(b) 97.5 percent
(c) 98 percent
(d) 99 percent
(e) none of the above

ANSWER: d

6.72 Rolf Steps is the production manager for a local manufacturing firm. This company produces staplers and other items. The annual demand for a particular stapler is 1,600 units. The holding cost is $2 per unit per year. The cost of setting up the production line is $25. There are 200 working days per year. The production rate for this product is 80 per day. If Rolf decided to produce 200 units each time he started production of the stapler, what would his maximum inventory level be?

(a) 200
(b) 180
(c) 100
(d) 90
(e) none of the above

ANSWER: b

6.73 In the ABC analysis of inventory, the A group items

(a) are critical to the functioning of the organization.
(b) are the most expensive class of items.
(c) typically account for over 70 percent of the company's business in dollars.
(d) typically account for about 10 percent of a company's inventory items.
(e) all of the above

ANSWER: e

6.74 With an annual demand of 2,400 units, daily demand of 10 units, and daily production rate of 40 units, a company has determined that each production run will be for 200 units. If production starts when the inventory level is at zero, how many units would actually be in the warehouse at the end of the first day of production? (Round answer to nearest unit.)

(a) 12
(b) 20
(c) 30
(d) 40
(e) none of the above

ANSWER: c

6.75 Jack Spratt is the production manager for a manufacturing firm that produces wizzy-gadgets and other items. The annual demand for a particular wizzy-gadget is 1,600 units. The holding cost is $2 per unit per year. The cost of setting up the production line is $25. There are 200 working days per year. The production rate for this product is 80 per day. If his maximum inventory level is 180 units, how many units did he produce each time he started production of the wizzy-gadgets?

(a) 200
(b) 180
(c) 100
(d) 90
(e) none of the above

ANSWER: a

6.76 Rose Arena is the production manager for a manufacturing firm that produces buggy whips and other items. The annual demand for a particular buggy whip is 1,600 units. The holding cost is $2 per unit per year. The cost of setting up the production line is $25. There are 200 working days per year. Rose decided to produce 200 units each time she started production of the buggy whips. If it took her 4 days to produce the 200 units, what was her production rate?

(a) 80 units/day
(b) 60 units/day
(c) 40 units/day
(d) 100 units/day
(e) none of the above

ANSWER: e

PROBLEMS

6.77 East Valve Distributors distributes industrial valves and control devices. The Eastern control device has an annual demand of 9,375 units and sells for $100 per unit. The cost of ordering is $40 per order and the average carrying cost per unit per year is $0.75. Determine the economic order quantity.

ANSWER: EOQ = 1,000 units

6.78 We use 1,200 of a certain spare part that costs \$25 for each order and has a \$24 annual holding cost. Calculate the total cost for order sizes of: 25, 40, 50, 60, and 100. Identify the economic order quantity and consider the implications for making an error in calculating the economic order quantity.

ANSWER:

Total Cost = total ordering cost + total holding cost

Q = 25 TC = 1200 + 300 = \$1,500
Q = 40 TC = 750 + 480 = \$1,230
Q = 50 TC = 600 + 600 = \$1,200
Q = 60 TC = 500 + 720 = \$1,220
Q = 100 TC = 300 + 1200 = \$1,500
$Q^* = [(2*1200*25)/24]^{1/2} = 50$ units per order

Small variations in order quantity will not have a significant impact on total costs.

6.79 David and Beth Sheba run a health food store. Their top selling item is called Heavenly Kelp. The annual demand for this is 810 units, and demand is constant throughout the year. The cost of placing an order is \$20, while the holding cost per unit per year is \$4.

(a) How many orders per year should be placed if they wish to minimize their total cost?
(b) What is the minimum possible annual holding cost?

ANSWER:

(a) EOQ = 90 units. Therefore, the number of orders per year is 810/90 = 9 orders per year.
(b) (90/2)4 = \$180 total holding cost

6.80 Everett Mann's Dream Store sells waterbeds and supplies. The best selling bed in the store has an annual demand of 400 units. The ordering cost is \$40, while the holding cost is \$5 per unit per year. There are 250 working days per year, and the lead-time is 6 days.

(a) To minimize total cost, how many units should be ordered each time an order is placed?
(b) If the holding cost per unit was \$6 instead of \$5, what would the optimal order quantity be?

ANSWER:

(a) EOQ = 80 units
(b) EOQ = 73.02 units if C_h=6.

6.81 Ivonne Callen sells beauty supplies. Her annual demand for a particular skin lotion is 1,000 units. The cost of placing an order is $20, while the holding cost per unit per year is 10 percent of the cost. This item currently costs $10 if the order quantity is less than 300. For orders of 300 units or more, the cost falls to $9.80. To minimize total cost, how many units should Ivonne order each time she places an order? What is the minimum total cost?

ANSWER:

With EOQ = 200, the total cost is $10,200.

With Q = 300 to obtain discount, the total cost is $10,013.67.

Therefore, she should order 300 units.

6.82 Susan Holland sells hand-painted shirts to vacationers who enter her gift shop. Her supplier can deliver only 10 of these per day, but if she orders more than this, the supplier will deliver 10 each day until the entire order is met. Her annual demand for these is 1,000, and the sales are relatively constant for each of the 250 days that her store is open. The cost of placing an order is $20, while the holding cost per unit per year is $2. If she could convince her supplier to deliver her entire order on a single day, would this increase or decrease her carrying plus ordering cost?

ANSWER:

Q(Production model) = 182.5 units. Total carrying cost: = (1/2)*(182.5*2)*(1 - 4/10)
= 182.5*.6 = $109.5

Q(Simple EOQ Model) = 141 units. Total carrying cost: = 70.5*2 = $141

Therefore, having the supplier deliver 10 units per day until he has filled her order is the alternative that minimizes the total carrying plus order costs.

6.83 ArtOrgan, Ltd. distributes mechanical replacements for human mitral heart valves. Its artificial valve has a demand of 12,765 units per year and sells for $7,900 per unit. The cost of ordering is $75 per order and the average carrying cost per unit per year is $150. Determine the economic order quantity.

ANSWER: EOQ = 113 units

6.84 Furniture Manufacturers Inc., uses 20,000 loads of lumber per year. A load of lumber costs $500 and the carrying cost is 10 percent of the unit cost. The cost to order is $200 per order and the lead-time is three working days. Determine (assume 200 working days):

(a) the economic order quantity
(b) the reorder point
(c) number of orders per year
(d) days between orders

ANSWER:

(a) EOQ = 400 units
(b) ROP = 100(3) = 300 units
(c) number of orders per year = D/Q = 2000/400 = 50 orders
(d) days between orders = 200/50 = 4 days

6.85 We use 1,500 per year of a certain subassembly that has an annual holding cost of $45 per unit. Each order placed costs us $150. We operate 300 days per year and have found that an order must be placed with our supplier 6 working days before we can expect to receive that order. For this subassembly, find:

(a) the economic order quantity
(b) the annual holding cost
(c) the annual ordering cost
(d) the reorder point

ANSWER:

(a) EOQ = 100
(b) annual holding cost = (100/2)(45) = 2250
(c) annual ordering cost = (1500/100)150 = 2250
(d) ROP = 5(6) = 30 units

6.86 The H.A.L. Computer Store sells a printer for $200. Demand for this is constant during the year, and annual demand is forecasted to be 600 units. The holding cost is $20 per unit per year, while the cost of ordering is $60 per order. Currently, the company is ordering 12 times per year (50 units each time). There are 250 working days per year and the lead-time is 10 days.

(a) Given the current policy of ordering 50 units at a time, what is the total of the annual ordering cost and the annual holding cost?
(b) If the company used the absolute best inventory policy, what would the total of the ordering and holding cost be?
(c) What is the reorder point?

ANSWER:

(a) TOC + THC = 720 + 500 = $1220
(b) If we order EOQ = 60 units, TOC + THC = 600 + 600 = $1,200
(c) ROP = (600/250)10 = 24 units

6.87 Purinnerds Dog Food is a very popular product at Kay Gnein's corner grocery. Demand for this is relatively constant, and the total demand for the year is 1,200 bags. The cost of placing an order is $50, while the holding cost is $3 per unit per year. The store is open 300 days per year. Lead-time for this is 8 days.

(a) If Kay places 50 orders per year, what would her ordering and holding costs be?
(b) If Kay wishes to minimize her total inventory cost, how many units should she order each time an order is placed?
(c) What is the reorder point?

ANSWER:

(a) With 50 orders per year, Q=24. TC = TOC + THC = 2500 + 36 = $2,536
(b) EOQ = 200
(c) ROP = (1200/300)8 = 32 units

6.88 We use 2,750 per year of a certain subassembly that has a purchase cost of $450, and an annual holding cost of $500 per unit. Each order placed costs us $150. We operate 300 days per year and have found that an order must be placed with our supplier 6 working days before we can expect to receive that order. For this subassembly, find:

(a) economic order quantity = 40.6
(b) annual holding cost (using EOQ) = $10155.60
(c) annual ordering cost (using EOQ) = $10155.60
(d) reorder point = 55

6.89 The H.A.L. Computer Store sells a printer for $400. Demand for this is constant during the year, and annual demand is forecasted to be 1100 units. The holding cost is $20 per unit per year, while the cost of ordering is $90 per order. Currently, the company is ordering 12 times per year (92 units each time). There are 270 working days per year and the lead-time is 8 days.

(a) Given the current policy of ordering 92 units at a time, what is the total of the annual ordering cost and the annual holding cost?
(b) If the company used the absolute best inventory policy, what would the total of the ordering and holding cost be?
(c) What is the reorder point?
(d) How many days between orders with 12 orders per year?

ANSWER:

(a) TC = $1,996.09
(b) Using EOQ of 99.5 units: TC = $1990.00
(c) ROP = 32.6 units
(d) Number of days between orders = 22.5

6.90 The Handy Manufacturing Company manufactures small air conditioner compressors. The estimated demand for the year is 12,000 units. The setup cost for the production process is $200 per run, and the carrying cost is $10.00 per unit per year. The daily production rate is 100 units per day, and demand has been 50 units per day. Determine the number of units to produce in each batch. (Problem assumes 240 operating days.)

ANSWER: Optimum production quantity = 979.8 units

6.91 Anne Beck recently took over a beauty supply store. Her predecessor always ordered shampoo in quantities of 100 units. Anne is reevaluating this policy. Based on her analysis, the cost to place each order is $35 and the holding cost is $8 per shampoo bottle per year. The annual demand for this product is 2500 bottles. Should Anne change the current order policy and, if so, how much can she save?

ANSWER:

Current inventory policy parameters:
D = 2500, Q = 100, # of orders = 25, Average inventory = 50, Order cost = $875,
Holding cost = $400, Total inventory cost = $875 + $400 = $1,275

Optimal inventory policy parameters:
Q* = 147.9, or 148 bottles, # of orders = 16.89, Average inventory = 74, Order cost = $591.15,
Holding cost = $592, Total inventory cost = $591.15 + $592 = $1,183.15

Savings = $1,275 - $1,183.15 = $91.85

6.92 Candy Incorporated stocks bubble gum game cards, an item that has a normally distributed demand during the reorder period with a mean of 12 dozen boxes and a standard deviation of two dozen boxes. If it is desirable to experience a stockout only 10 percent of the time, what is the appropriate safety stock?

ANSWER:

For 90 percent service level, we must have X = 12 + 1.28(2) = 14.56 dozen.

Since the mean is 12, the safety stock = 14.56 - 12 = 2.56

6.93 The purchasing manager for a firm is trying to determine what the safety stock should be for a particular product. She has developed the following table, which gives the distribution of demand during the lead-time and the probabilities:

Demand During Lead Time	Probability
40	0.20
50	0.25
60	0.25
70	0.20
80	0.10

The carrying cost is $5 per unit per year, the ordering cost is $30 per order, and the stockout cost is $40 per unit. The reorder point is 60 units, and 6 orders are placed each year. What level of safety stock should be maintained?

ANSWER:

Safety Stock	Additional Holding Cost	Stockout Cost	Total Cost
0	0	(10)(0.2)(40)(10)+(20)(0.1)(40)(10)	1600
10	50	(10)(0.1)(40)(10)	450
20	100	0	100

Therefore, 20 units of safety stock should be carried.

6.94 The purchasing manager for a firm is trying to determine what the safety stock should be for a particular product. She has developed the following table, which gives the distribution of demand during the lead-time and the probabilities:

Demand During Lead Time	Probability
40	0.10
50	0.20
60	0.25
70	0.25
80	0.20

The carrying cost is $5 per unit per year, the ordering cost is $30 per order, and the stockout cost is $40 per unit. The reorder point is 60 units, and 6 orders are placed each year. What level of safety stock should be maintained?

ANSWER:

Safety Stock	Additional Holding Cost	Stockout Cost	Total Cost ($)
0	0	(10)(0.25)(40)(10)+(20)(0.2)(40)(10)	2600
10	50	(10)(0.2)(40)(10)	850
20	100	0	100

Therefore, 20 units of safety stock should be carried.

SHORT ANSWER/ESSAY

6.95 Explain inventory's financial role in a company.

ANSWER: Inventory often represents a considerable amount of invested capital, thus inventory control is essential.

6.96 List three general categories of inventory.

ANSWER: raw material, work-in-process inventory, finished goods inventory

6.97 Explain how inventory can act as a buffer in the production process.

ANSWER: By storing some inventory, it helps to decouple the manufacturing process within the organization.

6.98 List three disadvantages of buying inventory in large quantities.

ANSWER: higher storage cost, more spoilage, damaged stock, theft, insurance, less cash to invest

6.99 List four significant inventory costs.

ANSWER: the inventory itself, order cost, carry cost, stockout cost

6.100 List three carrying-cost factors.

ANSWER: taxes, insurance, spoilage, theft, obsolescence, warehouse personnel wages

6.101 List three order cost factors.

ANSWER: sending a purchase order, inspecting incoming inventory, bill paying, inventory questions, purchasing department expenses, etc.

6.102 Explain the basic difference(s) between the simple EOQ model and the production run model.

ANSWER: In the simple EOQ, inventory delivery is assumed to occur instantaneously, while in the production run model, inventory is assumed to be produced (or "delivered") over time.

6.103 Discuss why it is sometimes prudent not to order the minimum level required to obtain a quantity discount.

ANSWER: The increased holding cost associated with ordering the minimum level required for the discount may outweigh the savings from the quantity discount.

CHAPTER 7
Linear Programming Models: Graphical and Computer Methods

TRUE/FALSE

7.1 Management resources that need control include machinery usage, labor volume, money spent, time used, warehouse space used, and material usage.

ANSWER: TRUE

7.2 In the term linear programming, the word programming comes from the phrase *computer programming*.

ANSWER: FALSE

7.3 Linear programming has few applications in the real world due to the assumption of certainty in the data and relationships of a problem.

ANSWER: FALSE

7.4 Any linear programming problem can be solved using the graphical solution procedure.

ANSWER: FALSE

7.5 An LP formulation typically requires finding the maximum value of an objective while simultaneously maximizing usage of the resource constraints.

ANSWER: FALSE

7.6 There are no limitations on the number of constraints or variables that can be graphed to solve an LP problem.

ANSWER: FALSE

7.7 Resource restrictions are called constraints.

ANSWER: TRUE

7.8 Industrial applications of linear programming might involve several thousand variables and constraints.

ANSWER: TRUE

7.9 The set of solution points that satisfies all of a linear programming problem's constraints simultaneously is defined as the feasible region in graphical linear programming.

ANSWER: TRUE

7.10 An objective function is necessary in a maximization problem but is not required in a minimization problem.

ANSWER: FALSE

7.11 In some instances, an infeasible solution may be the optimum found by the corner point method.

ANSWER: FALSE

7.12 The analytic postoptimality method attempts to determine a range of changes in problem parameters that will not affect the optimal solution or change the variables in the basis.

ANSWER: TRUE

7.13 The solution to a linear programming problem must always lie on a constraint.

ANSWER: TRUE

7.14 In a linear program, the constraints must be linear, but the objective function may be nonlinear.

ANSWER: FALSE

7.15 One can employ the same algorithm to solve both maximization and minimization problems.

ANSWER: TRUE

7.16 One converts a minimization problem to a maximization problem by reversing the direction of all constraints.

ANSWER: FALSE

7.17 The graphical method of solution illustrates that the only restriction on a solution is that the solution must lie along a constraint.

ANSWER: FALSE

7.18 Anytime we have an isoprofit line that is parallel to a constraint, we have the possibility of multiple solutions.

ANSWER: TRUE

7.19 If the isoprofit line is not parallel to a constraint, then the solution must be unique.

ANSWER: TRUE

7.20 When two or more constraints conflict with one another, we have a condition called unboundedness.

ANSWER: FALSE

7.21 The addition of a redundant constraint lowers the isoprofit line.

ANSWER: FALSE

7.22 Sensitivity analysis enables us to look only at the effects of changing the coefficients in the objective function.

ANSWER: FALSE

MULTIPLE CHOICE

7.23 Typical management resources include

(a) machinery usage.
(b) labor volume.
(c) warehouse space utilization.
(d) raw material usage.
(e) all of the above

ANSWER: e

7.24 Which of the following is not a property of all linear programming problems?

(a) the presence of restrictions
(b) optimization of some objective
(c) a computer program
(d) alternate courses of action to choose from
(e) usage of only linear equations and inequalities

ANSWER: c

7.25 A feasible solution to a linear programming problem

(a) must satisfy all of the problem's constraints simultaneously.
(b) need not satisfy all of the constraints, only the non-negativity constraints.
(c) must be a corner point of the feasible region.
(d) must give the maximum possible profit.

ANSWER: a

7.26 Infeasibility in a linear programming problem occurs when

(a) there is an infinite solution.
(b) a constraint is redundant.
(c) more than one solution is optimal.
(d) the feasible region is unbounded.
(e) there is no solution that satisfies all the constraints given.

ANSWER: e

7.27 In a maximization problem, when one or more of the solution variables and the profit can be made infinitely large without violating any constraints, then the linear program has

(a) an infeasible solution.
(b) an unbounded solution.
(c) a redundant constraint.
(d) alternate optimal solutions.
(e) none of the above

ANSWER: b

7.28 Which of the following is not a part of every linear programming problem formulation?

(a) an objective function
(b) a set of constraints
(c) non-negativity constraints
(d) a redundant constraint
(e) maximization or minimization of a linear function

ANSWER: d

7.29 When appropriate, the optimal solution to a maximization linear programming problem can be found by graphing the feasible region and

(a) finding the profit at every corner point of the feasible region to see which one gives the highest value.
(b) moving the isoprofit lines towards the origin in a parallel fashion until the last point in the feasible region is encountered.
(c) locating the point that is highest on the graph.
(d) none of the above
(e) all of the above

ANSWER: a

7.30 The graphical solution to a linear programming problem

(a) includes the corner point method and the isoprofit line solution method.
(b) is useful for four or fewer decision variables.
(c) is inappropriate for more than two constraints.
(d) is the most difficult approach, but is useful as a learning tool.
(e) can only be used if no inequalities exist.

ANSWER: a

7.31 The corner point solution method

(a) will yield different results from the isoprofit line solution method.
(b) requires that the profit from all corners of the feasible region be compared.
(c) will provide one, and only one, optimum.
(d) requires that all corners created by all constraints be compared.
(e) will not provide a solution at an intersection or corner where a non-negativity constraint is involved.

ANSWER: b

7.32 When a constraint line bounding a feasible region has the same slope as an isoprofit line,

(a) there may be more than one optimum solution.
(b) the problem involves redundancy.
(c) an error has been made in the problem formulation.
(d) a condition of infeasibility exists.
(e) none of the above

ANSWER: a

7.33 The simultaneous equation method is

(a) an alternative to the corner point method.
(b) useful only in minimization methods.
(c) an algebraic means for solving the intersection of two or more constraint equations.
(d) useful only when more than two product variables exist in a product mix problem.
(e) none of the above

ANSWER: c

7.34 Consider the following linear programming problem:

Maximize	$12X + 10Y$
Subject to:	$4X + 3Y \leq 480$
	$2X + 3Y \leq 360$
	all variables ≥ 0

The maximum possible value for the objective function is

(a) 360.
(b) 480.
(c) 1520.
(d) 1560.
(e) none of the above

ANSWER: c

7.35 Consider the following linear programming problem:

Maximize	$4X + 10Y$
Subject to:	$3X + 4Y \leq 480$
	$4X + 2Y \leq 360$
	all variables ≥ 0

The feasible corner points are (48,84), (0,120), (0,0), (90,0). What is the maximum possible value for the objective function?

(a) 1032
(b) 1200
(c) 360
(d) 1600
(e) none of the above

ANSWER: b

7.36 Consider the following linear programming problem:

Maximize	$5X + 6Y$
Subject to:	$4X + 2Y \leq 420$
	$1X + 2Y \leq 120$
	all variables ≥ 0

Which of the following points (X,Y) is not a feasible corner point?

(a) (0,60)
(b) (105,0)
(c) (120,0)
(d) (100,10)
(e) none of the above

ANSWER: c

7.37 Consider the following linear programming problem:

Maximize	$5X + 6Y$
Subject to:	$4X + 2Y \leq 420$
	$1X + 2Y \leq 120$
	all variables ≥ 0

Which of the following points (X,Y) is not feasible?
(a) (50,40)
(b) (20,50)
(c) (60,30)
(d) (90,10)
(e) none of the above

ANSWER: a

7.38 Two models of a product – Regular (X) and Deluxe (Y) – are produced by a company. A linear programming model is used to determine the production schedule. The formulation is as follows:

Maximize profit = $50X + 60Y$
Subject to:
$8X + 10Y \leq 800$ (labor hours)
$X + Y \leq 120$ (total units demanded)
$4X + 5Y \leq 500$ (raw materials)
all variables ≥ 0

The optimal solution is $X = 100$ $Y = 0$.

How many units of the regular model would be produced based on this solution?

(a) 0
(b) 100
(c) 50
(d) 120
(e) none of the above

ANSWER: b

7.39 Two models of a product – Regular (X) and Deluxe (Y) – are produced by a company. A linear programming model is used to determine the production schedule. The formulation is as follows:

Maximize profit = $50X + 60Y$
Subject to:
$8X + 10Y \leq 800$ (labor hours)
$X + Y \leq 120$ (total units demanded)
$4X + 10Y \leq 500$ (raw materials)
$X, Y \geq 0$

The optimal solution is X=100, Y=0.

Which of these constraints is redundant?

(a) the first constraint
(b) the second constraint
(c) the third constraint
(d) all of the above
(e) none of the above

ANSWER: b

7.40 Consider the following linear programming problem:

Minimize	$20X + 30Y$
Subject to	$2X + 4Y \leq 800$
	$6X + 3Y \geq 300$
	$X, Y \geq 0$

The optimum solution to this problem occurs at the point (X,Y).

(a) (0,0).
(b) (50,0).
(c) (0,100).
(d) (400,0).
(e) none of the above

ANSWER: b

7.41 Consider the following linear programming problem:

Maximize	$20X + 30Y$
Subject to:	$X + Y \leq 80$
	$6X + 12Y \leq 600$
	$X, Y \geq 0$

This is a special case of a linear programming problem in which

(a) there is no feasible solution.
(b) there is a redundant constraint.
(c) there are multiple optimal solutions.
(d) this cannot be solved graphically.
(e) none of the above

ANSWER: e

7.42 Consider the following linear programming problem:

Maximize	$20X + 30Y$
Subject to	$X + Y \leq 80$
	$8X + 9Y \leq 600$
	$3X + 2Y \geq 400$
	$X, Y \geq 0$

This is a special case of a linear programming problem in which
(a) there is no feasible solution.
(b) there is a redundant constraint.
(c) there are multiple optimal solutions.
(d) this cannot be solved graphically.
(e) none of the above

ANSWER: a

7.43 Adding a constraint to a linear programming (maximization) problem may result in, but is not necessarily limited to,

(a) a decrease in the value of the objective function.
(b) an increase in the value of the objective function.
(c) no change to the objective function.
(d) either (c) or (a) depending on the constraint.
(e) either (c) or (b) depending on the constraint.

ANSWER: d

7.44 Deleting a constraint from a linear programming (maximization) problem may result in, but is not limited to,

(a) a decrease in the value of the objective function.
(b) an increase in the value of the objective function.
(c) no change to the objective function.
(d) either (c) or (a) depending on the constraint.
(e) either (c) or (b) depending on the constraint.

ANSWER: e

7.45 Which of the following is not acceptable as a constraint in a linear programming problem (maximization)?

Constraint 1	$X + XY + Y \geq 12$
Constraint 2	$X - 2Y \leq 20$
Constraint 3	$X + 3Y = 48$
Constraint 4	$X + Y + Z \leq 150$

(a) Constraint 1
(b) Constraint 2
(c) Constraint 3
(d) Constraint 4
(e) none of the above

ANSWER: a

7.46 If two corner points tie for the best value of the objective function, then

(a) the solution is infeasible.
(b) there are an infinite number of optimal solutions.
(c) the problem is unbounded.
(d) the problem is degenerate.
(e) none of the above

ANSWER: b

7.47 If one changes the contribution rates in the objective function of an LP,

(a) the feasible region will change.
(b) the slope of the isoprofit or iso-cost line will change.
(c) the optimal solution to the LP is sure to no longer be optimal.
(d) all of the above
(e) none of the above

ANSWER: b

7.48 Sensitivity analysis may also be called

(a) postoptimality analysis.
(b) parametric programming.
(c) optimality analysis.
(d) all of the above
(e) none of the above

ANSWER: d

7.49 Sensitivity analyses are used to examine the effects of changes in

(a) contribution rates for each variable.
(b) technological coefficients.
(c) available resources.
(d) all of the above
(e) none of the above

ANSWER: d

7.50 Which of the following is a basic assumption of linear programming?

(a) The condition of uncertainty exists.
(b) Proportionality exists in the objective function and constraints.
(c) Independence exists for the activities.
(d) Divisibility exists, allowing only integer solutions.
(e) Solutions or variables may take values from $-\infty$ to $+\infty$.

ANSWER: b

7.51 The condition when there is no solution that satisfies all the constraints is called

(a) boundedness.
(b) redundancy.
(c) optimality.
(d) dependency.
(e) none of the above

ANSWER: e

7.52 In a minimization problem, when one or more of the solution variables and the cost can be made infinitely large without violating any constraints, then the linear program has

(a) an infeasible solution.
(b) an unbounded solution.
(c) a redundant constraint.
(d) alternate optimal solutions.
(e) none of the above

ANSWER: e

7.53 If the addition of a constraint to a linear programming problem does not change the solution, the constraint is said to be

(a) unbounded.
(b) non-negative.
(c) infeasible.
(d) redundant.
(e) bounded.

ANSWER: d

7.54 The graphical solution to a linear programming problem

(a) is a useful tool for solving practical problems.
(b) is useful for four or less decision variables.
(c) is useful primarily in helping one understand the linear programming solution process.
(d) is the most difficult approach.
(e) can only be used in a maximization problem.

ANSWER: c

7.55 In order for a linear programming problem to have a unique solution, the solution must exist

(a) at the intersection of the non-negativity constraints.
(b) at the intersection of a non-negativity constraint and a resource constraint.
(c) at the intersection of the objective function and a constraint.
(d) at the intersection of two or more constraints.
(e) none of the above

ANSWER: d

7.56 In order for a linear programming problem to have multiple solutions, the solution must exist

(a) at the intersection of the non-negativity constraints.
(b) on a non-redundant constraint parallel to the objective function.
(c) at the intersection of the objective function and a constraint.
(d) at the intersection of three or more constraints.
(e) none of the above

ANSWER: b

7.57 Consider the following linear programming problem:

Maximize	$12X + 10Y$
Subject to:	$2X + 3Y \leq 480$
	$4X + 3Y \leq 360$
	all variables ≥ 0

The maximum possible value for the objective function is

(a) 360.
(b) 480.
(c) 1520.
(d) 1560.
(e) none of the above

ANSWER: e

7.58 Consider the following linear programming problem:

Maximize	$12X + 10Y$
Subject to:	$4X + 3Y \leq 480$
	$2X + 3Y \leq 360$
	all variables ≥ 0

Which of the following points (X,Y) is feasible?

(a) (10,120)
(b) (120,10)
(c) (30,100)
(d) (60,90)
(e) none of the above

ANSWER: c

7.59 Consider the following linear programming problem:

Maximize	$5X + 6Y$
Subject to:	$4X + 2Y \leq 420$
	$1X + 2Y \leq 120$
	all variables ≥ 0

Which of the following points (X,Y) is in the feasible region?
(a) (30,60)
(b) (105,5)
(c) (0,210)
(d) (100,10)
(e) none of the above

ANSWER: d

7.60 Consider the following linear programming problem:

Maximize	$5X + 6Y$
Subject to:	$4X + 2Y \leq 420$
	$1X + 2Y \leq 120$
	all variables ≥ 0

Which of the following points (X,Y) is feasible?

(a) (50,40)
(b) (30,50)
(c) (60,30)
(d) (90,20)
(e) none of the above

ANSWER: c

7.61 Consider the following linear programming problem:

Maximize	$18X + 36Y$
Subject to:	$X + Y \leq 80$
	$6X + 12Y \leq 600$
	$X, Y \geq 0$

This is a special case of a linear programming problem in which

(a) there is no feasible solution.
(b) there is a redundant constraint.
(c) there are multiple optimal solutions.
(d) this cannot be solved graphically.
(e) none of the above

ANSWER: c

7.62 Consider the following linear programming problem:

Maximize	$20X + 30Y$
Subject to:	$X + Y \leq 80$
	$12X + 12Y \leq 600$
	$3X + 2Y \leq 400$
	$X, Y \geq 0$

This is a special case of a linear programming problem in which
(a) there is no feasible solution.
(b) there is a redundant constraint.
(c) there are multiple optimal solutions.
(d) this cannot be solved graphically.
(e) none of the above

ANSWER: b

7.63 Removing a constraint from a linear programming (maximization) problem may result in, but not be limited to,

(a) a decrease in the value of the objective function.
(b) an increase in the value of the objective function.
(c) either an increase or decrease in the value of the objective function.
(d) no change in the value of the objective function.
(e) either (b) or (d)

ANSWER: e

7.64 Adding a constraint to a linear programming (maximization) problem may result in, but not be limited to,

(a) a decrease in the value of the objective function.
(b) an increase in the value of the objective function.
(c) either an increase or decrease in the value of the objective function.
(d) no change in the value of the objective function.
(e) either a decrease or no change in the value of the objective function.

ANSWER: e

7.65 Which of the following is not acceptable as a constraint in a linear programming problem (minimization)?

Constraint 1	$X + Y \geq 12$
Constraint 2	$X - 2Y \leq 20$
Constraint 3	$X + 3Y = 48$
Constraint 4	$X + Y + Z \leq 150$
Constraint 5	$2X - 3Y + Z > 75$

(a) Constraint 1
(b) Constraint 2
(c) Constraint 3
(d) Constraint 4
(e) Constraint 5

ANSWER: e

7.66 Changes in the contribution rates in the objective function of an LP may represent

(a) changes in the technology used to produce the good.
(b) changes in the price for which the product can be sold.
(c) changes in government rules and regulations.
(d) changes in the raw materials used.
(e) none of the above

ANSWER: b

7.67 Consider the following linear programming problem:

Maximize	$10X + 30Y$
Subject to	$X + 2Y \le 80$
	$8X + 16Y \le 640$
	$4X + 2Y \ge 100$
	$X, Y \ge 0$

This is a special case of a linear programming problem in which

(a) there is no feasible solution.
(b) there is a redundant constraint.
(c) there are multiple optimal solutions.
(d) this cannot be solved graphically.
(e) none of the above

ANSWER: b

7.68 Consider the following linear programming problem:

Maximize	$12X + 10Y$
Subject to:	$4X + 3Y \le 480$
	$2X + 3Y \le 360$
	all variables ≥ 0

Which of the following points (X,Y) is feasible?

(a) (10,120)
(b) (120,10)
(c) (30,100)
(d) (60,90)
(e) none of the above

ANSWER: c

7.69 Consider the following linear programming problem:

Maximize	$5X + 6Y$
Subject to:	$4X + 2Y \le 420$
	$1X + 2Y \le 120$
	all variables ≥ 0

Which of the following points (X,Y) is not in the feasible region?

(a) (30,30)
(b) (60,40)
(c) (100,5)
(d) (20,40)
(e) none of the above

ANSWER: b

PROBLEMS

7.70 As a supervisor of a production department, you must decide the daily production totals of a certain product that has two models, the Deluxe and the Special. The profit on the Deluxe model is $12 per unit and the Special's profit is $10. Each model goes through two phases in the production process, and there are only 100 hours available daily at the construction stage and only 80 hours available at the finishing and inspection stage. Each Deluxe model requires 20 minutes of construction time and 10 minutes of finishing and inspection time. Each Special model requires 15 minutes of construction time and 15 minutes of finishing and inspection time. The company has also decided that the Special model must comprise at least 40 percent of the production total.

(a) Formulate this as a linear programming problem.
(b) Find the solution that gives the maximum profit.

ANSWER:

(a) Let X_1 = number of Deluxe models produced
X_2 = number of Special models produced

Maximize $12X_1 + 10X_2$

Subject to: $1/3X_1 + 1/4X_2 \le 100$

$1/6X_1 + 1/4X_2 \le 80$

$-0.4X_1 + 0.6X_2 \ge 0$

$X_1, X_2 \ge 0$

(b) Optimal solution: $X_1 = 120, X_2 = 240$ Profit = $3,840

7.71 The Fido Dog Food Company wishes to introduce a new brand of dog biscuits (composed of chicken and liver-flavored biscuits) that meets certain nutritional requirements. The liver-flavored biscuits contain 1 unit of nutrient A and 2 units of nutrient B, while the chicken-flavored ones contain 1 unit of nutrient A and 4 units of nutrient B. According to federal requirements, there must be at least 40 units of nutrient A and 60 units of nutrient B in a package of the new mix. In addition, the company has decided that there can be no more than 15 liver-flavored biscuits in a package. If it costs 1 cent to make a liver-flavored biscuit and 2 cents to make a chicken-flavored one, what is the optimal product mix for a package of the biscuits in order to minimize the firm's cost?

(a) Formulate this as a linear programming problem.
(b) Find the optimal solution for this problem graphically
(c) Are any constraints redundant? If so, which one or ones?
(d) What is the total cost of a package of dog biscuits using the optimal mix?

ANSWER:

(a) Let X_1 = number of liver-flavored biscuits in a package
X_2 = number of chicken-flavored biscuits in a package

Minimize $X_1 + 2X_2$

Subject to:

$$X_1 + X_2 \geq 40$$
$$2X_1 + 4X_2 \geq 60$$
$$X_1 \leq 15$$
$$X_1, X_2 \geq 0$$

(b) Corner points (0,40) and (15,25)
Optimal solution is (15,25) with cost of 65.

(c) $2X_1 + 4X_2 \geq 60$ is redundant

(d) minimum cost = 65 cents

7.72 Consider the following linear program:

Maximize $30X_1 + 10X_2$

Subject to:

$$3X_1 + X_2 \leq 300$$
$$X_1 + X_2 \leq 200$$
$$X_1 \leq 100$$
$$X_2 \geq 50$$
$$X_1 - X_2 \leq 0$$
$$X_1, X_2 \geq 0$$

(a) Solve the problem graphically. Is there more than one optimal solution? Explain.
(b) Are there any redundant constraints?

ANSWER:
(a) Corner points (0,50), (0,200), (50,50), (75,75), (50,150)
Optimum solutions: (75,75) and (50,150). Both yield a profit of $3,000.

(b) The constraint $X_1 \leq 100$ is redundant since $3X_1 + X_2 \leq 300$ also means that X_1 cannot exceed 100.

7.73 Solve the following linear programming problem using the corner point method:

Maximize $10X + 1Y$

Subject to:

$4X + 3Y \le 36$

$2X + 4Y \le 40$

$Y \ge 3$

$X, Y \ge 0$

ANSWER:

Feasible corner points (X,Y):
(0,3) (0,10) (2.4,8.8) (6.75,3)
Maximum profit 70.5 at (6.75,3).

7.74 Solve the following linear programming problem using the corner point method:

Maximize $3X + 5Y$

Subject to:

$4X + 4Y \le 48$

$1X + 2Y \le 20$

$Y \ge 2$

$X, Y \ge 0$

ANSWER:

Feasible corner points (X,Y): (0,2) (0,10) (4,8) (10,2)

Maximum profit is 52 at (4,8).

7.75 Billy Penny is trying to determine how many units of two types of lawn mowers to produce each day. One of these is the Standard model, while the other is the Deluxe model. The profit per unit on the Standard model is \$60, while the profit per unit on the Deluxe model is \$40. The Standard model requires 20 minutes of assembly time, while the Deluxe model requires 35 minutes of assembly time. The Standard model requires 10 minutes of inspection time, while the Deluxe model requires 15 minutes of inspection time. The company must fill an order for 6 Deluxe models. There are 450 minutes of assembly time and 180 minutes of inspection time available each day. How many units of each product should be manufactured to maximize profits?

ANSWER:

Let X = number of Standard models to produce
Y = number of Deluxe models to produce

Maximize $60X + 40Y$

Subject to:

$20X + 35Y \le 450$

$10X + 15Y \le 180$

$Y \ge 6$

$X, Y \ge 0$

Maximum profit is \$780 by producing 9 Standard and 6 Deluxe models.

7.76 Two advertising media are being considered for promotion of a product. Radio ads cost $400 each, while newspaper ads cost $600 each. The total budget is $7,200 per week. The total number of ads should be at least 15, with at least 2 of each type. Each newspaper ad reaches 6,000 people, while each radio ad reaches 2,000 people. The company wishes to reach as many people as possible while meeting all the constraints stated. How many ads of each type should be placed?

ANSWER:

Let R = number of radio ads placed
N = number of newspaper ads placed

$$
\begin{aligned}
\text{Maximize} \quad & 2000R + 6000N \\
\text{Subject to:} \quad & R + N \geq 15 \\
& 400R + 600N \leq 7200 \\
& R \geq 2 \\
& N \geq 2 \\
& R, N \geq 0
\end{aligned}
$$

Feasible corner points (R,N): (9,6) (13,2) (15,2)
Maximum exposure 54,000 with 9 radio and 6 newspaper ads.

7.77 Suppose a linear programming (maximization) problem has been solved and the optimal value of the objective function is $300. Suppose an additional constraint is added to this problem. Explain how this might affect each of the following:

(a) the feasible region
(b) the optimal value of the objective function

ANSWER:

(a) Adding a new constraint will reduce the size of the feasible region unless it is a redundant constraint. It can never make the feasible region any larger. However, it could make the problem infeasible.
(b) A new constraint can only reduce the size of the feasible region; therefore, the value of the objective function will either decrease or remain the same. If the original solution is still feasible, it will remain the optimal solution.

7.78 Upon retirement, Mr. Klaws started to make two types of children's wooden toys in his shop, Wuns and Toos. Wuns yield a variable profit of $9 each and Toos have a contribution margin of $8 each. Even though his electric saw overheats, he can make 7 Wuns or 14 Toos each day. Since he doesn't have equipment for drying the lacquer finish he puts on the toys, the drying operation limits him to 16 Wuns or 8 Toos per day.

(a) Solve this problem using the corner point method.
(b) For what profit ratios would the optimum solution remain the optimum solution?

ANSWER:

Let X_1 = numbers of wuns/day
X_2 = number of toos/day

Maximize $9X_1 + 8X_2$
Subject to:
$2X_1 + 1X_2 \leq 14$
$1X_1 + 2X_2 \leq 16$
$X_1, X_2 \geq 0$

Corner points (0,0), (7,0), (0,8), (4,6)

Optimum profit $84 at (4,6).

7.79 Susanna Nanna is the production manager for a furniture manufacturing company. The company produces tables (X) and chairs (Y). Each table generates a profit of $80 and requires 3 hours of assembly time and 4 hours of finishing time. Each chair generates $50 of profit and requires 3 hours of assembly time and 2 hours of finishing time. There are 360 hours of assembly time and 240 hours of finishing time available each month. The following linear programming problem represents this situation.

Maximize $80X + 50Y$
Subject to:
$3X + 3Y \leq 360$
$4X + 2Y \leq 240$
$X, Y \geq 0$

The optimal solution is X = 0, and Y = 120.

(a) What would the maximum possible profit be?
(b) How many hours of assembly time would be used to maximize profit?
(c) If a new constraint, $2X + 2Y \leq 400$, were added, what would happen to the maximum possible profit?

ANSWERS: (a) 6000, (b) 360, (c) It would not change.

7.80 As a supervisor of a production department, you must decide the daily production totals of a certain product that has two models, the Deluxe and the special. The profit on the Deluxe model is \$12 per unit, and the special's profit is \$10. Each model goes through two phases in the production process, and there are only 100 hours available daily at the construction stage and only 80 hours available at the finishing and inspection stage. Each Deluxe model requires 20 minutes of construction time and 10 minutes of finishing and inspection time. Each special model requires 15 minutes of construction time and 15 minutes of finishing and inspection time. The company has also decided that the special model must comprise at most 60 percent of the production total.

Formulate this as a linear programming problem.

ANSWER:

Let X_1 = number of Deluxe models produced
X_2 = number of special models produced

Maximize $12X_1 + 10X_2$

Subject to:

$$1/3X_1 + 1/4X_2 \le 100$$
$$1/6X_1 + 1/4X_2 \le 80$$
$$-1.5X_1 + X_2 \le 0$$
$$X_1, X_2 \ge 0$$

7.81 The Fido Dog Food Company wishes to introduce a new brand of dog biscuits (composed of chicken and liver-flavored biscuits) that meets certain nutritional requirements. The liver-flavored biscuits contain 1 unit of nutrient A and 2 units of nutrient B, while the chicken-flavored ones contain 1 unit of nutrient A and 4 units of nutrient B. According to federal requirements, there must be at least twice as many units of nutrient A as of nutrient B in a package of the new mix. In addition, the company has decided that there can be no more than 15 liver-flavored biscuits, and at least 10 chicken-flavored biscuits in a package. If it costs 1 cent to make a liver-flavored biscuit and 2 cents to make a chicken-flavored one, what is the optimal product mix for a package of the biscuits in order to minimize the firm's cost?

(a) Formulate this as a linear programming problem.
(b) Are any constraints impossible to achieve? If so which one(s)?

ANSWER:

(a) Let X_1 = number of liver-flavored biscuits in a package
X_2 = number of chicken-flavored biscuits in a package

Minimize $X_1 + 2X_2$

Subject to:

$$3X_1 + 7X_2 \le 0 \quad \text{(Ratio of A to B)}$$
$$X_1 \le 15 \quad \text{(Maximum liver)}$$
$$X_2 \ge 10 \quad \text{(Minimum chicken)}$$
$$X_1, X_2 \ge 0 \quad \text{(Non-negativity)}$$

(b) The constraint, $3X_1 + 7X_2 \le 0$, is impossible to achieve.

7.82 The No-Glare Company is making two types of antique-style lamps, type #1 and type #2. There is enough skilled labor to make either 1,000 type #1 or 2,000 type #2 lamps per day. There are only 6,000 inserts available per day, of which the type #1 requires 3 and the type #2 requires 4. Besides these shared constraints, there are only enough fancy switches to make 1,400 of the type #2 lamps per day. Management would like to make at least 10 percent more type #2 lamps than type #1 lamps; however, they do not believe that they can sell more than 25 percent more type #2 lamps than type #1 lamps. Marginal profit (contribution) is \$3 per type #1 lamp and \$4 per type #2 lamp.

(a) Formulate this as a linear program.
(b) What constraint may be unrealistic?

ANSWER:

(a) Let X_1 = the hundreds of type #1 lamps per day, etc.

Maximize: $300X_1 + 400X_2$

Subject to:

$0.10X_1 + 0.05X_2 \leq 1$	Labor
$3X_1 + 4X_2 \leq 60$	Inserts
$X_2 \leq 14$	Fancy switches
$1.1X_1 - X_2 \leq 0$	Minimum Type #2 to Type #1 ratio
$1.25X_1 - X_2 \geq 0$	Maximum Type #2 to Type #1 ratio
$X_1, X_2 \geq 0$	

(b) The labor constraint may be unrealistic because it assumes a continuous tradeoff between labor required for the Type #1 and Type #2 lamps.

7.83 Two advertising media are being considered for promotion of a product. Radio ads cost \$400 each, while newspaper ads cost \$600 each. The total budget is \$7,200 per week. The total number of ads should be at least 15, with at least 2 of each type, and there should be no more than 19 ads in total. The company does not want the number of newspaper ads to exceed the number of radio ads by more than 25 percent. Each newspaper ad reaches 6,000 people, 50 percent of whom will respond; while each radio ad reaches 2,000 people, 20 percent of whom will respond. The company wishes to reach as many respondents as possible while meeting all the constraints stated. Develop the appropriate LP model for determining the number of ads of each type that should be placed.

ANSWER:

Let R = number of radio ads placed
N = number of newspaper ads placed

Maximize: $0.20*2000R + 0.50*6000N$
or Maximize: $400R + 3000N$

Subject to:

$$R + N \geq 15$$
$$R + N \leq 19$$
$$400R + 600N \leq 7200$$
$$1.25R - N \geq 0$$
$$R \geq 2$$
$$N \geq 2$$
$$R, N \geq 0$$

7.84 Suppose a linear programming (maximization) problem has been solved and the optimal value of the objective function is $300. Suppose a constraint is removed from this problem. Explain how this might affect each of the following:

(a) the feasible region
(b) the optimal value of the objective function

ANSWER:

(a) Removing a constraint may, if the constraint is not redundant, increase the size of the feasible region. It can never make the feasible region any smaller. If the constraint was active in the solution, removing it will also result in a new optimal solution. However, removing an essential constraint could cause the problem to become unbounded.

(b) Removal of a constraint can only increase or leave the same the size of the feasible region; therefore, the value of the objective function will either increase or remain the same, assuming the problem has not become unbounded.

7.85 Suppose a linear programming (maximization) problem has been solved and the optimal value of the objective function is $300. Suppose an additional constraint (≥) is added to this problem. Explain how this might affect each of the following:

(a) the feasible region
(b) the optimal value of the objective function

ANSWER:

(a) Adding a new ≥ constraint will either leave the feasible region as it was, or make it smaller, or cause the problem to become infeasible.
(b) A new constraint can only reduce the size of the feasible region. Therefore, the value of the objective function will either stay the same or be lowered.

7.86 Consider the following formulation of a linear program. Determine what is possibly wrong.

Maximize: $15X1 + 25X2$

Subject to:

$$
\begin{aligned}
X1 + X2 &\geq 1000\\
X1 + X2 &\leq 500\\
50X1 + 20X2 &\leq 77000\\
125X1 - 100X2 &\geq 0\\
X1 &\geq 250\\
X2 &\geq 275\\
X1, X2 &\geq 0
\end{aligned}
$$

(a) There are too many constraints.
(b) There are not enough constraints.
(c) The formulation has redundancy.
(d) The formulation has unboundedness.
(e) The formulation has at least two constraints that conflict.
ANSWER: e

SHORT ANSWER/ESSAY

7.87 List at least three typical management resources that warrant control.

ANSWER: machinery usage, labor volume, dollars spent, time used, warehouse space usage, raw material usage

7.88 One basic assumption of linear programming is proportionality. Explain its need.

ANSWER: Rates of consumption exist and are constant. For example, if the production of 1 unit requires 4 units of a resource, then if 10 units are produced, 40 units of the resource are required. A change in the variable value results in a proportional change in the objective function value.

7.89 One basic assumption of linear programming is divisibility. Explain its need.

ANSWER: Solutions are real and non-negative; they can have fractional values and need not be whole numbers.

7.90 Define infeasibility with respect to an LP solution.

ANSWER: Occurs when there is no solution that can satisfy all constraints.

7.91 Define unboundedness with respect to an LP solution.

ANSWER: Typically occurs during maximization that causes the objective function value to increase without limit with all the constraints being satisfied.

7.92 Define alternate optimal solution with respect to an LP solution.

ANSWER: More than one optimal solution point exists because the objective function is parallel to a binding constraint.

7.93 How does alternate optimal solutions, as a special case in linear programming, compare to two other special cases of infeasibility and unboundedness?

ANSWER: With multiple alternate solutions, any answer is correct. In the other two cases, no single answer can be generated. Alternate solutions can occur when a problem is correctly formulated whereas the other two cases most likely have an incorrect formulation.

CHAPTER 8
Linear Programming Modeling Applications: With Computer Analyses in Excel and QM for Windows

TRUE/FALSE

8.1 Linear programming can be used to select effective media mixes, to allocate fixed or limited budgets across media, and to maximize audience exposure.

ANSWER: TRUE

8.2 Blending problems arise when one must decide which of two or more ingredients is to be chosen to produce a product.

ANSWER: FALSE

8.3 Linear programming can be used to select portfolio contents based on constraints such as corporate policies, legalities, and risks.

ANSWER: TRUE

8.4 Statistical pollsters might use the marketing research type of an LP problem model to handle a problem involving consumer surveys.

ANSWER: TRUE

8.5 Determining the mixture of ingredients for a most economical feed or diet combination would be described as a production mix type of linear program.

ANSWER: FALSE

8.6 A media selection LP application describes a method in which media producers select customers.

ANSWER: FALSE

8.7 The Delta Airlines Coldstart LP is designed to minimize the cost of in-flight meals while meeting human nutritional needs.

ANSWER: FALSE

8.8 An ingredient or blending problem is a special case of the more general problem known as diet and feed mix problems.

ANSWER: FALSE

8.9 In general, linear programming is unable to solve complex labor planning as the objective function is usually not definable.

ANSWER: FALSE

8.10 Linear programming variable names such as X_{11}, X_{12}, X_{13}, could possibly be used to represent production of a product (X_{1j}) over several months.

ANSWER: TRUE

8.11 Since the production mix linear program applications are a special situation, the number of decision variables are limited to two.

ANSWER: FALSE

8.12 In formulating the media selection linear programming model, we are unable to take into account the effectiveness of a particular presentation (e.g., the fact that only 5 percent of the people exposed to a radio ad will respond as desired).

ANSWER: FALSE

8.13 A marketing research linear programming model can help a researcher structure the least expensive, statistically meaningful sample.

ANSWER: TRUE

8.14 Before one can apply a marketing research linear programming model, he/she must identify the characteristics of a statistically meaningful sample.

ANSWER: TRUE

8.15 The marketing research linear programming model can be used to help one identify the characteristics of a statistically meaningful sample.

ANSWER: FALSE

8.16 The major use of a production mix linear programming model is to help one allocate multiple, interchangeable resources in the production of a product.

ANSWER: FALSE

8.17 The linear programming model of the production mix problem does not allow us to include the effect of quantity discounts on the cost of resources.

ANSWER: TRUE

8.18 The linear programming model of the production mix problem only includes constraints of the less than or equal form.

ANSWER: FALSE

8.19 The linear programming model of the production scheduling process can include the impact of hiring and firing, regular and overtime pay rates, and the desire to have a constant and stable production schedule over a several-month period.

ANSWER: TRUE

8.20 The linear programming model of the production scheduling process is usually used when we have to schedule the production of a single product, requiring a mix of resources, over time.

ANSWER: FALSE

8.21 The linear programming model of the production scheduling process is usually used when we have to schedule the production of multiple products, each of which requires a set of resources not required by the other products, over time.

ANSWER: FALSE

8.22 The assignment problem is the only linear programming problem for which we have a special solution method.

ANSWER: FALSE

8.23 In the linear programming formulation of the assignment problem, all constraint coefficients are equal to one.

ANSWER: TRUE

8.24 In the linear programming formulation of the assignment problem, making all the constraint coefficients and all the right-hand sides equal to one is equivalent to saying that every worker must be assigned a job, and every job must be done by someone.

ANSWER: TRUE

8.25 The linear programming formulation of the assignment problem cannot be used when there are more jobs than people to assign them to.

ANSWER: FALSE

8.26 If a linear programming problem has alternate solutions, the order in which you enter the constraints may affect the particular solution found.

ANSWER: TRUE

8.27 The linear programming portfolio selection model attempts to minimize the risk inherent in investing in the stock market.

ANSWER: FALSE

8.28 In the linear programming transportation model, the coefficients of the objective function can represent either the cost or the profit from shipping goods along a particular route.

ANSWER: TRUE

8.29 The linear programming transportation model allows us to solve problems where supply does not equal demand.

ANSWER: TRUE

8.30 The linear programming truck loading model always results in a practical solution.

ANSWER: FALSE

8.31 The linear programming ingredient or blending problem model allows one to include not only the cost of the resource, but also the differences in composition.

ANSWER: TRUE

MULTIPLE CHOICE

8.32 Using linear programming to maximize audience exposure in an advertising campaign is an example of the type of linear programming application known as

(a) media selection.
(b) marketing research.
(c) portfolio assessment.
(d) media budgeting.
(e) all of the above

ANSWER: a

8.33 A type of linear programming problem that is used in marketing is called the

(a) media selection problem.
(b) Madison Avenue problem.
(c) marketing allocation problem.
(d) All of the above are examples of marketing linear programming problems.
(e) None of the above are examples of marketing linear programming problems.

ANSWER: a

8.34 The selection of specific media from among a wide variety of alternatives is the type of LP problem known as

(a) the product mix problem.
(b) the investment banker problem.
(c) the Wall Street problem.
(d) the portfolio selection problem.
(e) none of the above

ANSWER: e

8.35 The following does not represent a factor a manager might consider when employing linear programming for a production scheduling:

(a) labor capacity
(b) space limitations
(c) product demand
(d) risk assessment
(e) inventory costs

ANSWER: d

The following exhibit pertains to questions 8.36 to 8.41.

EXHIBIT 8-1
A small furniture manufacturer produces tables and chairs. Each product must go through three stages of the manufacturing process—assembly, finishing, and inspection. Each table requires 3 hours of assembly, 2 hours of finishing, and 1 hour of inspection. Each chair requires 2 hours of assembly, 2 hours of finishing, and 1 hour of inspection. The profit per table is \$120 while the profit per chair is \$80. Currently, each week there are 200 hours of assembly time available, 180 hours of finishing time, and 40 hours of inspection time. Linear programming is to be used to develop a production schedule. Define the variables as follows:
T = number of tables produced each week C = number of chairs produced each week

8.36 According to Exhibit 8-1, which describes a production problem, what would the objective function be?

(a) Maximize T + C
(b) Maximize 120T + 80C
(c) Maximize 200T + 200 C
(d) Minimize 6T + 5C
(e) none of the above

ANSWER: b

8.37 According to Exhibit 8-1, which describes a production problem, which of the following would be a necessary constraint in the problem?

(a) $T + C \leq 40$
(b) $T + C \leq 200$
(c) $T + C \leq 180$
(d) $120T + 80C \geq 1000$
(e) none of the above

ANSWER: a

8.38 According to Exhibit 8-1, which describes a production problem, which of the following would be a necessary constraint in the problem?

(a) $T + C \geq 40$
(b) $3T + 2C \leq 200$
(c) $2T + 2C \leq 40$
(d) $120T + 80C \geq 1000$
(e) none of the above

ANSWER: b

8.39 According to Exhibit 8-1, which describes a production problem, suppose it is decided that there must be 4 chairs produced for every table. How would this constraint be written?

(a) $T \geq C$
(b) $T \leq C$
(c) $4T = C$
(d) $T = 4C$

ANSWER: c

8.40 According to Exhibit 8-1, which describes a production problem, suppose it is decided that the number of hours used in the assembly process must be at least 80 percent of the time available. How would this constraint be written?

(a) $3T + 2C \geq 160$
(b) $3T + 2C \geq 200$
(c) $3T + 2C \leq 200$
(d) $3T + 2C \leq 160$
(e) none of the above

ANSWER: a

8.41 According to Exhibit 8-1, which describes a production problem, suppose it is decided that the number of hours used in the assembly process must be at least 90 percent of the number of hours used in the finishing department. How would this constraint be written?

(a) $3T + 2C \geq 162$
(b) $3T + 2C \geq 0.9(2T + 2C)$
(c) $3T + 2C \leq 162$
(d) $3T + 2C \leq 0.9(2T + 2C)$
(e) none of the above

ANSWER: b

8.42 Which of the following does not represent a factor a manager might consider when employing linear programming for a production scheduling?

(a) labor capacity
(b) employee skill levels
(c) warehouse limitations
(d) shipping limitations
(e) none of the above

ANSWER: e

8.43 Production scheduling is amenable to solution by linear programming because

(a) the optimal product combination will minimize production risk.
(b) effective resource use will lead to optimal profits.
(c) linear programming will allow investment losses to be minimized.
(d) scheduling requires specific, narrowly defined constraints.
(e) objective functions and constraints can be readily developed and are relatively stable over time.

ANSWER: e

8.44 Determining the most efficient allocation of resources to the production of goods, etc., is characteristic of the LP problem type known as

(a) production scheduling.
(b) labor planning.
(c) assignment.
(d) blending.
(e) none of the above

ANSWER: a

8.45 When using Excel's Solver to input and solve a linear programming problem, it is essential that one perform an additional task before submitting the formulation. That important additional function is

(a) guessing the values of the variables.
(b) putting in a value for the objective function.
(c) choosing the options for assuming both a linear model and non-negative variables.
(d) resetting the parameters.
(e) none of the above

ANSWER: c

The following exhibit pertains to questions 8.46 to 8.50.

EXHIBIT 8-2
A small furniture manufacturer produces tables and chairs. Each product must go through three stages of the manufacturing process: assembly, finishing, and inspection. Each table requires 3 hours of assembly, 2 hours of finishing, and 1 hour of inspection. Each chair requires 2 hours of assembly, 2 hours of finishing, and 1 hour of inspection. The selling price per table is \$120 while the selling price per chair is \$80. Currently, each week there are 200 hours of assembly time available, 180 hours of finishing time, and 40 hours of inspection time. Assume that one hour of assembly time costs \$4.00; one hour of finishing time costs \$5.00; one hour of inspection time costs \$3.50; and that whatever labor hours are not required for the table and chairs can be applied to another product. Linear programming is to be used to develop a production schedule. Define the variables as follows:
T = number of tables produced each week C = number of chairs produced each week

8.46 According to Exhibit 8-2, which describes a production problem, what would the objective function be?

(a) Maximize T + C
(b) Maximize 120T + 80C
(c) Maximize 94.50T + 58.50C
(d) Minimize 6T + 5C
(e) none of the above

ANSWER: c

8.47 According to Exhibit 8-2, which describes a production problem, which of the following would not be a necessary constraint in the problem?

(a) $T + C \leq 40$
(b) $3T + 2C \leq 200$
(c) $2T + 2C \leq 200$
(d) all of the above
(e) none of the above

ANSWER: c

8.48 According to Exhibit 8-2, which describes a production problem, suppose it was decided that all the labor hours had to be paid for through the sale of the tables and chairs, regardless of whether or not all the labor hours were actually used. How would the objective function be written?

(a) Maximize T + C
(b) Minimize 120T + 80C
(c) Maximize 94.50T + 58.50C
(d) Maximize 120T + 80C
(e) none of the above

ANSWER: d

8.49 According to Exhibit 8-2, which describes a production problem, suppose you realize that you can trade off assembly hours for finishing hours, but that the total number of finishing hours, including the trade-off, cannot exceed 240 hours. How would this constraint be written?

(a) $3T + 2C \geq 160$
(b) $5T + 4C \leq 240$
(c) $3T + 2C \leq 200$
(d) $3T + 2C \leq 180$
(e) none of the above

ANSWER: e

8.50 Suppose that the problem described in Exhibit 8-2 is modified to specify that half the tables produced must have 4 chairs and half must have 2 chairs. How would this constraint be written?

(a) $C = 4T$
(b) $C = 2T$
(c) $C = 3T$
(d) $C = 6T$
(e) none of the above

ANSWER: c

The following exhibit pertains to questions 8.51 – 8.56.

	EXHIBIT 8-3
	Each coffee table produced by Timothy Kent Designers nets the firm a profit of \$9. Each bookcase yields a \$12 profit. Kent's firm is small and its resources limited. During any given production period (of 1 week), 10 gallons of varnish and 12 length of high quality redwood are available. Each coffee table requires approximately 1 gallon of varnish and 1 length of redwood. Each bookcase takes 1 gallon of varnish and 2 lengths of wood.
	T = number of tables produced each week B = number of bookcases produced each week

8.51 Referring to Exhibit 8-3, if we were to frame this as a linear programming problem, the objective function would be

(a) maximize $9B + 12C$
(b) maximize $9C + 12B$
(c) minimize $10C + 10B$
(d) maximize $12C + 10B$
(e) none of the above

ANSWER: b

8.52 Referring to Exhibit 8-3, which of the following constraints would be used?

(a) $10C + 12B \leq 12$
(b) $1C + 1B \leq 10$
(c) $1C + 2B \geq 12$
(d) all of the above
(e) none of the above

ANSWER: b

8.53 Referring to Exhibit 8-3, which of the following constraints would be used?

(a) Maximize $9C + 12B$
(b) $9C + 12B \geq 12$
(c) $12C + 9B \leq 10$
(d) $10C + 10B \geq 10$
(e) none of the above

ANSWER: e

8.54 Referring to Exhibit 8-3, suppose that this problem requires that you use all the varnish for the week. How would the linear programming representation change?

(a) $1B + 1C \leq 10$ will become $1B + 1C \leq 12$
(b) $1B + 1C \leq 10$ will be replaced by $1B + 1C \geq 10$
(c) $1B + 1C \leq 10$ will become $1B + 1C = 10$
(d) $2B + 1C \leq 12$ will become $2B + 1C = 12$
(e) none of the above

ANSWER: c

8.55 Referring to Exhibit 8-3, the solution to the problem is

(a) c=10,b= 0
(b) c= 0,b=10
(c) c= 0,b= 6
(d) c= 8,b=2
(e) none of the above

ANSWER: d

8.56 Referring to Exhibit 8-3, which of the following is unlikely to be an objective function for a linear program?

(a) maximize $5X + 6Y$
(b) minimize $X + Y + Z$
(c) minimize $X^2 + 2Y + 7Z$
(d) minimize $X + XY + 2Z$
(e) none of the above

ANSWER: c

8.57 Determining the most efficient allocation of people, machines, equipment, etc., is characteristic of the LP problem type known as

(a) production scheduling.
(b) labor planning.
(c) assignment.
(d) blending.
(e) none of the above

ANSWER: c

The following exhibit pertains to questions 8.58 to 8.62.

EXHIBIT 8-4

The following is a linear programming formulation of a labor planning problem. There are four overlapping shifts, and management must decide how many employees to schedule to start work on each shift. The objective is to minimize the total number of employees required while the constraints stipulate how many employees are required at each time of day. The variables X_1 - X_4 represent the number of employees starting work on each shift (shift 1 through shift 4).

Minimize $X_1 + X_2 + X_3 + X_4$

Subject to:

$X_1 + X_4 \geq 12$ (shift 1)
$X_1 + X_2 \geq 15$ (shift 2)
$X_2 + X_3 \geq 16$ (shift 3)
$X_3 + X_4 \geq 14$ (shift 4)
all variables ≥ 0

Final Optimal Solution:

Z = 29.000

Variable	Value
X_1	13.000
X_2	2.000
X_3	14.000
X_4	0.000

8.58 According to Exhibit 8-4, which describes a labor planning problem and its solution, how many workers would be assigned to shift 1?

(a) 12
(b) 13
(c) 0
(d) 2
(e) none of the above

ANSWER: b

8.59 According to Exhibit 8-4, which describes a labor planning problem and its solution, how many workers would be assigned to shift 3?

(a) 13
(b) 14
(c) 16
(d) 0
(e) none of the above

ANSWER: b

8.60 According to Exhibit 8-4, which describes a labor planning problem and its solution, how many workers would be assigned to shift 2?

(a) 2
(b) 0
(c) 14
(d) 15
(e) none of the above

ANSWER: a

8.61 According to Exhibit 8-4, which describes a labor planning problem and its solution, how many workers would be assigned to shift 4?

(a) 1
(b) 0
(c) 14
(d) 16
(e) none of the above

ANSWER: b

8.62 According to Exhibit 8-4, which describes a labor planning problem and its solution, how many workers would actually be on duty during shift 1?

(a) 12
(b) 13
(c) 0
(d) 29
(e) none of the above

ANSWER: b

8.63 This problem type is such a special case of linear programming that a special algorithm has been developed to solve it:

(a) the production mix problem.
(b) the assignment problem.
(c) the ingredient mix problem.
(d) the media selection problem.
(e) none of the above

ANSWER: b

8.64 Linear programming is used by managers involved in portfolio selection to

(a) maximize return on investment.
(b) maximize investment limitations.
(c) maximize risk.
(d) minimize risk.
(e) minimize expected return on investment.

ANSWER: a

8.65 The selection of specific investments from among a wide variety of alternatives is the type of LP problem known as

(a) the product mix problem.
(b) the investment banker problem.
(c) the Wall Street problem.
(d) the portfolio selection problem.
(e) none of the above

ANSWER: d

8.66 Linear programming is used by managers involved in portfolio selection to

(a) justify investment in specific financial instruments.
(b) maximize his/her possible investment.
(c) spread risk over several financial instruments.
(d) balance overall portfolio risk.
(e) none of the above

ANSWER: e

The following exhibit pertains to questions 8.67 to 8.69.

EXHIBIT 8-5

Ivana Myrocle wishes to invest her inheritance of $100,000 so that her return on investment is maximized, but she also wishes to keep her risk level relatively low. She has decided to invest her money in any of three possible ways—CDs, which pay a guaranteed 8 percent; stocks, which have an expected return of 12 percent; and a money market mutual fund, which is expected to return 10 percent. She has decided that any or all of the $100,000 may be invested, but any part (or all) of it may be put in any of the 3 alternatives. Thus, she may have some money invested in all three alternatives. In formulating this as a linear programming problem, define the variables as follows:

C = dollars invested in CDs
S = dollars invested in stocks
M = dollars invested in the money market mutual fund

8.67 According to Exhibit 8-5, which describes an investment problem, which of the following would be the most appropriate constraint in the linear programming problem?

(a) $0.08C + 0.12S + 0.10M \leq 100000$
(b) $C + S + M \geq 100000$
(c) $C + S + M = 100000$
(d) $C + S + M \leq 100000$
(e) none of the above

ANSWER: d

8.68 According to Exhibit 8-5, which describes an investment problem, suppose Ivana has decided that the amount invested in stocks cannot exceed one third of the total amount invested. Which is the best way to write this constraint?

(a) $S \leq 100{,}000/3$
(b) $0.12S \leq 0.08C + 0.10M$
(c) $S \leq (C + M + S)/3$
(d) $S \leq C + M$
(e) none of the above

ANSWER: c

8.69 According to Exhibit 8-5, which describes an investment problem, suppose Ivana has assigned the following risk factors to each investment instrument: CDs (C): 1.1; stocks (S): 4.7; money market mutual fund (M): 3.1. If Ivana decides that she wants the risk factor for the whole investment to be less than 3.4, how should the necessary constraint be written?

(a) $1.1C + 4.7S + 3.1M \leq 3.4$
(b) $C + S + M \leq 3.4$
(c) $(1.1C + 4.7S + 3.1M)/3 \leq 3.4$
(d) $1.1C + 4.7S + 3.1M \leq 3.4(C + S + M)$
(e) none of the above

ANSWER: d

8.70 When formulating transportation LP problems, constraints usually deal with the

(a) number of items to be transported.
(b) shipping cost associated with transporting goods.
(c) distance goods are to be transported.
(d) number of origins and destinations.
(e) capacities of origins and requirements of destinations.

ANSWER: e

8.71 The following problem type is such a special case of linear programming that a special algorithm has been developed to solve it:

(a) the production mix problem.
(b) the diet problem.
(c) the ingredient mix problem.
(d) the transportation problem.
(e) none of the above.

ANSWER: d

8.72 When formulating transportation LP problems, the objective function usually deals with the

(a) number of items to be transported.
(b) shipping cost associated with transporting goods.
(c) distance goods are to be transported.
(d) number of origins and destinations.
(e) capacities of origins and requirements of destinations.

ANSWER: b

8.73 The shipping problem in LP is also called the

(a) production mix problem.
(b) freight train problem.
(c) transportation problem.
(d) land and sea problem.
(e) none of the above

ANSWER: c

8.74 When applying linear programming to diet problems, the objective function is usually designed to

(a) maximize profits from blends of nutrients.
(b) maximize ingredient blends.
(c) minimize production losses.
(d) maximize the number of products to be produced.

(e) minimize the costs of nutrient blends.
ANSWER: e

PROBLEMS

8.75 Cedar Point amusement park management is preparing the park's annual promotional plan for the coming season. Several advertising alternatives exist: newspaper, television, radio, and displays at recreational shows. The information below shows the characteristics associated with each of the advertising alternatives, as well as the maximum number of placements available in each medium. Given an advertising budget of $250,000, how many placements should be made in each medium to maximize total audience exposure? Formulate this as a linear programming problem.

Type	Cost	Maximum number	Exposure (1000s)
Newspaper	1500	100	80
Television	2200	50	120
Radio	750	50	45
Shows	150	3	10

ANSWER: Let X_1 = number of newspaper placements
X_2 = number of television placements
X_3 = number of radio placements
X_4 = number of recreational shows

Maximize $80X_1 + 120X_2 + 45X_3 + 10X_4$

Subject to:

$$1500X_1 + 2200X_2 + 750X_3 + 150X_4 \le 250000$$
$$X_1 \le 100$$
$$X_2 \le 50$$
$$X_3 \le 50$$
$$X_4 \le 3$$
$$X_1, X_2, X_3, X_4 \ge 0$$

8.76 A small furniture manufacturer produces tables and chairs. Each product must go through three stages of the manufacturing process — assembly, finishing, and inspection. Each table requires 3 hours of assembly, 2 hours of finishing, and 1 hour of inspection. Each chair requires 2 hours of assembly, 2 hours of finishing, and 1 hour of inspection. The profit per table is $120, while the profit per chair is $80. Currently, each week there are 200 hours of assembly time available, 180 hours of finishing time, and 40 hours of inspection time. To keep a balance, the number of chairs produced should be at least twice the number of tables. Also, the number of chairs cannot exceed six times the number of tables. Formulate this as a linear programming problem. Carefully define all decision variables.
ANSWER: Let T = number of tables produced
C = number of chairs produced

Maximize $120T + 80C$

Subject to:

$$3T + 2C \le 200$$
$$2T + 2C \le 180$$
$$T + C \le 40$$
$$-2T + C \ge 0$$

$-6T + C \leq 0$
$C, T \geq 0$

8.77 Swearingen and McDonald, a small furniture manufacturer, produces fine hardwood tables and chairs. Each product must go through three stages of the manufacturing process — assembly, finishing, and inspection. Each table requires 12 hours of assembly, 20 hours of finishing, and 2 hours of inspection. Each chair requires 4 hours of assembly, 16 hours of finishing, and 3 hours of inspection. The profit per table is $150 while the profit per chair is $100. Currently, each week there are 300 hours of assembly time available, 220 hours of finishing time, and 30 hours of inspection time. To keep a balance, the number of chairs produced should be at least twice the number of tables. Also, the number of chairs cannot exceed 6 times the number of tables. Formulate this as a linear programming problem. Carefully define all decision variables. Find the solution.

ANSWER: Let T = number of tables produced
C = number of chairs produced

Maximize $150T + 100C$
Subject to:
$12T + 4C \leq 300$
$20T + 16C \leq 220$
$2T + 3C \leq 30$
$-2T + C \geq 0$
$-6T + C \leq 0$
$C, T \geq 0$

Solution: T = 3.75, C=7.5, Objective function = 1312.5

8.78 Solve the following linear program:

Minimize $1X + 2Y$
Subject to:
$1X + 3Y \geq 100$
$8X + 2Y \geq 180$
$3X + 2Y \leq 90$
$1Y \leq 85$

ANSWER: There is no feasible solution.

8.79 Solve the following linear program:

Maximize $1X + 2Y$
Subject to:
$1X + 3Y \geq 100$
$8X + 2Y \geq 180$
$3X + 2Y \leq 90$
$1Y \leq 85$

ANSWER: There is no feasible solution.

8.80 A manufacturer of microcomputers produces four models: Portable, Student, Office, and Network. The profit per unit on each of these four models is \$500, \$350, \$700, and \$1000, respectively. The models require the labor and materials per unit shown below.

	Portable	Student	Office	Network	Total
Labor (hrs/week)	5	5	6	8	4000
Chassis (unit/week)	1	1	1	1	400
Disk Drive (unit/week)	2	1	2	1	300
Hard Disk (unit/week)	0	0	0	1	20
Memory Chip (unit/week)	16	8	32	64	22000
Circuit Bds. (unit/week)	1	1	2	4	10000

Formulate this product mix problem using linear programming.

ANSWER: Let X_1 = portable
X_2 = student
X_3 = office
X_4 = network

Maximize $500X_1 + 350X_2 + 700X_3 + 1000X_4$

Subject to:

$$5X_1 + 5X_2 + 6X_3 + 8X_4 \le 4000$$
$$X_1 + X_2 + X_3 + X_4 \le 400$$
$$2X_1 + X_2 + 2X_3 + X_4 \le 300$$
$$X_4 \le 20$$
$$16X_1 + 8X_2 + 32X_3 + 64X_4 \le 22000$$
$$X_1 + X_2 + 2X_3 + 4X_4 \le 10000$$
$$X_1, X_2, X_3, X_4 \ge 0$$

8.81 Solve the following linear program:

Maximize $3X - Y$

Subject to:

$$11X + 2Y \ge 115$$
$$X + 12Y \ge 80$$
$$X + Y \ge 20$$
$$2X \ge 15$$

ANSWER: The problem is unbounded; in Excel, the Set Cells do not converge.

8.82 A fast food restaurant uses full-time and part-time help to meet fluctuating demand during the day. The following table presents projected need for workers at different times of the day:

Time	Workers needed
9:00–10:00	4
10:00–11:00	5
11:00–12:00	9
12:00–1:00	10
1:00–2:00	8
2:00–3:00	4
3:00–4:00	3
4:00–5:00	6

There is a maximum of four full-time workers and the other workers are part-time workers. Each full-time worker is there from 9:00 until 5:00, while the part-time workers will work for 4 consecutive hours at a cost of $4.00 per hour. The cost of the full-time worker is $50 per day. The company wishes to minimize total cost while meeting the demands. Formulate this as a linear programming problem. Carefully define all decision variables.

ANSWER: Let P_1 = number of part-time workers starting at 9:00
P_2 = number of part-time workers starting at 10:00
P_3 = number of part-time workers starting at 11:00
P_4 = number of part-time workers starting at 12:00
P_5 = number of part-time workers starting at 1:00
F = number of full-time workers

Minimize $50F + 16P_1 + 16P_2 + 16P_3 + 16P_4 + 16P_5$

Subject to:

$$
\begin{aligned}
F & \le 4 \\
F + P_1 & \ge 4 \\
F + P_1 + P_2 & \ge 5 \\
F + P_1 + P_2 + P_3 & \ge 9 \\
F + P_1 + P_2 + P_3 + P_4 & \ge 10 \\
F + P_2 + P_3 + P_4 + P_5 & \ge 8 \\
F + P_3 + P_4 + P_5 & \ge 4 \\
F + P_4 + P_5 & \ge 3 \\
F + P_5 & \ge 6 \\
\text{all variables} & \ge 0
\end{aligned}
$$

8.83 First Securities, Inc., an investment firm, has \$380,000 on account. The chief investment officer would like to reinvest the \$380,000 in a portfolio that would maximize return on investment while at the same time maintaining a relatively conservative mix of stocks and bonds. The following table shows the investment opportunities and rates of return.

Investment Opportunity	Rate of Return
Municipal Bonds	0.095
High Tech Stock	0.146
Blue Chip Stock	0.075
Federal Bonds	0.070

The Board of Directors has mandated that at least 60 percent of the investment consist of a combination of municipal and federal bonds, 25 percent Blue Chip Stock, and no more than 15 percent High Tech Stock. Formulate this portfolio selection problem using linear programming.

ANSWER: Let X_1 = \$ invested in Municipal Bonds
X_2 = \$ invested in High Tech Stock
X_3 = \$ invested in Blue Chip Stock
X_4 = \$ invested in Federal Bonds

Maximize $0.095X_1 + 0.146X_2 + 0.075X_3 + 0.07X_4$

Subject to:
$$X_1 + X_2 + X_3 + X_4 = 380000$$
$$X_1 + X_2 \geq 228000$$
$$X_3 = 95000$$
$$X_4 \leq 57000$$
$$X_1, X_2, X_3, X_4 \geq 0$$

8.84 Dr. Malcomb Heizer wishes to invest his retirement fund of \$2,050,000 so that his return on investment is maximized, but he also wishes to keep the risk level relatively low. He has decided to invest his money in any of three possible ways — CDs that pay a guaranteed 3 percent, stocks that have an expected return of 14 percent, and a money market mutual fund that is expected to return 18 percent. He has decided that the total \$2,000,000 will be invested, but any part (or all) of it may be put in any of the three alternatives. Thus, he may have some money invested in all three alternatives. He has also decided to invest, at most, 30 percent of this in stocks and at least 20 percent of this in money market funds. Formulate this as a linear programming problem and carefully define all the decision variables. Find the solution.

ANSWER: Let C = dollars invested in CDs
S = dollars invested in stocks
M = dollars invested in money market

Maximize $0.03C + 0.14S + 0.18M$

Subject to:
$$C + S + M = 2000000$$
$$S \leq 600000$$
$$C \geq 400000$$
$$C, S, M \geq 0$$

ANSWER: CD = \$400,000, Stock = \$600,000, Money market = \$1,000,000

8.85 Friendly Manufacturing has three factories (1, 2, and 3) and three warehouses (A, B, and C). The table below shows the shipping costs between each factory (in dollars) and warehouse, the factory manufacturing capabilities (in 1000s), and the warehouse capacities (in 1000s). Write the objective function and the constraint inequalities. Let X_{1A} = 1000s of units shipped from factory 1 to warehouse A, etc.

From		To		Production
	A	B	C	Capability
Factory 1	6	5	3	6
Factory 2	8	10	8	8
Factory 3	11	14	18	10
Capacity	7	12	5	

ANSWER:

Minimize $6X_{1A} + 5X_{1B} + 3X_{1C} + 8X_{2A} + 10X_{2B} + 8X_{2C} + 11X_{3A} + 14X_{3B} + 18X_{3C}$

Subject to:

$X_{1A} + X_{2A} + X_{3A} = 7$

$X_{1B} + X_{2B} + X_{3B} = 12$

$X_{1C} + X_{2C} + X_{3C} = 5$

$X_{1A} + X_{1B} + X_{1C} \le 6$

$X_{2A} + X_{2B} + X_{2C} \le 8$

$X_{3A} + X_{3B} + X_{3C} \le 10$

all variables ≥ 0

8.86 The following table provides shipping costs from each of two regional warehouses to each of three destinations. The supplies available and the demands are also given in the table.

FROM		TO		
	Houston	New Orleans	Atlanta	Supply (units)
Dallas	6	7	9	200
Huntsville	8	7	6	200
DEMAND	200	250	200	

Formulate this as a linear programming problem. Carefully define all decision variables.

ANSWER:

Let X_{11} = number of units shipped from Dallas to Houston

X_{12} = number of units shipped from Dallas to New Orleans

X_{13} = number of units shipped from Dallas to Atlanta

X_{21} = number of units shipped from Huntsville to Houston

X_{22} = number of units shipped from Huntsville to New Orleans

X_{23} = number of units shipped from Huntsville to Atlanta

Minimize $6X_{11} + 7X_{12} + 9X_{13} + 8X_{21} + 7X_{22} + 6\,X_{23}$

Subject to:

$X_{11} + X_{12} + X_{13} \le 200$

$X_{21} + X_{22} + X_{23} \le 200$

$X_{11} + X_{21} = 200$

$X_{12} + X_{22} = 250$

$X_{13} + X_{23} = 150$

all variables ≥ 0

8.87 Green Grass, Inc. just ran out of stock and suddenly has two emergency orders for grass seed blends: one is for 1500 pounds of normal, the other for 2300 pounds of special. At most, each pound of normal should contain 60 percent annual seed, while each pound of special should contain at least 70 percent perennial seed. Green Grass has two input mixtures, A and B. Mixture A contains 80 percent perennial and 15 percent annual seed. Mixture B contains 70 percent annual and 25 percent perennial seed. Mixture A costs 90 cents per pound and mixture B costs 50 cents per pound. Set up the constraints and the objective function to solve this blending problem.

Let X_1 = lbs. of mixture A used to produce the normal blend
X_2 = lbs. of mixture A used to produce the special blend
X_3 = lbs. of mixture B used to produce the normal blend
X_4 = lbs. of mixture B used to produce the special blend

ANSWER: Minimize $0.9X_1 + 0.9X_2 + 0.5X_3 + 0.5X_4$

Subject to:

$$X_1 + X_3 \geq 1500$$
$$X_2 + X_4 \geq 2300$$
$$0.45X_1 - 0.10X_3 \geq 0$$
$$0.10X_2 - 0.45X_4 \geq 0$$
$$X_1, X_2, X_3, X_4 \geq 0$$

8.88 Three types of gasoline are manufactured by a company – Regular, Super, and Extra. Regular should have at least 11percent additive 1 and 17 percent additive 2. Super should have at least 13 percent additive 1 and 22 percent additive 2. Extra should have at least 17 percent additive 1 and 19 percent additive 2. These are made by using two crudes – A and B. Crude A cost $28 per barrel and is 14 percent additive 1 and 18 percent additive 2. Crude B costs $30 per barrel and is 20 percent additive 1 and 24 percent additive 2. The demand for Regular is projected to be 1,000 barrels, while each of the others has a demand of 2,000 barrels. Formulate this as a linear programming problem to minimize cost while meeting all constraints. Carefully define all decision variables.

ANSWER:

Let AR = number of barrels of A to use in Regular
AS = number of barrels of A to use in Super
AE = number of barrels of A to use in Extra
BR = number of barrels of B to use in Regular
BS = number of barrels of B to use in Super
BE = number of barrels of B to use in Extra

Minimize $28AR + 28AS + 28AE + 30BR + 30BS + 30BE$

Subject to:

$$AR + BR = 1000$$
$$AS + BS = 2000$$
$$AE + BE = 2000$$
$$0.14AR + 0.20BR \geq 110$$
$$0.18AR + 0.24BR \geq 170$$
$$0.14AS + 0.20BS \geq 260$$
$$0.18AS + 0.24BS \geq 440$$
$$0.14AE + 0.20BE \geq 340$$
$$0.18AE + 0.24BE \geq 380$$

all variables ≥ 0

8.89 Three types of fertilizer are manufactured by a company — Regular, Supergro, and Jungle Feeder. Regular should have at least 10 percent nitrogen and 16 percent phosphorous. Supergro should have at least 12 percent nitrogen and 20 percent phosphorous, and Jungle Feeder should have at least 15 percent nitrogen and 18 percent phosphorous. These are made by using two components — A and B. Component A costs $0.30 per pound and is 14 percent nitrogen and 18 percent phosphorous. Component B costs $0.50 per pound and is 20 percent nitrogen and 24 percent phosphorous. The demand for Regular is projected to be 1,000 pounds, while each of the others has a demand of 2,000 pounds. Formulate the appropriate linear program.

Let X_1 = pounds of component A in Regular
X_2 = pounds of component A in Supergro
X_3 = pounds of component A in Jungle Feeder
X_4 = pounds of component B in Regular
X_5 = pounds of component B in Supergro
X_6 = pounds of component B in Jungle Feeder

ANSWER: Min. $Z = .3X_1 + .3X_2 + .3X_3 + .5X_4 + .5X_5 + .5X_6$

Subject to:

C1	$X_1 + X_4 = 1000$	(pounds of Regular needed)
C2	$X_2 + X_5 = 2000$	(pounds of Supergro needed)
C3	$X_3 + X_6 = 2000$	(pounds of Jungle Feeder needed)
C4	$0.14X_1 + 0.20X_4 \geq 100$	(nitrogen in Regular)
C5	$0.18X_1 + 0.24X_4 \geq 160$	(phosphorous in Regular)
C6	$0.14X_2 + 0.20X_5 \geq 240$	(nitrogen in Supergro)
C7	$0.18X_2 + 0.24X_5 \geq 400$	(phosphorous in Supergro)
C8	$0.14X_3 + 0.20X_6 \geq 300$	(nitrogen in Jungle Feeder)
C9	$0.18X_3 + 0.24X_6 \geq 360$	(phosphorous in Jungle Feeder)
	ALL $X_i \geq 0$	

8.90 A cruise line is planning its menu for the next trip. Vacationers like eating steak, lobster, and chicken. The cruise line has decided to plan for at least half of all booked passengers to have a steak dinner, for at least a quarter of all passengers to have lobster, and the rest to have chicken. Steak dinners cost the company $8, lobsters cost $15, and chicken costs the line $4. On the next cruise, there are 400 passengers booked. In addition, the cruise line has decided to plan for an additional 25% more meals than bookings. Formulate the appropriate linear program.

Let X1 = steak meals
X2 = lobster meals
X3 = chicken meals

ANSWER: Min. Z = 8X1 + 15X2 + 4X3
Subject to:

C1	X1			≥ 200	(booked meals of steak)
C2		X2		≥ 100	(booked meals of lobster)
C3	-X1	-X2	+X3	≥ 0	(booked meals of chicken)
C4	X1	+X2	+X3	≥ 500	(all meals)

8.91 A mail order firm, AmazingCo, can use one of 3 shipping couriers. Ajax Shipping charges $5 per pound and delivers in 2 days. Bilco Lanes charges $8 per pound but guarantees next day delivery. The final courier, Hobo Ltd., charges only $2 per pound but takes 4 days to deliver. AmazingCo has a quarterly budget of $250,000 and a reputation for timely delivery. Formulate the linear program so that the firm maintains its timely delivery reputation for 75,000 pounds of shipments per quarter.

Let X1 = pounds using Ajax
X2 = pounds using Bilco
X3 = pounds using Hobo Ltd

ANSWER: Min. Z = 2X1 + 1X2 + 4X3

Subject to:

C1	X1	+ X2	+ X3	= 75,000	(total pounds to be shipped)
C2	5X1	+8X2	+2X3	≤ 250,000	(budget for shipments)

SHORT ANSWER/ESSAY

8.92 What is one difference in the constraints between a maximization and a minimization linear program problem?

ANSWER: In a maximization problem, most of the constraints have inequalities that are greater than or equal to while in a minimization problem most of the constraints have inequalities that are less than or equal to.

8.93 Describe the marketing research linear programming application.

ANSWER: a decision aid for pollsters to make strategic decisions regarding survey coverage

8.94 Describe the production mix linear programming application.

ANSWER: a decision aid for the planning of the optimal mix of products to manufacture

8.95 Describe the production scheduling linear programming application.

ANSWER: a decision aid similar to the production mix application, but optimizes cost/profit over several future time periods

8.96 Describe the assignment linear programming application.

ANSWER: a decision aid in determining the most efficient assignment of humans to jobs, machines to tasks, sales people to territories, etc.

8.97 Describe the portfolio selection linear programming application.

ANSWER: a decision aid to effectively select specific investment components to compose an investment portfolio while maximizing investment return

8.98 Describe the truck loading linear programming application.

ANSWER: a decision aid to decide which items to load on a truck to maximize the value of the load shipped

8.99 Describe the shipping problem linear programming application.

ANSWER: The shipping problem (also called the transportation problem) is a decision aid to determine the amount of items to be transported from a number of origins to a number of destinations while minimizing shipping costs.

8.100 Describe a diet problem linear programming application.

ANSWER: a decision aid to help hospitals determine the most nutritious yet economical diet for patients

8.101 Describe the feed mix linear programming application.

ANSWER: a decision aid to specify a feed ingredient combination to minimize the total feed cost, yet still provide an adequate high protein diet

CHAPTER 9
Linear Programming: The Simplex Method

TRUE/FALSE

9.1 A basic feasible solution is a solution to a linear programming problem that corresponds to a corner point of the feasible region.

ANSWER: TRUE

9.2 A correctly formulated linear program, when solved with the simplex algorithm, will always yield a single optimal solution.

ANSWER: FALSE

9.3 If all of a resource represented by a slack variable is used, that slack variable will not be in the production mix column of a linear programming simplex tableau.

ANSWER: TRUE

9.4 In the simplex process, the new pivot row is found by dividing the pivot number by each number in the row.

ANSWER: FALSE

9.5 If a variable is part of the solution, its column in the body of the simplex table will have a single nonzero coefficient.

ANSWER: TRUE

9.6 In the simplex table, a coefficient of zero in a constraint implies that the variable with the zero coefficient has no influence on the solution for that iteration.

ANSWER: TRUE

9.7 The $C_j - Z_j$ row in the simplex table tells us whether the current solution is optimal, and if it is not, what variable will be in the optimal solution.

ANSWER: FALSE

9.8 For a maximization problem, the Z_j values in the body of the simplex table represent the gross profit given up by adding one unit of this variable into the current solution.

ANSWER: TRUE

9.9 In any linear programming problem, if a variable is to enter the solution, it must have a positive coefficient in the $C_j - Z_j$ row.

ANSWER: FALSE

9.10 In a maximization problem, the C_j - Z_j row gives the net loss from introducing one unit of each variable into the solution.

ANSWER: FALSE

9.11 In a maximization problem, if a variable is to enter the solution, it must have a positive coefficient in the C_j - Z_j row.

ANSWER: TRUE

9.12 A surplus variable is added to a $\geq$ constraint in order to create an equality, and represents a quantity of unused resource.

ANSWER: FALSE

9.13 The constraint $5X_1 + 6X_2 \geq 30$, when converted to an = constraint for use in the simplex algorithm, will be $5 X_1 + 6 X_2 - S + A = 30$.

ANSWER: TRUE

9.14 The constraint $5 X_1 + 6 X_2 \leq 30$, when converted to an = constraint for use in the simplex algorithm, will be $5 X_1 + 6 X_2 - S = 30$.

ANSWER: FALSE

9.15 The constraint $5 X_1 + 6 X_2 = 30$, when converted to an = constraint for use in the simplex algorithm, will be $5 X_1 + 6 X_2 - A = 30$.

ANSWER: FALSE

9.16 A surplus variable is added to an = constraint in order to utilize the simplex algorithm.

ANSWER: FALSE

9.17 If there are seven less-than-or-equal constraints in a problem, the simplex table contains seven slack variables.

ANSWER: TRUE

9.18 All variables in a linear programming problem (real, slack, surplus, or artificial) must be nonnegative.

ANSWER: TRUE

9.19 Artificial variables can be used in both maximization and minimization problems but are most often used in minimization problems.

ANSWER: TRUE

9.20 Slack and surplus variables are used in simplex only for the solution of maximization problems.

ANSWER: FALSE

9.21 We can solve a minimization problem by maximizing the negative of the minimization problem's objective function.

ANSWER: TRUE

9.22 In a maximization problem, if a variable is to enter the solution, it must have a negative coefficient in the $C_j - Z_j$ row.

ANSWER: FALSE

9.23 The basic process of the simplex algorithm is to find solutions to a set of simultaneous equations where we have more variables than equations.

ANSWER: TRUE

9.24 An infeasible solution is indicated when all the $C_j - Z_j$ row entries are of the proper sign to imply optimality, but an artificial variable remains in the solution.

ANSWER: TRUE

9.25 If all the numbers in the pivot column are negative, this implies that the solution is unbounded.

ANSWER: TRUE

9.26 As we are doing the ratio calculations for a simplex iteration, if there is a tie for the smallest ratio, the problem is degenerate.

ANSWER: TRUE

9.27 If, at an optimal solution, the $C_j - Z_j$ value for a real variable that is not in the solution mix has a value of one, there are multiple optimal solutions.

ANSWER: FALSE

9.28 Typically, real world applications of linear programming are solved with a computer program that utilizes the simplex algorithm.

ANSWER: TRUE

9.29 Sensitivity testing of basic variables involves reworking the initial simplex tableau.

ANSWER: FALSE

9.30 The shadow price is the value of one additional unit of a scarce resource.

ANSWER: TRUE

9.31 Shadow prices are the negatives of the numbers in the C_j - Z_j row's slack variable columns.

ANSWER: TRUE

9.32 Dual variables represent the potential value of resources.

ANSWER: TRUE

9.33 The dual problem formulation can be solved using the same simplex process used for the primal formulation.

ANSWER: TRUE

MULTIPLE CHOICE

9.34 The substitution rates give

(a) the number of units of each basic variable that must be removed from the solution if a new variable is entered.
(b) the gross profit or loss given up by adding one unit of a variable into the solution.
(c) the net profit or loss that will result from introducing one unit of the variable indicated in that column into the solution.
(d) the maximal value a variable can take on and still have all the constraints satisfied.
(e) none of the above

ANSWER: a

9.35 The contribution rate, C_j, gives

(a) the number of units of each basic variable that must be removed from the solution if a new variable is entered.
(b) the gross profit or loss given up by adding one unit of a variable into the solution.
(c) the net profit or loss that will result from introducing one unit of the variable indicated in that column into the solution.
(d) the maximal value a variable can take on and still have all the constraints satisfied.
(e) none of the above

ANSWER: e

9.36 Which of the following is not true about slack variables in a simplex tableau?

(a) They are used to convert ≤ constraint inequalities to equations.
(b) They represent unused resources.
(c) They require the addition of an artificial variable.
(d) They may represent machine time, labor hours, or warehouse space.
(e) They yield no profit.

ANSWER: c

9.37 Changes in the resources or right-hand side values of a linear programming problem

(a) will change the slope of the isoprofit or isocost line.
(b) result in no changes in the feasible region.
(c) are investigated by examining the ratios of the original LP solution and the slack column of the simplex tableau that is associated with the resource.
(d) all of the above

ANSWER: c

TABLE 9-1
Simplex Tableau: 1

C_j		10	20	0	0	
	Sol. Mix	X_1	X_2	S_1	S_2	Quantity
20	X_2	0.5	1	0.2	0	15
0	S_2	2.5	0	-	1	30
	Z_j	10	20	5	0	300
	C_j-Z_j	0	0	-5	0	

Final Optimal Solution Z =300

Variable	Value	Shadow Price
X_1	0	0
X_2	15	0

9.38 According to Table 9-1, the 0.500 in the X_1 column means that

(a) to produce 1 unit of X_1, 0.5 units of X_2 must be given up.
(b) to produce 1 unit of X_2, 0.5 units of X_1 must be given up.
(c) if 1 unit of X_1 is produced, profits on X_2 will decrease by 0.500.
(d) if 1 unit of X_1 is produced, profits on X_2 will increase by 0.500.
(e) none of the above

ANSWER: a

9.39 According to Table 9-1, which is the final simplex tableau for a problem with two variables and two constraints, what can be said about the optimal solution and the constraints?

(a) There is slack remaining in the first constraint.
(b) There is slack remaining in the second constraint.
(c) There is slack remaining in both constraints.
(d) There is no slack remaining in either constraint.
(e) none of the above

ANSWER: b

9.40 Consider the following general form of a linear programming problem:

Maximize Profit
Subject to: Amount of resource A used ≤ 100 units
Amount of resource B used ≤ 240 units
Amount of resource B used ≤ 150 units

The shadow price for S_1 is 25, for S_2 is 0, and for S_3 is 40. If the right-hand side of constraint 1 were changed from 100 to 101, what would happen to maximum possible profit?

(a) It would not change.
(b) It would increase by 25.
(c) It would decrease by 25.
(d) It would increase by 40.
(e) It would decrease by 40.

ANSWER: b

Table 9-2

Maximize profit $20X_1 + 30X_2 + 16X_3$

Subject to:

$8X_1 + 4X_2 \leq 64$ Resource A

$4X_1 + 12X_2 + 4X_3 \leq 96$ Resource B

All variables ≥ 0

C_j		20	30	16	0	0	
	Solution Mix	X1	X2	X3	S1	S2	Quantity
20	X_1	1	0.5	0	0.125	0	8
16	X_3	0	2.5	1	-0.125	0.25	16
	Z_j	20	50	16	0.5	4	416

9.41 According to Table 9-2, all of the resources are being used. If the amount of resource A were changed from 64 to 65, then the maximum possible total profit would be

(a) 416
(b) 417
(c) 416.5
(d) 415.5
(e) none of the above

ANSWER: c

9.42 According to Table 9-2, all of the resources are being used. If the amount of resource B were changed from 96 to 97, then the maximum possible total profit would be

(a) 416
(b) 417
(c) 419
(d) 420
(e) none of the above

ANSWER: d

9.43 According to Table 9-2, it is currently profitable to produce some units of X_1 and the current profit per unit of X_1 is \$20. What is the lowest value that this could be to allow this variable to remain in the basis?

(a) 8
(b) 16
(c) 20
(d) 30
(e) none of the above

ANSWER: b

9.44 The substitution rates

(a) are the coefficients in the quantity column.
(b) tell us the number of units of a basic variable that must be removed from the solution for another variable to enter the basis.
(c) tell the amount of one resource that can be substituted for another.
(d) tell us the amount of a resource that must be used to gain another unit of profit.
(e) none of the above

ANSWER: b

9.45 The $C_j - Z_j$ row of a simplex tableau gives

(a) the number of units of each basic variable that must be removed from the solution if a new variable is entered.
(b) the gross profit or loss given up by adding one unit of a variable into the solution.
(c) the net profit or loss that will result from introducing one unit of the variable indicated in that column into the solution.
(d) the maximal value a variable can take on and still have all the constraints satisfied.
(e) none of the above

ANSWER: c

9.46 The number –2 in the X_2 column and X_1 row of a simplex tableau implies that

(a) if 1 unit of X_2 is added to the solution, X_1 will decrease by 2.
(b) if 1 unit of X_1 is added to the solution, X_2 will decrease by 2.
(c) if 1 unit of X_2 is added to the solution, X_1 will increase by 2.
(d) if 1 unit of X_1 is added to the solution, X_2 will increase by 2.
(e) none of the above

ANSWER: c

9.47 If one changes the contribution rates in the objective function of an LP problem,

(a) the feasible region will change.
(b) the slope of the iso-profit or iso-cost line will change.
(c) the optimal solution to the LP will no longer be optimal.
(d) all of the above
(e) none of the above

ANSWER: b

9.48 Shadow prices

(a) can be derived from the coefficients of the slack variables in the $C_j - Z_j$ row of an optimal simplex tableau.
(b) represent the value of one additional unit of a resource.
(c) are found in the solution to the dual LP.
(d) all of the above
(e) none of the above

ANSWER: d

9.49 A shadow price is

(a) the coefficient of a constraint.
(b) the value over standard cost of one additional unit of a resource that becomes available.
(c) the coefficients that are deleted when transposing a matrix from a primal to a dual.
(d) any negative value in the Z_j row.
(e) the smallest result obtained when basic variable values in a column are divided into their respective row quantities.

ANSWER: b

9.50 Shadow prices represent

(a) the value of one additional unit of a basic variable.
(b) the value of one less unit of a basic variable.
(c) the value of one additional unit of a specific resource.
(d) the value of one less unit of a basic variable.
(e) none of the above

ANSWER: c

9.51 A slack variable

(a) is added to each ≤ constraint to facilitate the simplex process.
(b) is added to each ≥ constraint to facilitate the simplex process.
(c) is added to each ≤ or = constraint to facilitate the simplex process.
(d) is added to each = constraint to facilitate the simplex process.
(e) none of the above

ANSWER: a

9.52 Using the simplex method, we know we have an optimal solution when

(a) all slack variables have a zero value.
(b) all basic variables are negative.
(c) when all the real variables have a nonzero value.
(d) when all the artificial variables have a positive value.
(e) none of the above
ANSWER: e

Table 9-3

Maximize $Z = 12X_1 + 30X_2$
Subject to:
$32X_1 + 18X_2 \le 600$ Resource A
$24X_1 + 48X_2 \le 800$ Resource B

Final Optimal Solution: Z = 500

Variable	Solution	Shadow Price
X_1	0	3
X_2	16.667	0
S_1	300	0
S_2	0	0.625

Objective Coefficient Ranges

Variable	Min. C_j	Original	Max. C_j
X_1	$-\infty$	12	15
X_2	24	30	$+\infty$

Right-Hand Side Ranges

Constraint	Min.	Original	Max.
A	300	600	$+\infty$
B	0	800	1600

9.53 According to Table 9-3, which is a summarized solution output from simplex analysis, the optimal solution to this problem is

(a) $X_1 = 0, X_2 = 16.667, S_1 = 300, S_2 = 0$
(b) $X_1 = 0, X_2 = 16.667, S_1 = 0, S_2 = 0$
(c) $X_1 = 12, X_2 = 30, S_1 = 0, S_2 = 0.625$
(d) $X_1 = 12, X_2 = 30, S_1 = 0.625, S_2 = 0$
(e) none of the above

ANSWER: a

9.54 According to Table 9-3, which is a summarized solution output from simplex analysis, if the amount of resource A were decreased so that there were only 550 units available instead of 600, what would happen to total profits?

(a) They would decrease.
(b) They would increase.
(c) They would not change.
(d) Unable to determine from the given information.
(e) none of the above
ANSWER: c

9.55 If one changes a nonbasic objective function coefficient, the optimal solution of a maximization problem will remain optimal if

(a) the increase in the coefficient does not exceed the value of the Z_j associated with that nonbasic variable.
(b) the increase in the coefficient does not exceed the values of the Z_j's of every basic variable.
(c) the decrease in the coefficient does not exceed the value of the Z_j associated with the nonbasic variable.
(d) the new $C_j - Z_j$ associated with the nonbasic variable remains positive.
(e) none of the above

ANSWER: a

9.56 Which of the following is not true of artificial variables?

(a) They have no meaning in a physical sense — nothing more than a computational tool.
(b) In all linear programs, they appear in the objective function with a very low cost ($M).
(c) They are usually used with ≥ constraints.
(d) They are usually used with = constraints.
(e) none of the above

ANSWER: b

9.57 Consider the following linear programming problem:

Maximize $40 X_1 + 30 X_2 + 60X_3$

Subject to: $X_1 + X_2 + X_3 \geq 90$

$12 X_1 + 8 X_2 + 10 X_3 \leq 1500$

$X_1, X_2, X_3 \geq 0$

How many slack, surplus, and artificial variables would be necessary if the simplex were used to solve this problem?

(a) 3 slack, 3 surplus, and 3 artificial
(b) 1 slack, 2 surplus, and 2 artificial
(c) 1 slack, 4 surplus, and 4 artificial
(d) 1 slack, 1 surplus, and 1 artificial
(e) none of the above

ANSWER: d

9.58 Consider the following linear programming problem:

Maximize $40\ X_1 + 30\ X_2 + 60\ X_3$

Subject to:

$$X_1 + X_2 + X_3 \geq 90$$
$$12\ X_1 + 8\ X_2 + 10\ X_3 \leq 1500$$
$$X_1 = 20$$
$$X_3 \leq 100$$
$$X_1\ , X_2\ , X_3 \geq 0$$

How many slack, surplus, and artificial variables would be necessary if the simplex algorithm were used to solve this problem?

(a) 3 slack, 6 surplus, and 6 artificial
(b) 2 slack, 1 surplus, and 2 artificial
(c) 1 slack, 2 surplus, and 2 artificial
(d) 1 slack, 2 surplus, and 1 artificial
(e) none of the above

ANSWER: b

9.59 Which of the following is true about surplus variables in a simplex tableau?

(a) They are used to convert ≤ constraint inequalities to equations.
(b) They represent unused resources.
(c) They require the addition of an artificial variable.
(d) They may represent machine time, labor hours, or warehouse space.
(e) They yield a positive profit.

ANSWER: c

9.60 An artificial variable has no physical interpretation but

(a) is added to each ≤ constraint to facilitate the simplex process.
(b) is added to each ≥ constraint to facilitate the simplex process.
(c) is added to each ≤ or = constraint to facilitate the simplex process.
(d) is merely another manner of introducing a negative slack.
(e) none of the above

ANSWER: b

9.61 In applying the simplex solution procedure to a maximization problem to determine which variable enters the solution mix,

(a) pick the one with the smallest $C_j - Z_j$.
(b) pick the one with the largest nonnegative $C_j - Z_j$.
(c) pick the one with the largest C_j.
(d) pick the one with the smallest Z_j.
(e) pick the smallest nonnegative number formed by dividing each amount in the quantity column by the appropriate column at the exiting variable.

ANSWER: b

9.62 Nonbasic variables in the simplex method of linear programming are

(a) variables in the solution mix.
(b) variables not in the solution mix.
(c) the real variables in the initial solution.
(d) the slack variables in the optimum solution.
(e) always the slack, surplus, and artificial variables.

ANSWER: b

9.63 A solved LP problem indicated that the optimal solution was $X_1 = 5$, $X_2 = 10$, $A_1 = 40$. The first constraint was: $4X_1 + 2X_2 \geq 80$. This solution is:

(a) indeterminant.
(b) degenerate.
(c) infeasible.
(d) unbounded.
(e) none of the above

ANSWER: c

9.64 In solving a linear programming minimization problem using the simplex method,

(a) every time an artificial variable is added, a surplus variable must also be added.
(b) every time an artificial variable is added, a surplus variable must be subtracted.
(c) every time a surplus variable is added, an artificial variable must be added.
(d) every time a surplus variable is added, an artificial variable must be subtracted.
(e) none of the above

ANSWER: e

9.65 In using the simplex method for minimization linear programming problems,

(a) an optimal solution is reached when the $C_j - Z_j$ row values are negative.
(b) the pivot column is selected by the smallest positive number in the $C_j - Z_j$ row.
(c) the pivot column is selected by the most negative number in the $C_j - Z_j$ row.
(d) the pivot column is selected by the smallest negative number in the Z_j row.
(e) none of the above

ANSWER: c

9.66 In applying the simplex solution procedure to a minimization problem to determine which variable enters the solution mix,

(a) pick the one with the most negative $C_j - Z_j$.
(b) pick the one with the positive $C_j - Z_j$.
(c) pick the one with the largest C_j.
(d) pick the one with the smallest Z_j.
(e) pick the smallest nonnegative number formed by dividing each amount in the quantity column by the appropriate column at the exiting variable.

ANSWER: a

9.67 If, in the optimal tableau of a linear programming problem, an artificial variable is present in the solution mix, this implies

(a) infeasibility.
(b) unboundedness.
(c) degeneracy.
(d) alternate optimal solutions.
(e) a finite optimal solution.

ANSWER: a

9.68 If, in the final optimal simplex tableau, the $C_j - Z_j$ value for a nonbasic variable is zero, this implies

(a) infeasibility.
(b) unboundedness.
(c) degeneracy.
(d) alternate optimal solutions.
(e) none of the above

ANSWER: d

TABLE 9-4

C_j		5	3	6	0	
	Sol. Mix	X_1	X_2	S_1	S_2	Quantity
0	X2	0.667	1	0.083	0	20
6	S_2	2.667	0	-.167	1	40
	Z_j	26.667	40	3.33	0	800
	C_j–Z_j	-0.667	0	-3.33	0	

Final Optimal Solution Z = 800

Variable	Value	Shadow Price
X_1	0	6.667
X_2	20	0
S_1	0	3.333
S_2	40	0

9.69 According to Table 9-4, which is the final simplex tableau for a problem with two variables and two constraints, what are the values for all the variables in this solution?

(a) $X_1 = 20$, $X_2 = 40$, $S_1 = 0$, $S_2 = 0$
(b) $X_1 = 0$, $X_2 = 40$, $S_1 = 0$, $S_2 = 40$
(c) $X_1 = 0$, $X_2 = 20$, $S_1 = 0$, $S_2 = 40$
(d) $X_1 = 0$, $X_2 = 0$, $S_1 = 0$, $S_2 = 0$
(e) none of the above

ANSWER: c

9.70 According to Table 9-4, the 0.667 in the X_1 column means that

(a) to produce 1 unit of X_1, 0.667 units of X_2 must be given up.
(b) to produce 1 unit of X_2, 0.667 units of X_1 must be given up.
(c) if 1 unit of X_1 is produced, profits on X_2 will decrease by 0.667.
(d) if 1 unit of X_1 is produced, profits on X_2 will increase by 0.667.
(e) none of the above

ANSWER: a

9.71 According to Table 9-4, which is the final simplex tableau for a problem with two variables and two constraints, what can be said about the optimal solution and the constraints?

(a) There is slack remaining in the first constraint.
(b) There is slack remaining in the second constraint.
(c) There is slack remaining in both constraints.
(d) There is no slack remaining in either constraint.
(e) none of the above

ANSWER: b

9.72 According to Table 9-4, which is the final simplex tableau for a problem with two variables and two constraints, what is the maximum possible profit (objective function value) for this problem?

(a) 20
(b) 40
(c) 800
(d) 26.667
(e) none of the above

ANSWER: c

9.73 According to Table 9-4, which is the final simplex tableau for a linear programming problem (maximization), what would happen to profits if the X_1 column were selected as the pivot column and another iteration of the simplex algorithm were performed?

(a) Total profits would increase.
(b) Total profits would decrease.
(c) An infeasible solution would be found.
(d) Another optimal solution would be found.
(e) none of the above

ANSWER: b

9.74 Sensitivity analyses are used to examine the effects of changes in

(a) contribution rates for each variable.
(b) technological coefficients.
(c) available resources.
(d) all of the above

ANSWER: d

9.75 Sensitivity analysis may be used to

(a) experiment with possible future changes in the firm that may affect profits.
(b) determine whether a corner point of the feasible region actually yields optimal profit.
(c) replace the simplex method.
(d) reduce the number of variables in a complex LP problem.
(e) solve LP problems that require solutions only in whole numbers.

ANSWER: a

9.76 Right-hand side ranging

(a) tells us the number of units of a constraint that may be added or subtracted without changing the profit (objective function value).
(b) is a method to find the range over which shadow prices remain constant.
(c) requires computation of the dual before being accomplished.
(d) all of the above

ANSWER: b

9.77 Sensitivity analysis cannot be used to examine the effects of:

(a) changes in the contribution rates for each variable.
(b) changes in the technological coefficients.
(c) changes in the available resources.
(d) the addition or deletion of a constraint.
(e) none of the above

ANSWER: d

9.78 The solution to the dual LP problem

(a) presents the marginal profits of each additional unit of a resource.
(b) can always be derived by examining the Z_j row of the primal's optimal simplex tableau.
(c) is better than the solution to the primal.
(d) all of the above

ANSWER: a

9.79 For every primal

(a) that is a maximization problem, the dual is a minimization problem.
(b) the right-hand side quantities become the dual's objective function coefficients.
(c) constraint inequality signs are reversed in the dual.
(d) the transpose of the constraint coefficients become the dual's constraint coefficients.
(e) all of the above

ANSWER: e

9.80 The dual of a linear programming problem

(a) always exists.
(b) may be easier to solve.
(c) may contain economic information useful to management.
(d) while equivalent, is derived through an alternative procedure.
(e) all of the above

ANSWER: e

9.81 A primal linear programming problem has four variables and three constraints. The dual of this will have

(a) four variables and three constraints.
(b) three variables and four constraints.
(c) four variables and seven constraints.
(d) seven variables and four constraints.
(e) none of the above

ANSWER: b

PROBLEMS

9.82 Consider the following linear program:

$$
\begin{aligned}
\text{Maximize } Z &= 3X_1 + 2X_2 - X_3 \\
\text{Subject to: } & X_1 + X_2 + 2X_3 \le 10 \\
& 2X_1 - X_2 + X_3 \le 20 \\
& 3X_1 + X_2 \le 15 \\
& X_1, X_2, X_3 \ge 0
\end{aligned}
$$

(a) Convert the above constraints to equalities by adding the appropriate slack variables.
(b) Set up the initial simplex tableau and solve.

ANSWERS

(a)

$$
\begin{aligned}
\text{Maximize } Z &= 3X_1 + 2X_2 - X_3 + 0S_1 + 0S_2 + 0S_3 \\
\text{Subject to } & X_1 + X_2 + 2X_3 + S_1 = 10 \\
& 2X_1 - X_2 + X_3 + S_2 = 20 \\
& 3X_1 + X_2 + S_3 = 15 \\
& X_1, X_2, X_3 \ge 0
\end{aligned}
$$

(b)

C_j		3	2	–1	0	0	0	
	Sol. Mix	X_1	X_2	X_3	S_1	S_2	S_3	Quantity
0	S_1	1	1	2	1	0	0	10
0	S_2	2	–1	1	0	1	0	20
0	S_3	3	1		0	0	1	15
	Z_j	0	0	0	0	0	0	0
	$C_j–Z_j$	3	2	–1	0	0	0	

C_j		3	2	–1	0	0	0	
	Sol. Mix	X_1	X_2	X_3	S_1	S_2	S_3	Quantity
0	S_1	0	2/3	2	1	0	–1/3	5
0	S_2	0	–5/3	1	0	1	–2/3	10
3	X_3	1	1/3	0	0	0	1/3	5
	Z_j	3	1	0	0	0	1	15
	$C_j–Z_j$	0	1	–1	0	0	–1	

C_j		3	2	–1	0	0	0	
	Sol. Mix	X_1	X_2	X_3	S_1	S_2	S_3	Quantity
2	X_2	0	1	3	3/2	0	–1/2	15/2
0	S_2	0	0	6	5/2	1	–3/2	45/2
3	X_3	1	0	–1	–1/2	0	1/2	5/2
	Z_j	3	2	3	3/2	0	–1/2	45/2
	$C_j–Z_j$	0	0	–4	–3/2	0	–1/2	

9.83 Convert the following linear program into the simplex form:

Maximize $3x_1 + 2x_2$

Subject to:

$$7x_1 - 2x_2 \leq 0$$
$$5x_1 + x_2 \geq 10$$
$$x_1 + 7x_2 \geq 12$$
$$3x_1 + 3x_2 = 15$$

ANSWER:

Maximize

$$3x_1 + 2x_2 + 0S_1 + 0S_2 + 0S_3 + 0S_4 - MA_1 - MA_2 - MA_3$$

Subject to:

$$7x_1 - 2x_2 + 1S_1 - 0S_2 - 0S_3 - 0S_4 - 0A_2 - 0A_3 + 0A_4 = 0$$
$$5x_1 + x_2 - 0S_1 - 1S_2 - 0S_3 - 0S_4 + 1A_2 - 0A_3 + 0A_4 = 10$$
$$x_1 + 7x_2 - 0S_1 - 0S_2 - 1S_3 - 0S_4 - 0A_2 + 1A_3 + 0A_4 = 12$$
$$3x_1 + 3x_2 - 0S_1 - 0S_2 - 0S_3 - 0S_4 - 0A_2 - 0A_3 + 1A_4 = 15$$

9.84 Convert the following linear program into a simplex model form:

Maximize $8X + 10Y$

Subject to:

$$5X + 3Y \leq 34$$
$$2X + 3Y = 24$$
$$Y \geq 3$$
$$X, Y \geq 0$$

ANSWER:

Maximize $8X + 10Y + 0S1 + 0S3 - MA2 - MA3$

Subject to:

$$5X + 3Y + 1S1 + 0S3 + 0A2 + 0A3 = 34$$
$$2X + 3Y + 0S1 + 0S3 + 1A2 + 0A3 = 24$$
$$Y + 0S1 - 1S3 + 0A2 + 1A3 = 3$$
$$X, Y \geq 0$$

9.85 Write the dual of the following linear program:

Maximize $3X_1 + 5X_2$

Subject to:

$$4X_1 + 3X_2 \leq 48$$
$$X_1 + 2X_2 \leq 20$$
$$X_1, X_2 \geq 0$$

ANSWER:

Minimize $48U_1 + 20U_2$

Subject to:

$$4U_1 + 1U_2 \geq 3$$
$$3U_1 + 2U_2 \geq 5$$

$U_1, \quad U_2 \geq 0$

9.86 Write the dual of the following linear program:

Minimize $Z = 12X_1 + 30X_2$

Subject to:

$32X_1 + 18X_2 \geq 600$

$24X_1 + 48X_2 \geq 800$

$X_1, \quad X_2 \geq 0$

ANSWER:

Maximize $600U_1 + 800U_2$

Subject to:

$32U_1 + 24U_2 \leq 12$

$18U_1 + 48U_2 \leq 30$

$U_1, \quad U_2 \geq 0$

9.87 Solve the following linear programming problem using the simplex method.

Maximize $3X_1 + 5X_2$

Subject to:

$4X_1 + 3X_2 \leq 48$

$X_1 + 2X_2 \leq 20$

$X_1, X_2 \geq 0$

ANSWER:

C_j		3	5	0	0	
	Sol.Mix	X_1	X_2	S_1	S_2	Quantity
0	S_1	4	3	1	0	48
0	S_2	1	2	0	1	20
	Z_j	0	0	0	0	0
	$C_j - Z_j$	3	5	0	0	

Second tableau

C_j		3	5	0	0	
	Sol.Mix	X_1	X_2	S_1	S_2	Quantity
0	S_1	2.5	0	1	−1.5	18
5	X_2	0.5	1	0	0.5	10
	Z_j	2.5	5	0	2.5	50
	$C_j - Z_j$	0.5	0	0	−2.5	

Third tableau

C_j		3	5	0	0	
	Sol.Mix	X_1	X_2	S_1	S_2	Quantity
3	X_1	1	0	0.4	−0.6	7.2
5	X_2	0	1	−0.2	0.8	6.4
	Z_j	3	5	0.2	2.2	53.6

$C_j - Z_j$	0	0	−0.2	−2.2	

9.88 The following is a partial simplex tableau for a maximization problem after one iteration. Fill out the rest of this tableau, and then develop the next simplex tableau.

C_j		5	3	6	0	0	0	
	Sol.Mix	X_1	X_2	X_3	S_1	S_2	S_3	Quantity
	S_1	7/2	4/3	0	1	−1/6	0	24
	X_3	½	2/3	1	0	1/6	0	3
	S_3	3/2	2/3	0	0	1/6	1	15
	Z_j							
	$C_j - Z_j$							

ANSWER:

C_j		5	3	6	0	0	0	
	Sol.Mix	X_1	X_2	X_3	S_1	S_2	S_3	Quantity
0	S_1	7/2	4/3	0	1	−1/6	0	24
6	X_3	1/2	2/3	1	0	1/6	0	3
0	S_3	3/2	2/3	0	0	1/6	1	15
	Z_j	3	4	6	0	1	0	18
	$C_j - Z_j$	2	−1	0	0	−1	0	

Next tableau

C_j		5	3	6	0	0	0	
	Sol.Mix	X_1	X_2	X_3	S_1	S_2	S_3	Quantity
0	S_1	0	−10/3	−7	1	−4/3	0	3
5	X_1	1	4/3	2	0	1/3	0	6
0	S_3	0	−4/3	−3	0	−1/3	1	6
	Z_j	5	20/3	10	0	5/3	0	30
	$C_j - Z_j$	0	−11/3	−4	0	−5/3	0	

9.89 Upon retirement, Mr. Klaws started to make two types of children's wooden toys in his shop. Wuns yield a variable profit of \$8 each, and Toos have a contribution margin of \$9 each. Even though his electric saw overheats, he can make 7 Wuns or 14 Toos each day. Since he doesn't have equipment for drying the lacquer finish he puts on the toys, the drying operation limits him to 16 Wuns or 8 Toos per day. The final tableau for Mr. Klaws' problem would be:

C_j		8	9	0	0	
	Sol.Mix	X_1	X_2	S_1	S_2	Quantity
8	X_1	1	0	2/3	−1/3	4
9	X_2	0	1	−1/3	2/3	6
	Z_j	8	9	7/3	10/3	86
	$C_j–Z_j$	0	0	−7/3	−10/3	

(a) What would the value be of an additional unit of constraint #1?
(b) What would the value be of an additional unit of constraint #2?

ANSWER:

(a) \$7/3
(b) \$10/3

9.90 Add all necessary slack, surplus, and artificial variables to the following linear programming problem. Be sure to include these in the objective function with the appropriate coefficients.

Maximize $8X + 10Y$
Subject to:
$$5X + 3Y \leq 34$$
$$2X + 3Y = 24$$
$$Y \geq 3$$
$$X, Y \geq 0$$

ANSWER: Maximize $8X + 10Y + 0\,S_1 + 0\,S_2 - M\,A_1 - M\,A_2$
Subject to:
$$5X + 3Y + S_1 = 34$$
$$2X + 3Y + A1 = 24$$
$$Y - S_2 + A_2 = 3$$

9.91 Write the dual of the following problem.

Maximize $8X + 10Y$
Subject to:
$$5X + 3Y \leq 34$$
$$2X + 3Y \leq 24$$
$$Y \leq 3$$
$$X, Y \geq 0$$

ANSWER: Minimize $34U_1 + 24U_2 + 3U_3$
Subject to:
$$5U_1 + 2U_2 \geq 8$$
$$3U_1 + 3U_2 + U_3 \geq 10$$
All variables ≥ 0

9.92 Given the following dual linear program, write the primal program:

Maximize $3U_1 + 2U_2$

Subject to:

$7U_1 - 2U_2 \leq 0$
$5U_1 + U_2 \leq 10$
$U_1 + 7U_2 \leq 12$
$U_1, \quad U_2 \geq 0$

ANSWER:

Minimize $0X_1 + 10X_2 + 12X_3$

Subject to: $7X_1 + 5X_2 + 1X_3 \geq 3$
$-2X_1 + 1X_2 + 7X_3 \geq 2$
$X_1, \quad X_2, \quad X_3 \geq 0$

SHORT ANSWER/ESSAY

9.93 What does the $C_j - Z_j$ row represent in a simplex tableau?

ANSWER: the net profit/loss that will result from introducing one unit of the variable indicated by that column

9.94 Explain how a multiple optimal solution is recognized when using the simplex algorithm.

ANSWER: if the $C_j - Z_j$ value for a nonbasic variable is zero

9.95 Explain what the shadow price represents in a simplex final solution.

ANSWER: the value of one additional unit of a resource subject to limiting ranges

9.96 Explain what a surplus variable represents in a constraint.

ANSWER: the amount of overused resource for that constraint

9.97 Explain what an artificial variable represents in a constraint.

ANSWER: Nothing—it only acts as a tool to help generate an initial feasible solution.

9.98 Explain how no feasible solution is recognized when using the simplex algorithm.

ANSWER: if an artificial variable has a positive value in the final solution

9.99 Explain how an unbounded solution is recognized when calculating the simplex tableaus.

ANSWER: if all of the row ratios are negative or undefined

9.100 Explain how degeneracy is recognized when using the simplex algorithm.

ANSWER: when two rows tie for the smallest critical ratio

CHAPTER 10
Transportation and Assignment Models

TRUE/FALSE

10.1 Transportation and assignment problems are really linear programming techniques called network flow problems.

ANSWER: TRUE

10.2 Linear programming techniques can be used to solve transportation problems but are less efficient than special purpose algorithms. However, streamlined versions of the simplex method are helpful because they are fast.

ANSWER: TRUE

10.3 A typical transportation problem may ask the question, "How many of X should be shipped to point E from source A?"

ANSWER: TRUE

10.4 The objective of a transportation problem solution is to schedule shipments from sources to destinations while minimizing total transportation and production costs.

ANSWER: TRUE

10.5 In a transportation problem, each destination must be supplied by one and only one source.

ANSWER: FALSE

10.6 In a transportation problem, a single source may supply something to all destinations.

ANSWER: TRUE

10.7 In the transportation model, we must always make the total supply equal to the total demand.

ANSWER: TRUE

10.8 In a transportation problem, any solution is feasible as long as the constraints are met.

ANSWER: TRUE

10.9 In finding the maximum quantity that can be shipped on the least costly route using the stepping-stone method, one examines the closed path of plus and minus signs drawn and selects the smallest number found in those squares containing minus signs.

ANSWER: TRUE

10.10 The stepping-stone method is simply an orderly process for investigating the solution at each possible "corner point" of the multi-dimensioned solution space.

ANSWER: TRUE

10.11 In using the stepping-stone method, the path can turn at any box or cell that is unoccupied.

ANSWER: FALSE

10.12 Using the stepping-stone method to solve a maximization problem, we would choose the route with the largest positive index.

ANSWER: TRUE

10.13 One of the advantages of the stepping-stone method is that if, at a particular iteration, we accidentally choose a route that is not the best, the only penalty is to perform additional iterations.

ANSWER: TRUE

10.14 The northwest corner rule, stepping-stone, MODI, and Vogel's methods all produce integer solutions.

ANSWER: TRUE

10.15 Vogel's approximation method will often give a "good," if not "optimal," solution to an assignment problem.

ANSWER: TRUE

10.16 Both the assignment model and the transportation model can be used to solve unbalanced (supply does not equal demand) problems.

ANSWER: TRUE

10.17 It is possible to find an optimal solution to a transportation problem that is degenerate.

ANSWER: TRUE

10.18 A solution to the transportation problem can become degenerate at any iteration.

ANSWER: TRUE

10.19 The transportation method can be used to solve both minimization problems and maximization problems.

ANSWER: TRUE

10.20 Assignment problems involve determining the most efficient assignment of people to projects, salesmen to territories, contracts to bidders, and so on.

ANSWER: TRUE

10.21 The objective of an assignment problem solution most often is to minimize the total costs or time of performing the assigned tasks.

ANSWER: TRUE

10.22 In the assignment problem, the costs for a dummy row will be equal to the lowest cost of the column for each respective cell in that row.

ANSWER: FALSE

10.23 The Hungarian method is designed to solve transportation problems efficiently.

ANSWER: FALSE

10.24 The transportation and assignment problems are the only linear programming problems for which we have special solution techniques.

ANSWER: FALSE

10.25 Transportation and assignment problems can never have more than one optimal solution.

ANSWER: FALSE

10.26 In a transportation problem, a dummy source is given a zero cost, while in an assignment problem, a dummy source is given a very high cost.

ANSWER: FALSE

MULTIPLE CHOICE

Table 10-1

From \ To==>	1	2	3	Supply
A	20 (cost 3)	20 (cost 6)	(cost 4)	40
B	(cost 3)	30 (cost 4)	(cost 5)	30
C	(cost 5)	20 (cost 7)	10 (cost 6)	30
Demand	20	70	10	

10.27 What is the total cost represented by the solution shown in Table 10-1?

(a) 60
(b) 2500
(c) 2600
(d) 500
(e) none of the above

ANSWER: d

10.28 What is the value of the improvement index for cell B1 shown in Table 10-1?

(a) −50
(b) +3
(c) +2
(d) +1
(e) none of the above

ANSWER: c

Table 10-2

From \ To==>	1	2	3	Supply
A	cost 3; 20	cost 6; 30	cost 3	50
B	cost 4	cost 4; 40	cost 3	40
C	cost 5	cost 7; 10	cost 6; 15	25
Demand	20	80	15	

10.29 In Table 10-2, cell A3 should be selected to be filled in the next solution. If this was selected as the cell to be filled, and the next solution was found using the appropriate stepping-stone path, how many units would be assigned to this cell?

(a) 10
(b) 15
(c) 20
(d) 30
(e) none of the above

ANSWER: b

Table 10-3

From \ To==>	1	2	3	Dummy	Supply
A	10	8 80	12	0 20	100
B	6 120	7	4 30	0	150
C	10	9	6 170	0 80	250
Demand	120	80	200	100	

The following cell improvements are provided for Table 10-3	
Cell	Improvement Index
A1	+2
A3	+6
B2	+1
B-Dummy	+2
C1	+2
C2	+1

10.30 The cell improvement indices for Table 10-3 suggest that the optimal solution has been found. Based on this solution, how many units would actually be sent from source C?

(a) 10
(b) 170
(c) 180
(d) 250
(e) none of the above

ANSWER: b

10.31 In Table 10-3, suppose shipping cost from source C to point 2 was 8, which below would be true?

(a) There would be multiple optimal solutions.
(b) The minimum possible total cost would decrease.
(c) The minimum possible total cost would increase.
(d) Another dummy column would be needed.
(e) none of the above

ANSWER: a

10.32 A company must assign mechanics to each of four jobs. The time involved varies according to individual abilities. Table 10-4 shows how many minutes it takes each mechanic to perform each job. This was solved using the Hungarian method. Table 10-5 shows the solution.

Table 10-4					
	Job				
		1	2	3	4
Worker	A	4	6	5	4
	B	3	5	4	7
	C	5	6	5	4
	D	7	5	5	6

Table 10-5					
Final Table			Job		
		1	2	3	4
Worker	A	0	1	0	0
	B	0	1	0	4
	C	1	1	0	0
	D	3	0	0	2

If optimal assignments are made, how many total minutes would be required to complete the jobs?

(a) 0
(b) 4
(c) 17
(d) 20
(e) none of the above

ANSWER: c

10.33 According to Table 10-5, which is the final table for an assignment problem, which worker should be assigned to Job 1?

(a) either worker A or worker B
(b) only worker A could be assigned to Job 1
(c) only worker B could be assigned to Job 1
(d) any of the workers
(e) none of the workers

ANSWER: a

Table 10-6
Initial table–no allocations yet

From \ To==>	1	2	3	Supply
A	6	4	5	200
B	8	6	7	300
C	5	5	6	300
Demand	400	200	100	

Optimal Solution by the Modi Method

From \ To==>	1	2	3	Dummy	Supply
A	6 100	4	5 100	0	200
B	8	6 200	7	0 100	300
C	5 300	5	6	0	300
Demand	400	200	100	100	

10.34 In Table 10-6, which presents a MODI solution for a transportation problem, which below is true?

(a) There is no feasible solution to the problem.
(b) The total cost represented by the solution is $3,700.
(c) The original problem was unbalanced.
(d) This was a maximization problem.
(e) none of the above

ANSWER: c

10.35 According to Table 10-6, which presents a MODI solution for a transportation problem, if that solution is used, which of the following is true?

(a) Source A will ship 200 units to destination 1.
(b) Source B will ship only 200 units.
(c) Source C will ship only 200 units.
(d) Source A will ship 100 units to destination 2.
(e) none of the above

ANSWER: b

10.36 According to Table 10-6, which presents a MODI solution for a transportation problem, if that solution is used, which of the following is true?

(a) Total cost of shipping from A is $1,000.
(b) Total cost of shipping from B is $1,200.
(c) Total cost of shipping from C is $300.
(d) Total cost of shipping from B is $1,300.
(e) none of the above

ANSWER: b

Table 10-7
Initial table–no allocations yet

	To==>	1	2	3	Supply
From	A	4	6	4	100
	B	6	5	5	200
	C	5	7	6	200
	Demand	200	200	100	

Optimal solution by the MODI method

	To==>	1	2	3	Supply
From	A	4	6	4 100	100
	B	6	5 200	5	200
	C	5 200	7	6	200
	Demand	200	200	100	

10.37 According to Table 10-7, which presents a MODI solution for a transportation problem, if that solution is used, which of the following is true?

(a) 100 units will be shipped from source A to destination 1.
(b) The total cost is $500.
(c) The final solution is degenerate.
(d) The original problem was unbalanced.
(e) none of the above

ANSWER: c

10.38 According to Table 10-7, which presents a MODI solution for a transportation problem, if that solution is used, which of the following is true?

(a) The total shipping cost is $2,400.
(b) There is excess supply.
(c) There is excess demand.
(d) The total cost of shipping is $500.
(e) none of the above

ANSWER: a

Table 10-8 Input data	Jobs			
Person	1	2	3	4
1	5	7	5	6
2	5	4	5	4
3	6	5	6	4
4	6	6	5	7

Table 10-9 Final Revised Cost Table	Jobs			
Person	1	2	3	4
1	0	2	0	1
2	1	0	1	0
3	2	1	2	0
4	1	1	0	2

Table 10-10 Optimal Solution	Jobs			
Person	1	2	3	4
1	1	0	0	0
2	0	1	0	0
3	0	0	0	1
4	0	0	1	0
Value = 18				

10.39 According to Table 10-8, which displays the data for an assignment problem, if the rows represent the workers and the columns represent the jobs, what do the values in the cells represent?

(a) revenue generated by each person in each job
(b) profit gained by having a worker in a particular job
(c) cost associated with a person doing a specific job
(d) cannot be determined due to lack of information
(e) none of the above
ANSWER: c

10.40 According to Table 10-9, which displays the final revised cost data for an assignment problem, if the rows represent the workers and the columns represent the jobs, what do the zeroes in the cells signify?

(a) a non-optimal solution
(b) least favorable outcomes for assignment
(c) possible optimal options for assignment
(d) the final outcome is not yet derived
(e) none of the above
ANSWER: c

10.41 According to Table 10-10, which gives the optimal solution for an assignment problem, if the rows represent the workers and the columns represent the jobs, who will be assigned job 4?
(a) either worker 2 or worker 3
(b) worker 2 only
(c) worker 3 only
(d) Any worker may be assigned to job 4.
(e) none of the above
ANSWER: c

10.42 According to Table 10-10, which gives the optimal solution for an assignment problem, if the rows represent the workers and the columns represent the jobs, and if those assignments are made, how much will it cost to perform job 3?
(a) 4
(b) 2
(c) 6
(d) 5
(e) none of the above
ANSWER: d

10.43 Assuming that Table 10-11 represents the results of an iteration of a transportation model,

Table 10-11

	To==>	1	2	3	Suppl
Fro	A	[3] 20	[6] 20	[4]	40
	B	[3]	[4] 30	[5]	30
	C	[5]	[7] 20	[6] 10	30
	Demand	20	70	10	

The next tableau will be:

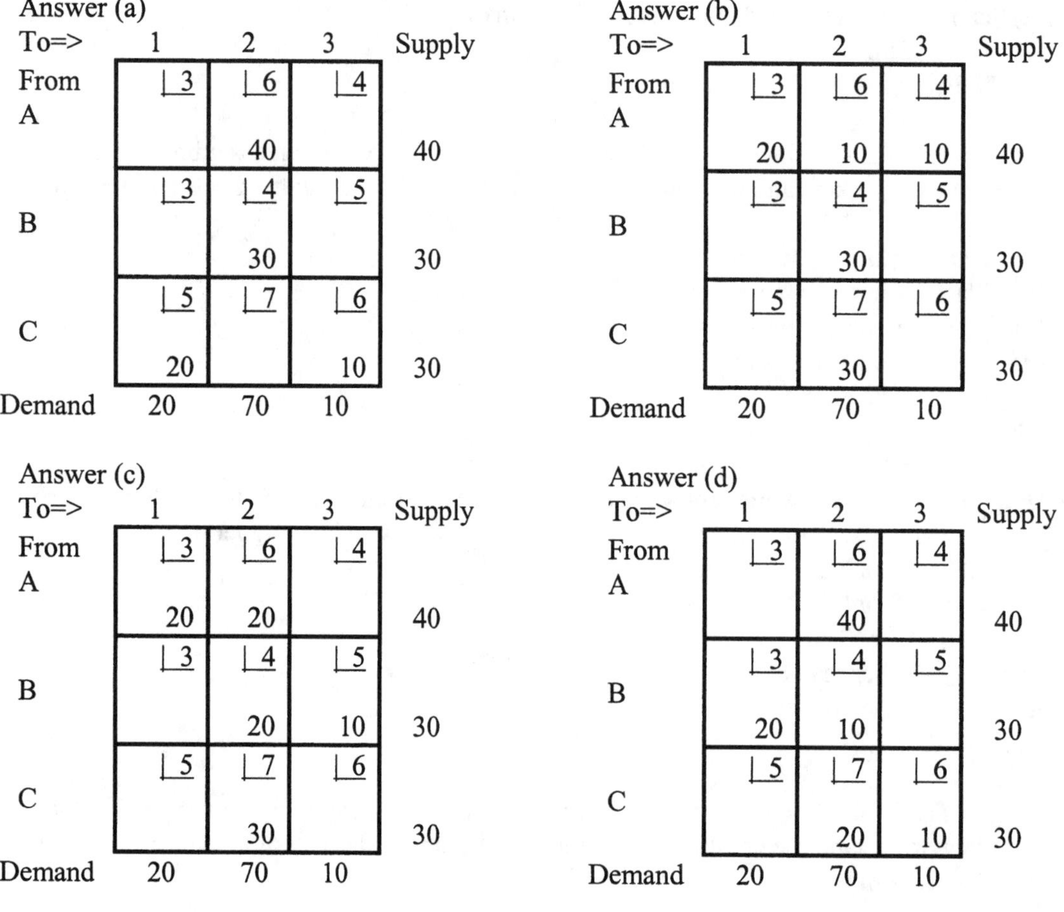

Answer (a)

To=> From	1	2	3	Supply
A	[3]	[6] 40	[4]	40
B	[3]	[4] 30	[5]	30
C	[5] 20	[7]	[6] 10	30
Demand	20	70	10	

Answer (b)

To=> From	1	2	3	Supply
A	[3] 20	[6] 10	[4] 10	40
B	[3]	[4] 30	[5]	30
C	[5]	[7] 30	[6]	30
Demand	20	70	10	

Answer (c)

To=> From	1	2	3	Supply
A	[3] 20	[6] 20	[4]	40
B	[3]	[4] 20	[5] 10	30
C	[5]	[7] 30	[6]	30
Demand	20	70	10	

Answer (d)

To=> From	1	2	3	Supply
A	[3]	[6] 40	[4]	40
B	[3] 20	[4] 10	[5]	30
C	[5]	[7] 20	[6] 10	30
Demand	20	70	10	

(e) none of the above

ANSWER: b

Table 10-12

To=> From	1	2	3	Supply
A	3	6 40	4	40
B	3	4 30	5	30
C	5 20	7	6 10	30
Demand	20	70	10	

10.44 Table 10-12 represents a solution that is

(a) an initial solution.
(b) infeasible.
(c) degenerate.
(d) all of the above
(e) none of the above

ANSWER: c

10.45 In Table 10-13, if cell A3 is filled on the next iteration, what is the improvement in the objective function?

Table 10-13

From \ To==>	1	2	3	Supply
A	3 20	6 30	3	50
B	4	4 40	3	40
C	5	7 10	6 15	25
Demand	20	80	15	

(a) 60
(b) 30
(c) 530
(d) 590
(e) none of the above

ANSWER: b

10.46 A transportation problem

(a) is a special case of the linear programming problem.
(b) can be solved by linear programming, but is solved more efficiently by a special-purpose algorithm.
(c) may give an initial feasible solution rather than the optimal solution.
(d) requires the same assumptions that are required for linear programming problems.
(e) all of the above

ANSWER: e

Table 10-14

From \ To==>	1	2	3	Dummy	Supply
A	(10)	80 (8)	(12)	20 (0)	100
B	120 (6)	40 (7)	30 (4)	(0)	150
C	(10)	10 (9)	170 (6)	80 (0)	250
Demand	120	80	200	100	

10.47 Table 10-14 illustrates a(n)

(a) optimal solution.
(b) degenerate solution.
(c) unbounded solution.
(d) infeasible solution.
(e) none of the above

ANSWER: d

Table 10-15	
Cell	Improvement Indices
A1	+2
A3	+6
B2	+1
B-Dummy	+2
C1	+2
C2	+1

10.48 The cell improvements shown in Table 10-15 have been calculated using the MODI method. If this is a maximization problem, which cell should be filled next?

(a) A1
(b) A3
(c) B2
(d) C1
(e) none of the above

ANSWER: b

10.49 The only restriction we place on the initial solution of a transportation problem is that

(a) we must have nonzero quantities in a majority of the boxes.
(b) all constraints must be satisfied.
(c) demand must be less than supply.
(d) we must have a number (equal to the number of rows plus the number of columns minus one) of boxes that contain nonzero quantities.
(e) none of the above

ANSWER: b

Table 10-16

From \ To==>	1	2	3	Dummy	Supply
A	[10]	[8] 80	[12]	[0] 20	100
B	[6] 120	[7] 40	[4] 30	[0]	150
C	[10]	[9] 10	[6] 170	[0] 80	250
Demand	120	80	200	100	

10.50 What is wrong with Table 10-16?

(a) The solution is infeasible.
(b) The solution is degenerate.
(c) The solution is unbounded.
(d) Nothing is wrong.
(e) The solution is inefficient in that it is possible to use fewer routes.

ANSWER: a

10.51 In Table 10-17, which cell should be filled on the next iteration?

Table 10-17

	To==>	1	2	3	Dummy	Supply
From	A	10	8 80	12 20	0	100
	B	6 120	7	4 30	0	150
	C	10	9	6 150	0 100	250
	Demand	120	80	200	100	

(a) A1
(b) ADum
(c) B2
(d) C1
(e) C2

ANSWER: b

10.52 The solution presented in Table 10-18 is

(a) infeasible.
(b) degenerate.
(c) unbounded.
(d) optimal.
(e) none of the above

ANSWER: d

Table 10-18

	To==>	1	2	3	Dummy	Supply
From	A	10	8 80	12	0 20	100
	B	6 120	7	4 30	0	150
	C	10	9	6 170	0 80	250
	Demand	120	80	200	100	

10.53 What is wrong with Table 10-19?

Table 10-19

	To==>	1	2	3	Dummy	Supply
From	A	10	8 70	12 10	0 20	100
	B	6 100	7	4 50	0	150
	C	10 20	9 10	6 140	0 80	250
	Demand	120	80	200	100	

(a) The solution is infeasible.
(b) The solution is degenerate.
(c) The solution is unbounded.
(d) Nothing is wrong.
(e) There are too many filled cells.

ANSWER: e

10.54 The solution shown in Table 10-20 was obtained by Vogel's approximation. The difference between the objective function for this solution and that for the optimal is

(a) 40
(b) 60
(c) 80
(d) 100
(e) none of the above

ANSWER: c

Table 10-20

	To==>	1	2	3	Dummy	Supply
From	A	10	8	12	0 100	100
	B	6 120	7	4 30	0	150
	C	10	9 80	6 170	0	250
	Demand	120	80	200	100	

Table 10-21		Job (Time in Minutes)			
		1	2	3	4
Worker	A	5	9	5	7
	B	3	8	4	4
	C	5	5	8	4
	D	7	4	5	5

10.55 A company must assign mechanics to each of four jobs. The time involved varies according to individual abilities. Table 10-21 shows how many minutes it takes each mechanic to perform each job. If the optimal assignments are made, how many total minutes would be required for completing the jobs?

(a) 0
(b) 4
(c) 17
(d) 16
(e) none of the above

ANSWER: d

Table 10-22		Job (Time in Minutes)			
		1	2	3	4
Worker	A	0	0	2	1
	B	1	3	1	0
	C	1	0	1	1
	D	0	1	0	3

10.56 Given Table 10-22, the final table for an assignment problem, who should be assigned to job 2?

(a) worker A
(b) worker C
(c) either worker A or worker C
(d) neither worker A nor worker C
(e) worker D

ANSWER: b

Table 10-23

From \ To==	1	2	3	Supply
A	6	4	5	200
B	8	6	7	300
C	5	5	6	300
Demand	400	200	100	

10.57 Table 10-23 provides information about a transportation problem. This problem is

(a) unbounded.
(b) unbalanced.
(c) infeasible.
(d) all of the above
(e) none of the above

ANSWER: (b)

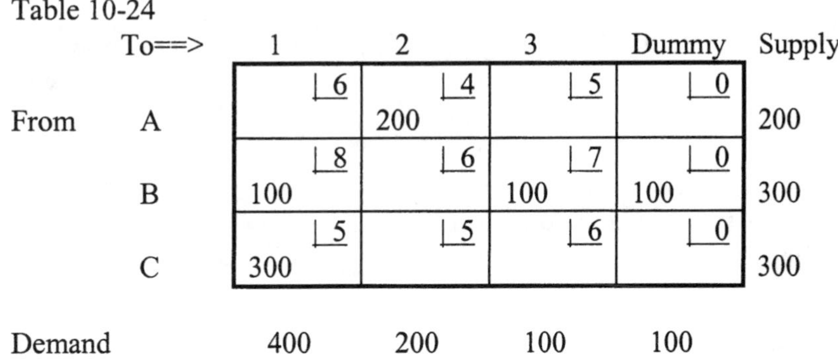

Table 10-24

From \ To==>	1	2	3	Dummy	Supply
A	6	200 (4)	5	0	200
B	100 (8)	6	100 (7)	100 (0)	300
C	300 (5)	5	6	0	300
Demand	400	200	100	100	

10.58 According to Table 10-24, which presents a solution to a transportation problem obtained by Vogel's approximation, which of the following is true?

(a) The solution is degenerate.
(b) The total cost represented by the solution is 3,800.
(c) The original problem was unbalanced.
(d) all of the above
(e) none of the above

ANSWER: d

Table 10-25

From \ To==>	1	2	3	4	5	6	Supply
A	[5]	[6]	[4]	[6]	[6]	[4] 100	100
B	[6]	[5] 200	[7]	[6]	[5]	[6]	200
C	[5] 100	[7]	[6]	[7]	[5] 200	[6]	300
D	[9] 50	[7] 200	[6]	[5] 100	[7]	[7]	350
E	[5] 50	[7]	[4] 100	[6]	[7]	[4]	150
Demand	200	400	100	100	200	100	

10.59 Table 10-25 shows a solution to a transportation problem. The solution shown is

(a) infeasible.
(n) unbounded.
(c) degenerate.
(d) all of the above
(e) none of the above

ANSWER: c

10.60 To solve the problem in Table 10-25, showing a solution to a transportation problem, one should

(a) do nothing.
(n) start over.
(c) place a zero in an unoccupied cell.
(d) add a dummy source and/or destination.
(e) none of the above

ANSWER: c

10.61 Table 10-25 shows a solution to a transportation problem. What is the total transportation cost for all shipments from source C?

(a) 1,000
(b) 500
(c) 1,950
(d) 1,500
(e) none of the above

ANSWER: d

10.62 Table 10-25 shows a solution to a transportation problem. What is the total transportation cost for all shipments going to destination 2?

(a) 1,000
(b) 1,400
(c) 2,300
(d) 1,800
(e) none of the above

ANSWER: e

10.63 Table 10-25 shows a solution to a transportation problem. If this solution is used, the total cost is

(a) 6,400.
(b) 6,800.
(c) 7,200.
(d) 6,200.
(e) none of the above

ANSWER: e

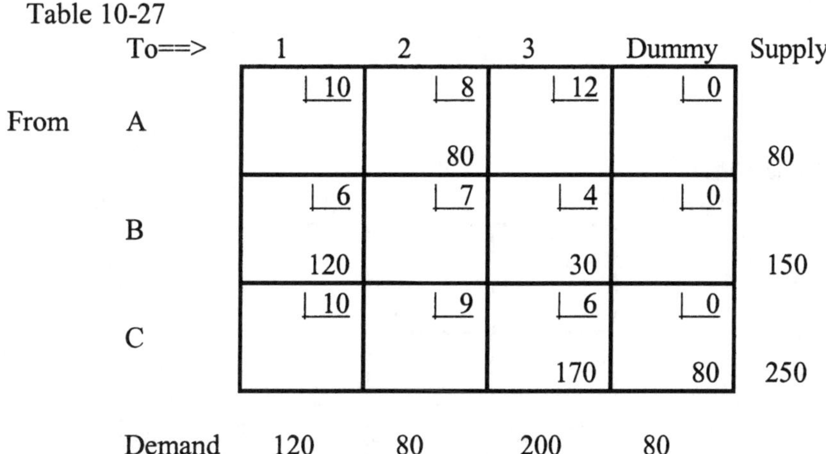

Table 10-27

From \ To==>	1	2	3	Dummy	Supply
A	[10]	[8] 80	[12]	[0]	80
B	[6] 120	[7]	[4] 30	[0]	150
C	[10]	[9]	[6] 170	[0] 80	250
Demand	120	80	200	80	

10.64 The solution presented in Table 10-27 is

(a) infeasible.
(b) degenerate.
(c) unbounded.
(d) optimal.
(e) both b and d

ANSWER: e

Table 10-28

From \ To==>	1	2	3	Dummy	Supply
A	10	8 80	12	0 20	100
B	6 100	7	4 50	0	150
C	10 20	9	6 150	0 80	250
Demand	120	80	200	100	

10.65 The solution shown in Table 10-28 is

(a) infeasible.
(b) degenerate.
(c) unbounded.
(d) optimal.
(e) none of the above

ANSWER: e

Table 10-29

From \ To==>	1	2	3	Dummy	Supply
A	10	8 40	12	0 10	50
B	6 60	7	4 15	0	75
C	10	9	6 85	0 40	125
Demand	60	40	100	50	

10.66 The solution shown in Table 10-29 is

(a) infeasible.
(b) one of a number of alternate solutions.
(c) unbounded.
(d) optimal.
(e) none of the above

ANSWER: d

10.67 A certain firm has three different operations that must be assigned to four locations. The profit (in thousands of dollars) associated with each operation at each location is presented below. The firm's vice president would like to assign the various operations so that the total profit is maximized. Find the appropriate assignments.

	Table 10-30			
Operations	Location			
	1	2	3	4
W	9	11	7	10
X	10	12	6	12
Y	8	10	13	9
Z	12	8	11	10

ANSWER: Assign W to 2, X to 4, Y to 3, and Z to 1. Total profit = $48 (thousand)

10.68 Given Table 10-31, the final table for an assignment problem, which assignment would you make first?

(a) worker A
(b) worker B
(c) worker C
(d) Either worker B or worker C
(e) Either worker A or worker C

ANSWER: e

Table 10-31		Job (Time in Minutes)			
		1	2	3	4
Worker	A	0	1	2	3
	B	0	0	0	1
	C	2	2	5	0
	D	4	0	0	2

10.69 Given Table 10-32, the final assignment table for a problem, who would be assigned to job 3?

(a) worker A
(b) worker B
(c) worker C
(d) worker B or worker D
(e) none of the above

ANSWER: d

Table 10-32		Job (Time in Minutes)			
		1	2	3	4
Worker	A	0	1	2	3
	B	0	0	0	1
	C	2	2	5	0
	D	4	0	0	2

10.70 Given the following assignment problem, to which job should we assign worker B?

(a) job 4
(b) job 3
(c) job 2
(d) job 1
(e) It doesn't matter; the cost will remain the same because multiple solutions exist.

ANSWER: e

Table 10-33		Job (Time in Minutes)			
Worker		1	2	3	4
	A	5	7	9	11
	B	7	9	11	13
	C	9	11	13	15
	D	11	13	15	17

10.71 Which of the following techniques can be used for moving from an initial feasible solution to an optimal solution in a transportation problem?

(a) stepping-stone method
(b) northwest corner rule
(c) Vogel's approximation method
(d) all of the above

ANSWER: a

10.72 Which of the following is an applicable characteristic in using the stepping-stone method?

(a) Only an unoccupied square may be used as a "stepping-stone."
(b) Only an occupied square may be used as a "stepping-stone."
(c) Only the column and row with the highest factory capacity may be used as a "stepping-stone."
(d) all of the above
(e) none of the above

ANSWER: b

10.73 After testing each unused cell by the stepping-stone method in the transportation problem and finding only one cell with a negative improvement index,

(a) you would make that improvement and then check all unused cells again.
(b) once you make that improvement, you would definitely have an optimum solution.
(c) once you make that improvement, you would definitely have the optimum solution.
(d) you should check to be sure that you don't have to add a dummy source or dummy destination.
(e) none of the above

ANSWER: a

10.74 In the transportation problem, using the stepping-stone method,

(a) you may not skip over an empty cell.
(b) you may not skip over a used cell.
(c) your path may not cross over itself.
(d) if you have an optimum solution and get an improvement index of zero, there is another optimum solution.
(e) none of the above

ANSWER: d

10.75 In using the stepping-stone or the MODI solution method, which of the following rules must first be observed in order to apply the method?

(a) The supply must be less than the demand.
(b) The demand must be less than the supply.
(c) The number of occupied routes must always equal one less than the sum of the number of rows plus the number of columns.
(d) The number of occupied routes must equal the number of columns plus the number of rows.
(e) none of the above

ANSWER: c

10.76 Which method usually gives a very good initial solution and often results in the optimal solution to a transportation problem?

(a) northwest corner rule
(b) Vogel's approximation method
(c) MODI method
(d) stepping-stone method
(e) none of the above

ANSWER: b

10.77 In applying Vogel's approximation method to a cost minimization problem, row and column penalties are determined by

(a) finding the largest unit cost in each row or column.
(b) finding the smallest unit cost in each row or column.
(c) finding the sum of the unit costs in each row or column.
(d) finding the difference between the two lowest unit costs in each row and column.
(e) finding the difference between the two highest unit costs in each row and column.

ANSWER: d

10.78 If we want to quickly arrive at a "good," but not necessarily "optimal" solution to the transportation problem, we will use the

(a) stepping-stone method.
(b) northwest corner rule.
(c) Vogel's approximation method.
(d) MODI method.
(e) any of the above

ANSWER: c

10.79 Which method usually gives a very good solution to the transportation problem?

(a) northwest corner rule
(b) Vogel's approximation method
(c) MODI method
(d) stepping-stone method
(e) none of the above

ANSWER: b

10.80 When the solution of a transportation problem by Vogel's approximation method is done, we know that

(a) we have the optimal solution.
(b) we have the same initial solution as we would have obtained using the northwest corner rule.
(c) we have the same final solution as we would have obtained using the northwest corner rule.
(d) we must test the solution to see that it is optimal.
(e) none of the above

ANSWER: d

10.81 If the total supply from the sources does not equal the total demand from the destinations in the transportation problem,

(a) if supply is greater than demand, add a dummy source or factory.
(b) if demand is greater than supply, add a dummy destination or warehouse.
(c) the amount put in a dummy source or destination should make supply and demand equal.
(d) all of the above

ANSWER: c

10.82 In a transportation problem, degeneracy occurs when

(a) the number of used (or full) cells does not equal the number of rows plus columns minus one.
(b) in an initial solution, both a row total and a column total are satisfied simultaneously.
(c) during an improvement, two negative cells contain the same smallest amount.
(d) all of the above

ANSWER: d

10.83 In the transportation problem, if a degenerate situation occurs,

(a) you may shift some quantities out of used cells as long as you don't alter the totals from each source and to each demand.
(b) you may place an artificial quantity (such as a zero) in an unused cell that cannot be checked by the stepping-stone approach, so that all unused cells can then be checked.
(c) you may put an artificial quantity in any unused cell.
(d) you have made a mistake and should start again with a different initial solution.
(e) you should add a dummy factory or warehouse, as appropriate.

ANSWER: b

10.84 In Vogel's method for a profit maximization problem, row and column penalties are determined by

(a) finding the largest unit cost in each row or column.
(b) finding the smallest unit cost in each row or column.
(c) finding the sum of the unit costs in each row or column.
(d) finding the difference between the two lowest unit costs in each row and column.
(e) finding the difference between the two highest unit costs in each row and column.

ANSWER: e

10.85 Which of the following is not a step in the Hungarian method of assignment?

(a) find the opportunity-cost table
(b) test for an optimal assignment
(c) enumerate all possible solutions
(d) revise the opportunity-cost table
(e) none of the above

ANSWER: c

10.86 Objectives of the assignment problem include

(a) minimize total costs.
(b) minimize total time to perform the tasks at hand.
(c) minimize opportunity costs.
(d) all of the above

ANSWER: d

10.87 In an assignment problem

(a) the number of rows and columns must be equal.
(b) the number of rows must exceed the number of columns.
(c) the number of rows must equal or exceed the number of columns.
(d) the number of columns must equal or exceed the number of rows.
(e) none of the above

ANSWER: a

10.88 In revising the opportunity cost table of the assignment problem, after drawing lines through all of the zeros

(a) the smallest uncovered number is added to all zeros.
(b) the smallest uncovered number is added to all uncovered numbers.
(c) the smallest uncovered number is added to all numbers at the intersection of lines.
(d) all of the above

ANSWER: c

10.89 Which of the following methods is used only with the assignment problem?

(a) the Hungarian method
(b) stepping-stone method
(c) MODI method
(d) Vogel's approximation method
(e) the simplex method

ANSWER: a

10.90 Objectives of the assignment problem can include

(a) minimize total costs.
(b) minimize total time to perform the tasks at hand.
(c) minimize opportunity costs.
(d) maximize profit.
(e) all of the above

ANSWER: e

10.91 In solving maximization assignment problems,

(a) just reverse all the decision rules used in the minimizing algorithm (if it says subtract, now add, and so on).
(b) use the Australian transformation process and convert the data.
(c) convert the problem to an equivalent minimization problem.
(d) all of the above

ANSWER: c

PROBLEMS

10.92 Find the solution to the transportation problem depicted below.

Table 10-34

From \ To==>	1	2	3	Dummy	Supply
A	10	8	12	0	50
B	6	7	4	0	75
C	10	9	6	0	125
Demand	60	40	100	50	

(a)

Table 10-34 a

From \ To==>	1	2	3	Dummy	Supply
A	10	8 40	12	0 10	50
B	6 60	7	4 15	0	75
C	10	9	6 85	0 40	125
Demand	60	40	100	50	

(b)

Table 10-34 b

From \ To==>	1	2	3	Dummy	Supply
A	10	8 20	12	0 30	50
B	6 60	7	4 15	0	75
C	10	9 20	6 85	0 20	125
Demand	60	40	100	50	

(c)

Table 10-34 c

From	To==>	1	2	3	Dummy	Supply
	A	10 40	8	12	0 10	50
	B	6	7 15	4 25	0 35	75
	C	10 20	9	6 100	0 5	125
	Demand	60	40	100	50	

(d)

Table 10-34 d

From	To==>	1	2	3	Dummy	Supply
	A	10 50	8	12	0	50
	B	6	7	4 75	0	75
	C	10 10	9 40	6 25	0 50	125
	Demand	60	40	100	50	

(e) none of the above

ANSWER: a

10.93 Solve the following transportation table:

Table 10-35

From \ To==>	1	2	3	Dummy	Supply
A	5 / 50	8	8	0	40
B	6	9	4 / 75	0	85
C	6 / 10	9 / 40	6 / 25	0 / 50	110
Demand	50	60	85	40	

(a)

Table 10-35a Solution?

From \ To==>	1	2	3	Dummy	Supply
A	5 / 50	8	8	0	40
B	6	9	4 / 75	0	85
C	6 / 10	9 / 40	6 / 25	0 / 50	110
Demand	50	60	85	40	

(b)

Table 10-35b Solution?

From \ To==>	1	2	3	Dummy	Supply
A	5 / 50	8	8	0	40
B	6	9	4 / 75	0	85
C	6 / 10	9 / 40	6 / 25	0 / 50	110
Demand	50	60	85	40	

(c)

Table 10-35c Solution?

From	To==>	1	2	3	Dummy	Supply
	A	5 40	8	8	0	40
	B	6 10	9 60	4 15	0	85
	C	6	9	6 70	0 40	110
	Demand	50	60	85	40	

(d)

Table 10-35d Solution?

From	To==>	1	2	3	Dummy	Supply
	A	5	8	8	0 40	40
	B	6	9	4 85	0	85
	C	6 50	9 60	6	0	110
	Demand	50	60	85	40	

(e) none of the above

ANSWER: e

10.94 Use Vogel's approximation to find the solution to the transportation problem shown in Table 10-36.

Table 10-36

From \ To==>	1	2	3	Dummy	Supply
A	5	7	8	0	20
B	3	9	9	0	65
C	5	9	6	0	90
Demand	30	40	85	20	

(a)

Table 10-36a Solution?

From \ To==>	1	2	3	Dummy	Supply
A	5	7	8	0 20	20
B	3	9	9 65	0	65
C	5 30	9 40	6 20	0	90
Demand	30	40	85	20	

(b)

Table 10-36b Solution?

From \ To==>	1	2	3	Dummy	Supply
A	5	7 20	8	0	20
B	3 30	9	9 35	0	65
C	5	9 20	6 50	0 20	90
Demand	30	40	85	20	

(c)

Table 10-36c Solution?

	To==>	1	2	3	Dummy	Supply
From	A	5	7 20	8	0	20
	B	3 30	9 15	9	0 20	65
	C	5	9 5	6 85	0	90
	Demand	30	40	85	20	

(d)

Table 10-36d Solution?

	To==>	1	2	3	Dummy	Supply
From	A	5 10	7	8	0 10	20
	B	3	9 40	9	0 5	65
	C	5	9	6 85	0 5	90
	Demand	30	40	85	20	

(e) none of the above

ANSWER: c

10.95 The table below describes a transportation problem. Find the solution to this problem using Vogel's approximation.

Table 10-37

From \ To==>	1	2	3	4	Supply
A	4	7	10	12	2000
B	7	5	8	11	2500
C	9	8	6	10	2200
Demand	1000	2200	2300	1200	

(a)

(a) Table 10-37a Solution?

From \ To==>	1	2	3	4	Supply
A	4 1000	7	10 1000	12	2000
B	7	5 1000	8 300	11 1200	2500
C	9	8 1200	6 1000	10	2200
Demand	1000	2200	2300	1200	

(b)

Table 10-37b Solution?

From \ To==>	1	2	3	4	Supply
A	4	7 200	10 800	12 1200	2000
B	7 1000	5	8 1500	11	2500
C	9	8 2000	6 200	10	2200
Demand	1000	2200	2300	1200	

(c)

Table 10-37c Solution?

From	To==>	1	2	3	4	Supply
	A	4	7 / 2000	10	12	2000
	B	7 / 1000	5	8 / 300	11 / 1200	2500
	C	9	8 / 200	6 / 1800	10	2200
	Demand	1000	2200	2300	1200	

(d)

Table 10-37d Solution?

From	To==>	1	2	3	4	Supply
	A	4 / 1000	7	10	12 / 1000	2000
	B	7	5 / 2200	8 / 100	11 / 200	2500
	C	9	8	6 / 2200	10	2200
	Demand	1000	2200	2300	1200	

(e) none of the above

ANSWER: d

10.96 Table 10-38 describes a transportation problem:

Table 10-38

From	To==>	D	E	F	Supply
	A	[2]	[5]	[2]	40
	B	[1]	[4]	[2]	30
	C	[4]	[3]	[2]	30
Demand		20	30	50	100

(a) Use the northwest corner method to get an initial solution.
(b) What is the cost of the initial solution?
(c) Use the stepping-stone method to find the optimal solution.
(d) What is the cost of the optimal solution?
(e) Is there an alternate optimal solution?

ANSWER: (a)

From	To==>	D	E	F	Supply
	A	[2] 20	[5] 20	[2]	40
	B	[1]	[4] 10	[2] 20	30
	C	[4]	[3]	[2] 30	30
Demand		20	30	50	100

(b) Cost = 280

(c) Optimal solution:

From	To==>	D	E	F	Supply
	A	[2]	[5]	[2] 40	40
	B	[1] 20	[4]	[2] 10	30
	C	[4]	[3] 30	[2]	30
Demand		20	30	50	100

(d) Cost = 210

(e) no

SHORT ANSWER/ESSAY

10.97 Describe a general transportation problem.

ANSWER: a specific case of linear programming concerned with scheduling shipments from sources to destinations while minimizing transportation costs

10.98 What is meant by a balanced transportation problem?

ANSWER: a situation in which total demand equals total supply exactly

10.99 What is meant by an unbalanced transportation problem?

ANSWER: a situation in which total demand does not equal total supply

10.100 When is a dummy destination added to a transportation problem?

ANSWER: when total supply exceeds total demand

CHAPTER 11
Integer Programming, Goal Programming, and Nonlinear Programming

TRUE/FALSE

11.1 If conditions require that all decision variables must have an integer solution, then the class of problem described is an integer programming problem.

ANSWER: TRUE

11.2 An integer programming solution can never produce a greater profit objective than the LP solution to the same problem.

ANSWER: TRUE

11.3 0–1 integer programming might be applicable to selecting the best gymnastics team to represent a country from among all identified teams.

ANSWER: TRUE

11.4 For the same linear program, the optimal integer solution may vary significantly from the standard simplex derived solution.

ANSWER: TRUE

11.5 In a linear program formulation, a constraint requiring an integer outcome may not be included in the constraint set of the formulation.

ANSWER: FALSE

11.6 In goal programming, if all the goals are achieved, then the value of the objective function will always be zero.

ANSWER: TRUE

11.7 Unfortunately, multiple goals in goal programming are not able to be prioritized and solved.

ANSWER: FALSE

11.8 Typically, in goal programming, the constraints are prioritized.

ANSWER: TRUE

11.9 Goal programming permits multiple objectives to be satisfied.

ANSWER: TRUE

11.10 The constraint $X_1 + X_2 \leq 1$ with 0–1 integer programming allows for either X_1 or X_2 to be a part of the optimal solution, but not both.

ANSWER: TRUE

11.11 Requiring an integer solution to a linear programming problem decreases the size of the feasible region.

ANSWER: TRUE

11.12 The transportation problem is a good example of a pure-integer programming problem.

ANSWER: TRUE

11.13 The development of a stock portfolio is an example of an integer programming problem.

ANSWER: TRUE

11.14 The branch and bound method provides a guide as we search through the possible solutions.

ANSWER: TRUE

11.15 When solving very large integer programming problems, we sometimes have to settle for a "good," not necessarily optimal, answer.

ANSWER: TRUE

11.16 Goal programming can be used to ensure that we maximize profit, while at the same time we use the entire amount of an available resource.

ANSWER: FALSE

11.17 In goal programming, our goal is to drive the deviational variables in the objective function as close to zero as possible.

ANSWER: TRUE

11.18 A problem, where we wished to maximize profit, and profit per unit was a function of the number of units produced, could be solved as a mixed integer programming problem.

ANSWER: FALSE

11.19 A branch and bound method can be used to solve assignment problems.

ANSWER: TRUE

11.20 A zero-one programming representation could be used to assign sections of a course to specific classrooms.

ANSWER: TRUE

11.21 In goal programming, the deviational variables have the same objective function coefficients as the surplus and slack variables in a normal linear program.

ANSWER: FALSE

11.22 Unfortunately, goal programming, while able to handle multiple objectives, is unable to prioritize these objectives.

ANSWER: FALSE

11.23 One positive feature of the branch and bound algorithm is that it evaluates only a relatively small subset of all possible solutions, while not precluding the evaluation of any solution.

ANSWER: TRUE

MULTIPLE CHOICE

11.24 A model containing a linear objective function and linear constraints but requiring that one or more of the decision variables take on an integer value in the final solution is called

(a) an integer programming problem.
(b) a goal programming problem.
(c) a nonlinear programming problem.
(d) a multiple objective LP problem.
(e) none of the above

ANSWER: a

11.25 Assignment problems solved previously by linear programming techniques are also examples of

(a) pure-integer programming problems.
(b) mixed-integer programming problems.
(c) zero-one integer programming problems.
(d) goal programming problems.
(e) nonlinear programming problems.

ANSWER: c

11.26 A mathematical programming model that permits decision makers to set and prioritize multiple objective functions is called a

(a) pure-integer programming problem.
(b) mixed-integer programming problem.
(c) zero-one integer programming problem.
(d) goal programming problem.
(e) nonlinear programming problem.

ANSWER: d

11.27 Goal programming differs from linear programming in which of the following aspects?

(a) It tries to maximize deviations between set goals and what can be achieved within the constraints.
(b) It minimizes instead of maximizing as in LP.
(c) It permits multiple goals to be combined into one objective function.
(d) all of the above
(e) none of the above

ANSWER: c

11.28 Which of the following is a category of mathematical programming techniques that doesn't assume linearity in the objective function and/or constraints?

(a) integer programs
(b) goal programming problems
(c) nonlinear programs
(d) multiple objective programming problems
(e) none of the above

ANSWER: c

11.29 The branch and bound method is often used when

(a) solving integer programming problems.
(b) the problem cannot be graphically solved.
(c) there are fewer than three variables.
(d) one or more variables are negative.
(e) computer facilities are not available.

ANSWER: a

11.30 A mathematical model designed to handle decision problems with multiple outcomes measured in different units is

(a) the branch and bound method.
(b) linear programming.
(c) integer programming.
(d) goal programming.
(e) mixed-integer programming.

ANSWER: d

11.31 A type of integer programming is

(a) pure.
(b) mixed.
(c) zero-one.
(d) all of the above

ANSWER: d

11.32 Goal programming and linear programming differ in that

(a) in LP, the objective function is maximized or minimized, while in goal programming, the deviation between goals and possible achievement is minimized.
(b) slack and surplus variables have 0 profit/cost in LP, while deviational variables do not in goal programming.
(c) slack and surplus variables are the only variables in the objective function in goal programming, but only part of the objective function in LP.
(d) all of the above
(e) none of the above

ANSWER: d

11.33 Goal programming is characterized by

(a) all maximization problems.
(b) setting of lower and upper bounds.
(c) the deviation from a high-priority goal must be minimized before the next-highest-priority goal may be considered.
(d) all of the above
(e) none of the above

ANSWER: c

11.34 An integer programming (maximization) problem was first solved as a linear programming problem, and the objective function value (profit) was \$253.67. The two decision variables (X, Y) in the problem had values of X = 12.45 and Y = 32.75. If there is a single optimal solution, which of the following must be true for the optimal integer solution to this problem?

(a) X = 12 Y = 32
(b) X = 12 Y = 33
(c) the objective function value must be less than \$253.67
(d) the objective function value will be greater than \$253.67
(e) none of the above

ANSWER: c

11.35 An integer programming (minimization) problem was first solved as a linear programming problem, and the objective function value (cost) was \$253.67. The two decision variables (X, Y) in the problem had values of X = 12.45 and Y = 32.75. If there is a single optimal solution, which of the following must be true for the optimal integer solution to this problem?

(a) X = 13 Y = 33
(b) X = 12 Y = 32
(c) the objective function value must be less than \$253.67
(d) the objective function value will be greater than \$253.67
(e) none of the above

ANSWER: d

11.36 In a goal programming problem with two goals at the same priority level, all the deviational variables are equal to zero in the optimal solution. This means

(a) there is no feasible solution to the problem.
(b) all goals are fully achieved.
(c) nonlinear programming must be used to solve this.
(d) this problem was an integer programming problem.
(e) none of the above

ANSWER: b

11.37 A goal programming problem had two goals (with no priorities assigned). Goal number 1 was to achieve a profit of $2,400 and goal number 2 was to have no idle time for workers in the factory. The optimal solution to this problem resulted in a profit of $2,300 and no idle time. What was the value for the objective function for this goal programming problem?

(a) 2300
(b) 100
(c) –100
(d) 0
(e) none of the above

ANSWER: b

11.38 A goal programming problem had two goals (with no priorities assigned). Goal number 1 was to achieve a profit of $3,600 and goal number 2 was to have no wasted material. The optimal solution to this problem resulted in a profit of $3,300 and no wasted material. What was the value for the objective function for this goal programming problem?

(a) 300
(b) –300
(c) 3300
(d) 0
(e) none of the above

ANSWER: a

11.39 In an integer programming problem, if it is desired to have variable X be exactly twice the value of variable Y, the constraint would be written:

(a) $2X + Y = 0$
(b) $X + 2Y = 0$
(c) $2X - Y = 0$
(d) $X - 2Y = 0$
(e) none of the above

ANSWER: d

Table 11-1
A company has decided to use 0–1 integer programming to help make some investment decisions. There are three possible investment alternatives from which to choose, but if it is decided that a particular alternative is to be selected, the entire cost of that alternative will be incurred (i.e., it is impossible to build one-half of a factory). The integer programming model is as follows:
Maximize $5000X_1 + 7000X_2 + 9000X_3$ Subject to: $X_1 + X_2 + X_3 \leq 2$ (only 2 may be chosen) $25000X_1 + 32000X_2 + 29000X_3 \leq 62{,}000$ (budget limit) $16X_1 + 14X_2 + 19X_3 \leq 36$ (resource limitation) all variables = 0 or 1
where $X_1 = 1$ if alternative 1 is selected, 0 otherwise $X_2 = 1$ if alternative 2 is selected, 0 otherwise $X_3 = 1$ if alternative 3 is selected, 0 otherwise
The optimal solution is $X_1 = 0$, $X_2 = 1$, $X_3 = 1$

11.40 According to Table 11-1, which presents an integer programming problem, if the optimal solution is used, what would the value of the objective function be?

(a) 21,000
(b) 12,000
(c) 16,000
(d) 2
(e) none of the above

ANSWER: c

11.41 According to Table 11-1, which presents an integer programming problem, if the optimal solution is used, how much of the budget would be spent?

(a) $32,000
(b) $29,000
(c) $61,000
(d) $62,000
(e) none of the above

ANSWER: c

11.42 In Table 11-1, which presents an integer programming problem, using the optimal solution means only two of the alternatives would be selected. How much slack is there in the third constraint?

(a) 0
(b) 3
(c) 33
(d) 36
(e) none of the above

ANSWER: b

11.43 According to Table 11-1, which presents an integer programming problem, the optimal solution is to select only two of the alternatives. Suppose you wished to add a constraint that stipulated that alternative 2 could only be selected if alternative 1 is also selected (i.e., if alternative 1 is not selected, you may not select alternative 2; however, you may select #1 and not select #2). How would this constraint be written?

(a) $X_1 = X_2$
(b) $X_1 \leq X_2$
(c) $X_1 \geq X_2$
(d) $X_1 + X_2 = 2$
(e) none of the above

ANSWER: c

11.44 Suppose the branch and bound method is used to solve an integer programming problem. When the linear solution is found, X_1=3.6. If branching is done on this variable, two branches would be generated. The constraint $X_1 \leq 3$ is added to one branch. What constraint would be added to the other branch?

(a) $X_1 \geq 3$
(b) $X_1 \geq 2$
(c) $X_1 \geq 4$
(d) $X_1 = 3$
(e) none of the above

ANSWER: c

11.45 Suppose the branch and bound method is used to solve an integer programming problem. When the linear solution is found, $X_1 = 6.35$. If branching is done on this variable, two branches would be generated. The constraint $X_1 \leq 6$ is added to one branch. What constraint would be added to the other branch?

(a) $X_1 \geq 7$
(b) $X_1 \geq 6$
(c) $X_1 \geq 5$
(d) $X_1 = 6$
(e) none of the above

ANSWER: a

Table 11-2						
Minimize $Z = P_1 d_1^+ + P_1 d_1^- + P_1 d_2^+ + P_1 d_2^- + P_1 d_3^+ + P_1 d_3^-$						
Subject to: $4 X_1 + 3 X_2 + 5 X_3 + d_1^- - d_1^+ = 240$ $24 X_1 + 30 X_2 + 32 X_3 + d_2^- - d_2^+ = 1500$ $1 X_1 + 2 X_2 + X_3 + d_3^- - d_3^+ = 50$						
Optimal Solution Data:						
Decision Variable	Solution Value	Goal	d^+	d^-	Priority	Non-achievement
X_1	12.5	1	0	2.5	P_1	2.5
X_2	0	2	0	0		
X_3	37.5	3	0	0		

11.46 According to Table 11-2, which presents a solution to a goal programming problem, there are three goals (each represented by a constraint). Which goals are totally achieved?

(a) number 1 only
(b) number 1 and number 2
(c) number 2 and number 3
(d) number 1 and number 3
(e) none of the above

ANSWER: c

11.47 According to Table 11-2, which presents a solution to a goal programming problem, there are three goals (each represented by a constraint). Goal number 2 represents a profit goal. How much profit would be achieved by this solution?

(a) 1,500
(b) 0
(c) 2.5
(d) 32
(e) none of the above

ANSWER: a

11.48 According to Table 11-2, which presents a solution to a goal programming problem, there are three goals (each represented by a constraint). Goal number 1 represents a labor-utilization goal — the company would like to utilize 240 hours per week. How many hours would be utilized if the optimal solution were used?

(a) 240.0
(b) 237.5
(c) 227.5
(d) 2.5
(e) none of the above

ANSWER: b

Table 11-3	
Maximize	$Z = 34X_1 + 43X_2 + 29X_3$
Subject to:	$5X_1 + 4X_2 + 7X_3 \leq 50$
	$1X_1 + 2X_2 + 2X_3 \leq 16$
	$3X_1 + 4X_2 + 1X_3 \leq 9$
	All X_i are integer and non-negative

Final Integer Solution Z = 208

Decision Variable	Solution
X_1	1
X_2	0
X_3	6

11.49 According to Table 11-3, which presents a solution for an integer programming problem, what is the maximum possible profit for the integer programming problem?

(a) 174
(b) 208
(c) 221
(d) 222
(e) none of the above

ANSWER: b

11.50 According to Table 11-3, which presents a solution for an integer programming problem, what are the values for X_1, X_2, and X_3 in the solution to the integer problem?

(a) 0, 0.542, and 6.833
(b) 0, 0, and 6
(c) 0, 0, and 7
(d) 1, 0, and 6
(e) none of the above

ANSWER: d

Table 11-4	
Maximize	$Z = 400 X_1 + 400 X_2 + 350 X_3$
Subject to:	$7 X_1 + 7 X_2 + 12 X_3 \leq 80$
	$3 X_1 + 6 X_2 + 5 X_3 \leq 50$
	$4 X_1 + 5 X_2 + 2 X_3 \leq 23$
	All X are integer and non-negative
Initial Solution $Z = 3001.471$	
Decision Variable	Solution
X_1	3.412
X_2	0
X_3	4.676
Final Integer Solution $Z = 2650$	
Decision Variable	Solution
X1	3
X2	1
X3	3
Alternative Final Integer Solution $Z = 2650$	
Decision Variable	Solution
X1	4
X2	0
X3	3

11.51 According to Table 11-4, which presents a solution for an integer programming problem, what is the maximum possible profit that may be achieved for the integer problem?

(a) 3001.471
(b) 3001
(c) 3002
(d) 2650
(e) none of the above

ANSWER: d

11.52 According to Table 11-4, which presents a solution for an integer programming problem, what would happen if the initial real solution were rounded to $X_1 = 3$, $X_2 = 0$, and $X_3 = 5$?

(a) An infeasible solution would be found.
(b) A feasible but suboptimal solution would be found.
(c) The optimal solution would be found.
(d) none of the above
(e) all of the above

ANSWER: a

11.53 According to Table 11-4, which presents a solution for an integer programming problem, what would happen if the constraint $X_1 \geq 3$ were added to the problem?

(a) Profit of 2650 could not be achieved.
(b) Profit of 2650 could still be achieved.
(c) The problem would have to be run again on the computer.
(d) all of the above
(e) none of the above

ANSWER: b

11.54 According to Table 11-4, which presents a solution for an integer programming problem, the branch and bound method was used to find the optimal solutions. Which of the following constraints could have been included in the final problem that yielded the optimal solutions?

(a) $X_3 \geq 5$
(b) $X_3 \geq 4$
(c) $X_3 \geq 3$
(d) $X_3 \leq 2$
(e) none of the above

ANSWER: c

11.55 According to Table 11-4, which presents a solution for an integer programming problem, there are two optimal solutions. Which of the following must be true?

(a) Any point on the line between these two points is also optimal.
(b) One of these points is infeasible.
(c) The solution is unbounded.
(d) The problem is a 0–1 problem.
(e) none of the above

ANSWER: e

11.56 A transportation problem is an example of

(a) a pure-integer programming problem.
(b) a mixed-integer programming problem.
(c) a zero-one integer programming problem.
(d) a goal programming problem.
(e) a nonlinear programming problem.

ANSWER: a

11.57 If we wish to develop a stock portfolio wherein we maximize return and minimize risk, we would have to use

(a) pure-integer programming.
(b) goal programming.
(c) zero-one integer programming.
(d) mixed-integer programming.
(e) nonlinear programming.

ANSWER: b

11.58 If we wish to select a location for a new manufacturing plant, the best approach would be to use

(a) zero-one integer programming.
(b) mixed-integer programming.
(c) any integer programming model.
(d) an assignment model.
(e) a goal programming model.

ANSWER: e

11.59 Maximize: $7X_1 + 3X_2$

Subject to:

$$5X_1 + 7X_2 \le 27$$
$$4X_1 + X_2 \le 14$$
$$3X_1 - 2X_2 \le 9$$
$$X_1, \quad X_2 \ge 0$$
$$X_1 \text{ integer}$$

represents a

(a) mixed integer programming problem.
(b) goal programming problem.
(c) nonlinear programming problem.
(d) multiple-objective programming problem.
(e) none of the above

ANSWER: a

11.60 Solving an integer programming problem by rounding off answers obtained by solving it as a linear programming problem (using simplex) to values in the feasible region, we find that

(a) the values of decision variables obtained by rounding off are always very close to the optimal values.
(b) the value of the objective function for a maximization problem will likely be less than that for the simplex solution.
(c) the value of the objective function for a minimization problem will likely be less than that for the simplex solution.
(d) all constraints are satisfied exactly.
(e) none of the above

ANSWER: b

11.61 When using the branch and bound method, we

(a) enumerate all the feasible solutions.
(b) solve problems that cannot be solved using the computer.
(c) must have problems with fewer than three variables.
(d) are solving a nonlinear programming problem.
(e) none of the above

ANSWER: e

11.62 In a standard linear programming problem formulation

(a) we are restricted to having fewer than 100 decision variables.
(b) all constraints must be measured in the same units.
(c) the number of constraints must be less than or equal to the number of decision variables.
(d) all variables must be nonnegative.
(e) none of the constraint coefficients may be negative.

ANSWER: d

11.63 Assume that you are to solve the minimization assignment problem depicted in Table 11-5 using the branch and bound method. With what lower bound would you begin?

Table 11-5		Job (Time in Minutes)			
		1	2	3	4
Worker	A	5	9	5	7
	B	3	8	4	4
	C	5	5	8	4
	D	7	4	5	5

(a) 19
(b) 16
(c) 17
(d) 14
(e) 20

ANSWER: b
A3, B1, C4, D2 = (5+3+4+4) = 16

11.64 Assume that you are to solve the maximization assignment problem depicted in Table 11-6 using the branch and bound method. With what upper bound would you begin?

Table 11-6		Job (Profit in dollars)			
		1	2	3	4
Worker	A	5	9	5	7
	B	3	8	4	4
	C	5	5	8	4
	D	7	4	5	5

(a) 16
(b) 30
(c) 32
(d) 34
(e) 15

ANSWER: b
A4, B2, C3, D1 = (7+8+8+7) = 30

11.65 Goal programming is characterized by

(a) nonlinear constraints.
(b) satisficing.
(c) multiple objective functions.
(d) all of the above
(e) none of the above

ANSWER: b

11.66 Consider the following 0–1 integer programming problem:

Minimize $20X + 36Y + 24Z$
Subject to: $2X + 4Y + 3Z \geq 7$
$12X + 8Y + 10Z \geq 25$
X, Y, Z must be 0 or 1

If we wish to add the constraint that no more than two of these variables must be positive, how would this be written?

(a) $2X + 2Y + 2Z \leq 3$
(b) $X + Y + Z \leq 2$
(c) $X \leq 2$, and $Y \leq 2$, and $Z \leq 2$
(d) $X, Y, Z \leq 2$
(e) none of the above

ANSWER: b

11.67 Consider the following 0–1 integer programming problem:

Minimize $20X + 36Y + 24Z$
Subject to: $2X + 4Y + 3Z \geq 7$
$12X + 8Y + 10Z \geq 25$
X, Y, Z must be 0 or 1

If we wish to add the constraint that X must be positive, and that only Y or Z but not both can be positive, how would the additional constraint(s) be written?

(a) $X + Y + Z \leq 3$, $Y + Z \leq 1$
(b) $X \leq 1$, $Y + Z = 1$
(c) $X \leq 2$, and $Y \leq 2$, and $Z \leq 2$
(d) $X = 1$, $Y + Z \leq 1$
(e) none of the above

ANSWER: d

11.68 An integer programming (maximization) problem was first solved as a linear programming problem, and the objective function value (profit) was \$253.67. The two decision variables (X, Y) in the problem had values of X = 12.45 and Y = 32.75. Which of the following must be true for the optimal integer solution to this problem?

(a) X = 12 Y = 32
(b) X = 12 Y = 33
(c) X = 12
(d) Y = 32
(e) none of the above

ANSWER: e

11.69 A goal programming problem had two goals (with no priorities assigned). Goal number 1 was to achieve a cost of \$2,400 and goal number 2 was to have no idle time for workers in the factory. The optimal solution to this problem resulted in a cost of \$2,400 and no idle time. What was the value for the objective function for this goal programming problem?

(a) 2300
(b) 100
(c) –100
(d) 0
(e) none of the above

ANSWER: d

11.70 A goal programming problem had two goals (with no priorities assigned). Goal number 1 was to achieve a cost of $3,600 and goal number 2 was to have no wasted material. The optimal solution to this problem resulted in a cost of $3,900 and no wasted material. What was the value for the objective function for this goal programming problem?

(a) 300
(b) –300
(c) 3300
(d) 0
(e) none of the above

ANSWER: a

Table 11-7				
A company has decided to use 0–1 integer programming to help make some investment decisions. There are three possible investment alternatives from which to choose, but if it is decided that a particular alternative is to be selected, the entire cost of that alternative will be incurred (i.e., it is impossible to build one-half of a factory). The integer programming model is as follows:				
Maximize	$5000X_1 +$	$7000X_2 +$	$9000X_3$	
Subject to:	$X_1 +$	$X_2 +$	$X_3 \leq 2$	Constraint 1
	$-X_1 +$	X_2	≤ 0	Constraint 2
	$25{,}000X_1 +$	$32{,}000X_2 +$	$29{,}000X_3 \leq 62{,}000$	(budget limit)
	$16X_1 +$	$14X_2 +$	$19X_3 \leq 36$	(resource limitation)
		all variables = 0 or 1		
where	$X_1 = 1$ if alternative 1 is selected, 0 otherwise			
	$X_2 = 1$ if alternative 2 is selected, 0 otherwise			
	$X_3 = 1$ if alternative 3 is selected, 0 otherwise			
The optimal solution is $X_1 = 1, X_2 = 0, X_3 = 1$				

11.71 Table 11-7 presents an integer programming problem. What is the meaning of Constraint 1?

(a) If X_1 is selected, X_2 must also be selected.
(b) No more than two alternatives may be selected.
(c) At least two alternatives must be selected.
(d) If X_2 is selected, X_1 must also be selected.
(e) none of the above

ANSWER: b

11.72 Table 11-7 presents an integer programming problem. What is the meaning of Constraint 2?

(a) Both alternatives 1 and 2 must be selected.
(b) If alternative 2 is selected, alternative 1 must also be selected.
(c) Either alternative 1 or alternative 2 must be selected.
(d) No more than one alternative may be selected.
(e) none of the above

ANSWER: b

11.73 Table 11-7 presents an integer programming problem. If the optimal solution is used, then only two of the alternatives would be selected. How much slack would there be in the third constraint?

(a) 1000
(b) 5000
(c) 3300
(d) 8000
(e) none of the above

ANSWER: d

11.74 Table 11-7 presents an integer programming problem. Suppose you wish to add a constraint that stipulates that both alternative 2 and alternative 3 must be selected, or neither can be selected. How would this constraint be written?

(a) $X_2 = X_3$
(b) $X_2 \leq X_3$
(c) $X_2 \geq X_3$
(d) $X_2 + X_3 = 1$
(e) none of the above

ANSWER: a

Table 11-8						
Minimize $Z = P_1 d_1^+ + P_1 d_1^- + P_1 d_2^+ + P_1 d_2^- + P_1 d_3^+ + P_1 d_3^-$						
Subject to: $4 X_1 + 3 X_2 + 5 X_3 + d_1^- - d_1^+ = 240$ $24 X_1 + 30 X_2 + 32 X_3 + d_2^- - d_2^+ = 1500$ $1 X_1 + 2 X_2 + X_3 + d_3^- - d_3^+ = 50$						
Optimal Solution Data:						
Decision Variable	Solution Value	Goal	d^+	d^-	Priority	Non-achievement
X_1	12.5	1	0	2.5	P_1	2.5
X_2	0	2	0	0		
X_3	37.5	3	0	0		

11.75 Table 11-8 represents a solution to a goal programming problem. There are three goals (each represented by a constraint). Which goals are only partly achieved?

(a) number 1 only
(b) number 1 and number 2
(c) number 2 and number 3
(d) number 1 and number 3
(e) none of the above

ANSWER: a

11.76 Table 11-8 represents a solution to a goal programming problem. There are three goals (each represented by a constraint). Goal number 3 represents a resource usage goal. How much of this resource would be used by this solution?

(a) 50 units
(b) 70 units
(c) 2500 units
(d) 240 units
(e) none of the above

ANSWER: a

11.77 Table 11-8 represents a solution to a goal programming problem. There are three goals (each represented by a constraint). Goal number 1 represents a labor utilization goal – the company would like to utilize 240 hours per week. Which of the following does the optimal solution use?

(a) more than 240 hours
(b) exactly 240 hours
(c) less than 240 hours
(d) 50 hours
(e) none of the above

ANSWER: c

Table 11-9	
Maximize	$Z = 34X_1 + 43X_2 + 29X_3$
Subject to:	$5X_1 + 4X_2 + 7X_3 \leq 50$
	$1X_1 + 2X_2 + 2X_3 \leq 16$
	$3X_1 + 4X_2 + 1X_3 \leq 9$
All X_i are integer and non-negative	
Final Integer Solution $Z = 208$	
Decision Variable	Solution
X_1	1
X_2	0
X_3	6

11.78 Table 11-9 represents a solution for an integer programming problem. If this problem had been solved as a simple linear programming problem, what would you expect the value of the objective function to be?

(a) less than 208
(b) greater than 208
(c) exactly 208
(d) (a) or (c)
(e) (b) or (c)

ANSWER: e

11.79 Table 11-9 represents a solution for an integer programming problem. If one uses the optimal solution presented, how much slack is there in the first equation?

(a) 0 units
(b) 5 units
(c) 3 units
(d) 2 units
(e) none of the above

ANSWER: c

11.80 A model containing a linear objective function and requiring that one or more of the decision variables take on an integer value in the final solution is called

(a) an integer programming problem.
(b) a goal programming problem.
(c) a nonlinear programming problem.
(d) a multiple objective LP problem.
(e) insufficient information.

ANSWER: e

11.81 Goal programming and linear programming differ in that

(a) in LP, the objective function is maximized or minimized, while in goal programming, the deviation between goals and possible achievement is minimized.
(b) slack variables are used in LP, while deviational variables are used in goal programming.
(c) deviational variables have positive objective function coefficients in goal programming, but slack variables have 0 coefficients in LP.
(d) all of the above
(e) none of the above

ANSWER: d

11.82 A goal programming problem had two goals (with no priorities assigned). Goal number 1 was to achieve a cost of $3,600 and goal number 2 was to complete the task in 400 hours or fewer. The optimal solution to this problem resulted in a cost of $3,600 and a completion time of 420 hours. What was the value for the objective function for this goal programming problem?

(a) 400
(b) -400
(c) 20
(d) 0
(e) none of the above

ANSWER: c

PROBLEMS

11.83 The Elastic Firm has two products coming on the market: Zigs and Zags. To make a Zig, the firm needs 10 units of product A and 15 units of product B. To make a Zag, they need 20 units of product A and 15 units of product B. There are only 2,000 units of product A and 3,000 units of product B available to the firm. The profit on a Zig is \$4 and on a Zag it is \$6. Management objectives in order of their priority are:

(1) Produce at least 50 Zigs.
(2) Achieve a target profit of at least \$750.
(3) Use all of the product B available.

Formulate this as a goal programming problem.

ANSWER: Let X_1 = number of Zigs, X_2 = number of Zags.
d_1^- = underachievement of Zig goal
d_1^+ = overachievement of Zig goal
d_2^- = underachievement of profit target
d_2^+ = overachievement of profit target
d_3^- = unused product B
d_3^+ = additional amount of product B needed

Minimize $P_1 d_1^- + P_2 d_2^- + P_3 d_3^-$

Subject to:

$X_1 + d_1^- - d_1^+ = 50$ (Zig constraint)

$4X_1 + 6X_2 + d_2^- - d_2^+ = 750$ (profit)

$15X_1 + 15X_2 + d_3^- - d_3^+ = 3000$ (product B)

$10X_1 + 20X_2 \leq 2000$ (product A)

all variables ≥ 0

11.84 Classify the following problems as to whether they are pure-integer, mixed-integer, zero-one, goal, or nonlinear programming problems.

(a) Maximize $Z = 5X_1 + 6X_1X_2 + 2X_2$
Subject to:
$3X_1 + 2X_2 \geq 6$
$X_1 + X_2 \leq 8$
$X_1, X_2 \geq 0$

(b) Minimize $Z = 8X_1 + 6X_2$
Subject to:
$4X_1 + 5X_2 \geq 10$
$X_1 + X_2 \leq 3$
$X_1, X_2 \geq 0$
X_1 integer

(c) Maximize $Z = 10X_1 + 5X_2$
Subject to:
$8X_1 + 10X_2 = 10$
$4X_1 + 6X_2 \geq 5$
$X_1, X_2 = 0$ or 1

(d) Minimize $Z = 8X_1^2 + 4X_1X_2 + 12X_2^2$
Subject to:
$6X_1 + X_2 \geq 50$
$X_1 + X_2 \geq 40$

ANSWER:
(a) nonlinear
(b) mixed-integer
(c) zero-one
(d) nonlinear

11.85 A package express carrier is considering expanding the fleet of aircraft used to transport packages. There is a total of $200 million allocated for purchases. Two types of aircraft may be purchased—the C1A and the C1B. The C1A costs $25 million, while the C1B costs $18 million. The C1A can carry 60,000 pounds of packages, while the C1B can only carry 40,000 pounds of packages. The company needs at least ten new aircraft. Formulate this as an integer programming problem to maximize the number of pounds that may be carried.

ANSWER: Let A = number of C1As to purchase
B = number of C1Bs to purchase

Maximize $60000A + 40000B$

Subject to:
$25A + 18B \leq 200$ (budget in millions)
$A + B \geq 10$ (aircraft)
$A, B \geq 0$ and integer

11.86 Smalltime Investments Inc. is going to purchase new computers for most of the employees. There are ten employees, and at least eight computers must be purchased. The cost of the basic personal computer with monitor and disk drive is $2,000, while the deluxe version with VGA and advanced processor is $3,500. Due to internal politics, the number of deluxe computers must be no more than half the number of regular computers, but at least three deluxe computers must be purchased. The budget is $27,000. Formulate this as an integer programming problem to maximize the number of computers purchased.

ANSWER: Let R = number of regular computers purchased
D = number of deluxe computers purchased

Maximize $R + D$

Subject to:

$$2000R + 3500D \leq 27{,}000 \text{ (budget)}$$
$$-0.5R + D \leq 0 \text{ (political limitation)}$$
$$D \geq 3 \text{ (minimum \# of deluxe)}$$
$$R + D \geq 8 \text{ (minimum \# of computers)}$$

all variables ≥ 0 and integer

11.87 Smalltime Investments Inc. is going to purchase new computers. There are ten employees, and the company would like one for each employee. The cost of the basic personal computer with monitor and disk drive is $2,000, while the deluxe version with VGA and advanced processor is $3,500. Due to internal politics, the number of deluxe computers should be less than half the number of regular computers, but at least three deluxe computers must be purchased. The budget is $27,000, although additional money could be used if it were deemed necessary. All of these are goals that the company has identified. Formulate this as a goal programming problem.

ANSWER:

Let R = number of regular computers purchased
D = number of deluxe computers purchased
d_1^- = underachievement of goal of 10 computers to purchase
d_1^+ = overachievement of goal of 10 computers to purchase
d_2^- = unused budget
d_2^+ = additional monies required
d_3^- = underachievement of goal of the number of deluxe computers should be less than half the number of regular computers
d_3^+ = underachievement of goal of the number of deluxe computers should be less than half the number of regular computers
d_4^- = underachievement of goal that the number of deluxe computers should be at least three
d_4^+ = underachievement of goal that the number of deluxe computers should be at least three

Minimize $d_1^- + d_1^+ + d_3^+ + d_4^-$

Subject to:

$$R + D + d_1^- - d_1^+ = 10$$
$$2000R + 3500D + d_2^- - d_2^+ = 27{,}000$$
$$-0.5R + D + d_3^- - d_3^+ = 0$$
$$D + d_4^- - d_4^+ = 3$$

all variables ≥ 0

11.88 Allied Manufacturing has three factories located in Dallas, Houston, and New Orleans. They each produce the same product and ship to three regional warehouses — #1, #2, and #3. The cost of shipping one unit of each product to each of the three destinations is given below.

TO==>	#1	#2	#3	
FROM Dallas 4	6	5	100	
Houston	5	7	8	100
New Orleans	4	3	5	100
DEMAND	120	130	150	

There is no way to meet the demand for each warehouse. Therefore, the company has decided to set the following goals: (1) the number shipped from each source should be as close to 100 units as possible (overtime may be used if necessary), (2) the number shipped to each destination should be as close to the demand as possible, (3) the total cost should be close to \$1,400. Formulate this as a goal programming problem.

ANSWER:

Let X_{11} = number of units shipped from Dallas to #1
X_{12} = number of units shipped from Dallas to #2
X_{13} = number of units shipped from Dallas to #3
X_{21} = number of units shipped from Houston to #1
X_{22} = number of units shipped from Houston to #2
X_{23} = number of units shipped from Houston to #3
X_{31} = number of units shipped from New Orleans to #1
X_{32} = number of units shipped from New Orleans to #2
X_{33} = number of units shipped from New Orleans to #3

d_1^- = underachievement of goal to ship 100 units from Dallas
d_1^+ = overachievement of goal to ship 100 units from Dallas
d_2^- = underachievement of goal to ship 100 units from Houston
d_2^+ = overachievement of goal to ship 100 units from Houston
d_3^- = underachievement of goal to ship 100 units from New Orleans
d_3^+ = underachievement of goal to ship 100 units from New Orleans
d_4^- = underachievement of target to ship to warehouse #1 close to its demand
d_4^+ = overachievement of target to ship to warehouse #1 close to its demand
d_5^- = underachievement of target to ship to warehouse #2 close to its demand
d_5^+ = overachievement of target to ship to warehouse #2 close to its demand
d_6^- = underachievement of target to ship to warehouse #3 close to its demand
d_6^+ = overachievement of target to ship to warehouse #3 close to its demand
d_7^- = underachievement of target total cost
d_7^+ = overachievement of target total cost

Minimize $d_1^+ + d_2^+ + d_3^+ + d_4^+ + d_4^- + d_5^- + d_5^+ + d_6^+ + d_6^- + d_7^+$

Subject to:

$$X_{11} + X_{12} + X_{13} + d_1^- - d_1^+ = 100$$
$$X_{21} + X_{22} + X_{23} + d_2^- - d_2^+ = 100$$
$$X_{31} + X_{32} + X_{33} + d_3^- - d_3^+ = 100$$
$$X_{11} + X_{21} + X_{31} + d_4^- - d_4^+ = 120$$
$$X_{12} + X_{22} + X_{32} + d_5^- - d_5^+ = 130$$
$$X_{13} + X_{23} + X_{33} + d_6^- - d_6^+ = 150$$
$$4\,X_{11} + 6\,X_{12} + 5\,X_{13} + 5\,X_{21} + 7\,X_{22} + 8\,X_{23} + 4\,X_{31} + 3\,X_{32} + 5\,X_{33} + d_7^- - d_7^+ = 1400$$

all variables ≥ 0

11.89 The Elastic Firm has two products coming on the market, Zigs and Zags. To make a Zig, the firm needs 10 units of product A and 15 units of product B. To make a Zag, they need 20 units of product A and 15 units of product B. There are only 2,000 units of product A and 3,000 units of product B available to the firm. The profit on a Zig is \$4 and on a Zag it is \$6. Management objectives in order of their priority are:

(1) Produce at least 40 Zags.
(2) Achieve a target profit of at least \$750.
(3) Use all of the product A available.
(4) Use all of the product B available.
(5) Avoid the requirement for more product A.

Formulate this as a goal programming problem.

ANSWER: Let X_1 = number of Zigs, X_2 = number of Zags.
d_1^- = underachievement of Zag goal
d_1^+ = overachievement of Zag goal
d_2^- = underachievement of profit target
d_2^+ = overachievement of profit target
d_3^- = unused product A
d_3^+ = additional amount of product A needed
d_4^- = unused product B
d_4^+ = additional amount of product B needed

Minimize $P_1 d_1^- + P_2 d_2^- + P_3 d_3^- + P_4 d_4^+ + P_5 d_3^-$

Subject to:

$X_1 + d_1^- - d_1^+ = 40$ (Zig constraint)
$4 X_1 + 6 X_2 + d_2^- - d_2^+ = 750$ (profit)
$10 X_1 + 20 X_2 + d_3^- - d_3^+ = 2000$ (product A)
$15 X_1 + 15 X_2 + d_4^- - d_4^+ = 3000$ (product B)
all variables ≥ 0

11.90 Data Equipment Inc. produces two models of a retail price scanner, a sophisticated model that can be networked to a central processing unit and a stand-alone model for small retailers. The major limitations of the manufacturing of these two products are labor and material capacities. The following table summarizes the usages and capacities associated with each product.

Product	Labor Hr/Unit	Materials Components/Unit	Profit $/Unit
Network (X_1)	8	20	$160
Basic (X_2)	5	7	$ 95
Capacity	800 hr/day	1,500 comp/day	

The typical LP formulation for this problem is:

Maximize $P = \$160\ X_1 + \$95\ X_2$

Subject to:

$$8\ X_1 + 5\ X_2 \le 800$$
$$20\ X_1 + 7\ X_2 \le 1500$$
$$X_1, X_2 \ge 0$$

However, the management of DEI has prioritized several goals that are to be attained by manufacturing:

(1) Since the labor situation at the plant is uneasy (i.e., there are rumors that a local union is considering an organizing campaign), management wants to assure full employment of all its employees.
(2) Management has established a profit goal of $12,000 per day.
(3) Due to the high prices of components from nonroutine suppliers, management wants to minimize the purchase of additional materials.

Given the above additional information, set this up as a goal programming problem.

ANSWER: Let
d_1^- = underachievement of full employment goal
d_1^+ = overachievement of full employment goal
d_2^- = underachievement of profit target
d_2^+ = overachievement of profit target
d_3^- = unused components
d_3^+ = additional amount of components needed

Minimize $P_1 d_1^- + P_2 d_2^- + P_3 d_3^+$

Subject to:

$$8\ X_1 + 5\ X_2 + d_1^- - d_1^+ = 800$$
$$160\ X_1 + 95\ X_2 + d_2^- - d_2^+ = 12000$$
$$20\ X_1 + 7\ X_2 + d_3^- - d_3^+ = 1500$$
$$\text{all variables} \ge 0$$

11.91 Data Equipment Inc. produces two models of a retail price scanner, a sophisticated model that can be networked to a central processing unit and a stand-alone model for small retailers. The major limitations of the manufacturing of these two products are labor and material capacities. The following table summarizes the usages and capacities associated with each product.

Product	Labor Hr/Unit	Materials Components/Unit	Profit $/Unit
Network (X_1)	8	20	$160
Basic (X_2)	5	7	$ 95
Capacity	800 hr/day	1,500 comp/day	

The typical LP formulation for this problem is:

Maximize $P = \$160\ X_1 + \$95\ X_2$

Subject to:

$$8\ X_1 + 5\ X_2 \le 800$$
$$20\ X_1 + 7\ X_2 \le 1500$$
$$X_1, X_2 \ \ge 0$$

However, the management of DEI has prioritized several goals that are to be attained by manufacturing:

(1) Management had decided to severely limit overtime.
(2) Management has established a profit goal of $15,000 per day.
(3) Due to the difficulty of obtaining components from non-routine suppliers, management wants to end production with at least 50 units of each component remaining in stock.
(4) Management also believes that they should produce at least 30 units of the network model.

Given the above additional information, set this up as a goal programming problem.

ANSWER: Let d_1^- = underachievement of labor hours
d_1^+ = overachievement of labor hours
d_2^- = underachievement of profit target
d_2^+ = overachievement of profit target
d_3^- = unused components
d_3^+ = additional amount of components needed
d_4^- = underachievement of target for number of network models
d_4^+ = overachievement of target for number of network models

Minimize $P_1\ d_1^+ + P_2\ d_2^- + P_3\ d_3^+ + P_4\ d_4^-$

Subject to:

$$8\ X_1 + 5\ X_2 + d_1^- - d_1^+ = 800$$
$$160\ X_1 + 95\ X_2 + d_2^- - d_2^+ = 15000$$
$$20\ X_1 + 7\ X_2 + d_3^- - d_3^+ = 1450$$
$$X_1 \quad + d_4^- - d_4^+ = 30$$
all variables ≥ 0

11.92 A package express carrier is considering expanding the fleet of aircraft used to transport packages. Of primary importance is that there is a total of $350 million allocated for purchases. Two types of aircraft may be purchased—the C1A and the C1B. The C1A costs $25 million, while the C1B costs $18 million. The C1A can carry 60,000 pounds of packages, while the C1B can only carry 40,000 pounds of packages. Of secondary importance is that the company needs at least 10 new aircraft. It takes 150 hours per month to maintain the C1A, and 100 hours to maintain the C1B. The least level of importance is that there are a total of 1,200 hours of maintenance time available per month.

(a) First, formulate this as an integer programming problem to maximize the number of pounds that may be carried.

(b) Second, rework the problem differently than in part (a) to suppose the company decides that what is most important to them is that they keep the ratio of C1Bs to C1As in their fleet as close to 1.2 as possible to allow for flexibility in serving their routes. Formulate the goal programming representation of this problem.

ANSWER:

(a) Let A = number of C1As to purchase
B = number of C1Bs to purchase

Maximize $60000A + 40000B$

Subject to:

$$\begin{aligned} 25A + 18B &\leq 350 \text{ (budget, in millions)} \\ A + B &\geq 10 \text{ (minimum number of aircraft)} \\ 150A + 100B &\leq 1200 \text{ (maintenance)} \\ A, B &\geq 0 \text{ and integer} \end{aligned}$$

(b) Let A = number of C1As to purchase
B = number of C1Bs to purchase
d_1^- = underachievement of ratio of C1B to C1A
d_1^+ = overachievement of ratio of C1B to C1A
d_2^- = underachievement of budget target
d_2^+ = overachievement of budget target
d_3^- = underachievement of planes
d_3^+ = overachievement of planes
d_4^- = underachievement of maintenance hours
d_4^+ = overachievement of maintenance hours

Minimize $d_1^+ + d_2^+ + d_3^- + d_3^+ + d_4^- + d_4^+$

Subject to:

$$\begin{aligned} -1.2A + B + d_1^- - d_1^+ &= 0 \text{ (ratio of 1.2 C1Bs to C1As)} \\ 25A + 18B + d_2^- - d_2^+ &= 350 \text{ (budget, in millions)} \\ A + B + d_3^- - d_3^+ &= 10 \text{ (minimum number of aircraft)} \\ 150A + 100B + d_4^- - d_4^+ &= 1200 \text{ (maintenance)} \\ \text{all variables} &\geq 0 \end{aligned}$$

11.93 Bastille College is going to purchase new computers for both faculty and staff. There is a total of 50 people who need new machines – 30 faculty and 20 staff. The cost of the basic personal computer with monitor and disk drive is \$2,000, while the deluxe version with VGA and advanced processor is \$3,500. Due to internal politics, the number of deluxe computers assigned to staff must be less than half the number of deluxe computers assigned to faculty. Staff members do feel somewhat "put upon" by having this limit placed upon the number of deluxe machines purchased for their use, so the College would like to purchase as many deluxe machines for the staff as possible. The College feels that it must purchase at least 5 deluxe computers for the faculty; if possible, it would like to purchase as many as 20 deluxe computers for the faculty. The budget is \$100,000. Develop the mathematical programming formulation of this problem that would maximize the number of computers purchased.

ANSWER:
Can be formulated as either an integer program or goal program
The IP formulation:

Let F_R = number of regular computers purchased for faculty use
F_D = number of deluxe computers purchased for faculty use
S_R = number of regular computers purchased for staff use
S_D = number of deluxe computers purchased for staff use

Maximize $C = F_R + F_D + S_R + S_D$

Subject to:

$F_D \geq 5$ (minimum deluxe faculty)
$F_D \leq 20$ (max. deluxe faculty)
$F_R + F_D \leq 30$ (total faculty computers)
$S_R + S_D \leq 20$ (total staff computers)
$-0.5F_D + S_D \leq 0$ (faculty to staff deluxe ratio)
$2000\,F_R + 3500\,F_D + 2000\,S_R + 3500\,S_D \leq 10000$ (budget)
all variables ≥ 0 and integer

The goal programming formulation:

d_1^- = underachievement of minimum faculty deluxe computers
d_1^+ = overachievement of minimum faculty deluxe computers
d_2^- = underachievement of maximum faculty deluxe computers
d_2^+ = overachievement of maximum faculty deluxe computers
d_3^- = underachievement of deluxe ratio
d_3^+ = overachievement of deluxe ratio
d_4^- = underachievement of total faculty computers
d_4^+ = overachievement of total faculty computers
d_5^- = underachievement of maximum staff deluxe computers
d_5^+ = overachievement of maximum staff deluxe computers
d_6^- = underachievement of total staff computers
d_6^+ = overachievement of total staff computers
d_7^- = underachievement of budget
d_7^+ = overachievement of budget

(answer continued on next page)

Minimize $d_1^- + d_2^+ + d_3^+ + d_4^- + d_5^- + d_6^- + d_7^+$

Subject to:

$F_D +$	$d_1^- - d_1^+ =$	5	Deluxe faculty
$F_D +$	$d_2^- - d_2^+ =$	20	Deluxe faculty
$-0.5F_D +$	$S_D + d_3^- - d_3^+ =$	0	Deluxe ratio
$F_D + \quad F_R +$	$d_4^- - d_4^+ =$	30	Total faculty
	$S_D + d_5^- - d_5^+ =$	20	Staff
$S_R +$	$S_D + d_6^- - d_6^+ =$	20	Total staff
$3500F_D + 2000F_R + 2000S_R + 3500S_D +$	$d_7^- - d_7^+ =$	100000	Budget

all variables ≥ 0

11.94 Allied Manufacturing has three factories located in Dallas, Houston, and New Orleans. They each produce the same 277 products and ship to three regional warehouses — #1, #2, and #3. The cost of shipping one unit of each product to each of the three destinations is given in the table below.

TO==>		#1	#2	#3	SUPPLY
FROM	Dallas	4	6	5	100
	Houston	5	7	8	100
	New Orleans	4	3	5	100
	DEMAND	120	130	150	

There is no way to meet the demand for each warehouse. Therefore, the company has decided to set the following goals: (1) each source should ship as much of its capacity as possible, (2) the number shipped to each destination should be as close to the demand as possible, (3) the capacity of New Orleans should be divided as evenly as possible between warehouses #1 and #2, and (4) the total cost should be less than $1,400. Formulate this as a goal programming problem.

ANSWER:

Let X_{11} = number of units shipped from Dallas to #1
X_{12} = number of units shipped from Dallas to #2
X_{13} = number of units shipped from Dallas to #3
X_{21} = number of units shipped from Houston to #1
X_{22} = number of units shipped from Houston to #2
X_{23} = number of units shipped from Houston to #3
X_{31} = number of units shipped from New Orleans to #1
X_{32} = number of units shipped from New Orleans to #2
X_{33} = number of units shipped from New Orleans to #3
d_1^- = underachievement of goal to ship 100 units from Dallas
d_1^+ = overachievement of goal to ship 100 units from Dallas
d_2^- = underachievement of goal to ship 100 units from Houston
d_2^+ = overachievement of goal to ship 100 units from Houston
d_3^- = underachievement of goal to ship 100 units from New Orleans
d_3^+ = overachievement of goal to ship 100 units from New Orleans
d_4^- = underachievement of target to ship to warehouse #1 close to its demand
d_4^+ = overachievement of target to ship to warehouse #1 close to its demand
d_5^- = underachievement of target to ship to warehouse #2 close to its demand
d_5^+ = overachievement of target to ship to warehouse #2 close to its demand
d_6^- = underachievement of target to ship to warehouse #3 close to its demand
d_6^+ = overachievement of target to ship to warehouse #3 close to its demand
d_7^- = underachievement of target to ship about same quantities from New Orleans to warehouse 1 and 2
d_7^+ = overachievement of target to ship about same quantities from New Orleans to warehouse 1 and 2
d_8^- = underachievement of target total cost
d_8^+ = overachievement of target total cost

Minimize $d_1^- + d_2^- + d_3^- + d_4^- + d_4^+ + d_5^- + d_5^+ + d_6^- + d_6^+ + d_7^- + d_7^+ + d_8^+$

Subject to:
$X_{11} + X_{12} + X_{13} + d_1^- - d_1^+ = 100$
$X_{21} + X_{22} + X_{23} + d_2^- - d_2^+ = 100$
$X_{31} + X_{32} + X_{33} + d_3^- - d_3^+ = 100$
$X_{11} + X_{21} + X_{31} + d_4^- - d_4^+ = 120$
$X_{12} + X_{22} + X_{32} + d_5^- - d_5^+ = 130$
$X_{13} + X_{23} + X_{33} + d_6^- - d_6^+ = 150$
$X_{31} - X_{32} + d_7^- - d_7^+ = 0$
$4 X_{11} + 6 X_{12} + 5 X_{13} + 5 X_{21} + 7 X_{22} + 8 X_{23} + 4 X_{31} + 3 X_{32} + 5 X_{33} + d_8^- - d_8^+ = 1400$
all variables ≥ 0

SHORT ANSWER/ESSAY

11.95 Define deviational variables.

ANSWER: They constitute the objective function terms and capture the gap between set goals and what can be actually achieved given the constraints.

11.96 Briefly describe how the branch and bound method searches for an optimal solution.

ANSWER: The feasible solution area is broken into smaller subparts until an optimal solution is found, a rudimentary divide-and-conquer strategy.

11.97 State the advantage of goal programming over linear programming.

ANSWER: Goal programming allows for multiple goals, unlike linear programming.

11.98 What is the primary difference between linear programming and goal programming?

ANSWER: Goal programming establishes a hierarchy of importance among goals so that lower-priority goals are tackled only after higher-priority goals are satisfied. Goal programming attempts to reach a satisfactory level of multiple objectives; LP tries to find the best possible outcome for a single objective.

CHAPTER 12
Network Models

TRUE/FALSE

12.1 The minimal-spanning tree technique finds the shortest route to a series of destinations.

ANSWER: FALSE

12.2 In the minimal-spanning tree technique, it is necessary to start at the last node in the network.

ANSWER: FALSE

12.3 The maximal-flow technique would be helpful to city planners in determining how freeways should be expanded.

ANSWER: TRUE

12.4 The shortest-route technique requires that each node in the network be connected to at least one other node.

ANSWER: FALSE

12.5 The shortest-route technique is the same as the minimal-spanning tree technique.

ANSWER: FALSE

12.6 Busy highways are often analyzed with the maximal-flow technique.

ANSWER: TRUE

12.7 Transportation companies would definitely be interested in the shortest-route technique to optimize travel.

ANSWER: TRUE

12.8 Cable television companies would employ the shortest-route technique to lay out the cables connecting individual houses.

ANSWER: FALSE

12.9 We may begin the maximal-flow technique by picking an arbitrary path through the network.

ANSWER: TRUE

12.10 In the maximal-flow technique, pathways are indicated by nodes, and the connections between them by lines.

ANSWER: TRUE

12.11 The maximal-flow technique might be used by the U.S. Army Corps of Engineers to study water run-off in an attempt to minimize the danger from floods.

ANSWER: TRUE

12.12 The shortest-route technique might be used by someone planning a vacation in order to minimize the required amount of driving.

ANSWER: TRUE

12.13 The maximal-flow technique might be used by New York City traffic engineers to study the impact of different stop light sequences on traffic moving through the city.

ANSWER: FALSE

12.14 In the shortest-route technique, locations are indicated by nodes, and the pathways connecting them by lines.

ANSWER: TRUE

12.15 A traveling salesperson might use the shortest route technique to minimize the distance traveled to reach one of his/her customers.

ANSWER: TRUE

12.16 For a traveling salesperson attempting to plan his/her route between customers, the shortest-route model would be of greater assistance than the minimal spanning tree model.

ANSWER: TRUE

12.17 The maximal flow model might be of use to an engineer looking for spare capacity in an oil pipeline system.

ANSWER: TRUE

12.18 The shortest route model assumes that one is trying to connect two end points in the shortest manner possible, rather than attempting to connect all the nodes in the model.

ANSWER: TRUE

12.19 The maximal-flow model assumes that there are alternate arcs between each pair of nodes.

ANSWER: FALSE

12.20 The maximal-flow model assumes that there is a net flow from "source" to "sink."

ANSWER: TRUE

MULTIPLE CHOICE

12.21 If your goal was to construct a network in which all points were connected and the distance between them was as short as possible, the technique that you would use is

(a) shortest-route.
(b) maximal-flow.
(c) minimal-spanning tree.
(d) none of the above

ANSWER: c

12.22 The minimal-spanning technique would best be used

(a) to determine LAN network wiring within a building.
(b) to minimize traffic flow on a busy highway.
(c) by a trucking company making frequent but repeatable drops.
(d) none of the above

ANSWER: a

12.23 The maximal-flow technique would best be used

(a) to determine LAN network wiring within a building.
(b) to maximize traffic flow on a busy highway.
(c) by a trucking company making frequent but repeatable drops.
(d) none of the above

ANSWER: b

12.24 A technique that allows a researcher to determine the greatest amount of material that can move through a network is called

(a) maximal-flow.
(b) maximal-spanning.
(c) shortest-route.
(d) none of the above

ANSWER: a

12.25 The first step in the maximal-flow technique is to

(a) pick the node with the maximum flow.
(b) pick any path with some flow.
(c) eliminate any node that has a zero flow.
(d) add a dummy flow from the start to the finish.
(e) none of the above

ANSWER: b

12.26 The shortest-route technique would best be used to

(a) determine the amount of LAN network wiring within a building.
(b) minimize the amount of traffic flow on a busy highway.
(c) determine the path for a truck making frequent but repeatable drops.
(d) none of the above

ANSWER: c

12.27 When using the shortest-route technique, the first step is to

(a) connect the nearest node that minimizes the total distance to the origin.
(b) trace the path from the warehouse to the plant.
(c) determine the average distance traveled from source to end.
(d) find the nearest node to the origin and put a distance box by the node.
(e) none of the above

ANSWER: d

12.28 The shortest route technique might be logically used for

(a) finding the longest time to travel between two points.
(b) finding the shortest travel distance between two points.
(c) finding the most scenic route to allow travel to several places during a trip on spring break.
(d) connecting all the points of a network together while minimizing the distance between them.
(e) none of the above

ANSWER: b

12.29 All the nodes must be connected in which of the following techniques?

(a) shortest-route
(b) maximal-flow
(c) minimal-spanning tree
(d) all of the above

ANSWER: c

12.30 The minimal-spanning technique would best be used

(a) by an architect to lay out corridors between offices in a new office building.
(b) by a telephone company attempting to lay out wires in a new housing development.
(c) by an airline laying out flight routes.
(d) none of the above
(e) all of the above

ANSWER: b

12.31 The maximal-flow technique might be used

(a) to help design the moving sidewalks transporting passengers from one terminal to another in a busy airport.
(b) by someone designing the traffic approaches to an airport.
(c) by someone attempting to design roads that would limit the flow of traffic through an area.
(d) all of the above
(e) none of the above

ANSWER: d

12.32 The second step in the maximal-flow technique is to

(a) pick the node with the maximum flow.
(b) pick any path with some flow.
(c) increase the flow as much as possible.
(d) add capacity to the path with minimum flow.
(e) none of the above

ANSWER: c

12.33 The shortest-route technique would best be used to

(a) plan the routes for a vacation driving tour.
(b) plan the route for a school bus.
(c) determine the path for a truck making frequent runs from a factory to a warehouse.
(d) all of the above
(e) none of the above

ANSWER: d

12.34 When using the shortest-route technique, the second step is to

(a) find the next-nearest node to the origin and put the distance in a box by the node.
(b) trace the path from the warehouse to the plant.
(c) determine the average distance traveled from source to end.
(d) find the nearest node to the origin and put a distance box by the node.
(e) none of the above

ANSWER: a

12.35 The shortest route technique might be logically used for

(a) finding the longest distance to travel between two points.
(b) finding the shortest time to travel between two points.
(c) finding the most scenic route to allow travel to several places during a trip on spring break.
(d) connecting all the points of a network together while minimizing the number of pathways.
(e) none of the above

ANSWER: b

PROBLEMS

12.36 Given the following distances between destination nodes, what is the minimum distance that connects all the nodes?

From	To	Distance
1	2	100
2	3	150
1	3	200

(a) 100
(b) 250
(c) 350
(d) 450
(e) none of the above

ANSWER: b

12.37 Given the following distances between destination nodes, what is the minimum distance that connects all the nodes?

From	To	Distance
1	2	200
1	3	300
2	3	350
2	4	350
3	4	250

(a) 100
(b) 750
(c) 850
(d) 900
(e) none of the above

ANSWER: b

12.38 Given the following distances between destination nodes, what is the minimum distance that connects all the nodes?

	To	Distance
1	2	100
2	4	150
1	3	200
2	3	50
3	4	175
4	5	250
3	5	300

(a) 100
(b) 150
(c) 550
(d) 1225
(e) none of the above
ANSWER: c

12.39 Given the following distances between destination nodes, what is the minimum distance that connects all the nodes?

From	To	Distance
1	2	100
1	3	50
2	3	200
2	5	325
1	4	50
3	4	350
3	5	400
4	5	450

(a) 300
(b) 525
(c) 675
(d) 1925
(e) none of the above

ANSWER: b

12.40 Pipeline fluid flows are indicated below. Determine the maximum flow from Node 1 to Node 3.

From Node	To Node	Fluid Flow
1	3	400
3	1	100
1	2	300
2	1	0
2	3	100
3	2	100

(a) 100
(b) 400
(c) 500
(d) 700
(e) none of the above

ANSWER: c

12.41 Pipeline fluid flows are indicated below. Determine the maximum flow from Node 1 to Node 4.

From Node	To Node	Fluid Flow
1	2	400
2	1	0
1	4	200
4	1	200
1	3	200
3	1	0
2	4	200
4	2	200
3	4	300
4	3	300

(a) 200
(b) 300
(c) 600
(d) 700
(e) none of the above

ANSWER: c

12.42 Find the shortest route from Node 1 to Node 4 using the shortest-route technique.

From Node	To Node	Distance
1	2	100
1	3	200
2	3	50
2	4	350
3	4	250

(a) 250
(b) 400
(c) 450
(d) 600
(e) none of the above

ANSWER: b

12.43 Find the shortest route from Node 1 to Node 4.

From Node	To Node	Distance
1	2	250
1	3	150
1	4	400
2	3	50
2	4	100
3	4	200

(a) 300
(b) 350
(c) 400
(d) 450
(e) none of the above

ANSWER: a

12.44 Find the shortest route from Node 1 to Node 6.

From Node	To Node	Distance
1	2	150
1	3	200
2	4	200
2	3	50
4	6	100
3	4	300
3	5	350
5	6	100

(a) 300
(b) 450
(c) 550
(d) 650
(e) none of the above

ANSWER: b

12.45 Given the following distances between destination nodes, what is the minimum distance that connects all the nodes?

From	To	Distance
1	2	120
2	3	100
1	3	200
2	4	150
3	5	90
4	5	170

(a) 290
(b) 310
(c) 620
(d) 460
(e) none of the above

ANSWER: d

12.46 Given the following distances between destination nodes, what is the minimum distance that connects all the nodes?

From	To	Distance
1	2	200
1	3	300
1	5	400
2	3	300
2	4	400
3	4	200
3	5	200
4	5	100
4	6	300
5	6	400

(a) 1000
(b) 800
(c) 700
(d) 1100
(e) none of the above

ANSWER: d

12.47 Given the following distances between destination nodes, what is the minimum distance that connects all the nodes?

From	To	Distance
1	2	100
1	3	200
2	3	100
2	4	150
2	5	200
3	4	150
3	5	300
4	5	250
4	6	200
5	6	100

(a) 900
(b) 650
(c) 400
(d) 1200
(e) none of the above

ANSWER: b

12.48 Given the following distances between destination nodes, what is the minimum distance that connects all the nodes?

From	To	Distance
1	2	100
1	3	50
2	3	200
2	5	300
1	4	50
3	4	350
3	5	400
3	6	400
4	5	450
4	6	350
5	6	200

(a) 900
(b) 1200
(c) 1100
(d) 700
(e) none of the above

ANSWER: d

12.49 Pipeline fluid flows are indicated below. Determine the maximum flow from Node 1 to Node 4.

From Node	To Node	Fluid Flow
1	3	200
3	1	0
1	2	150
2	1	50
2	3	100
3	2	100
3	4	150
4	3	50

(a) 100
(b) 150
(c) 200
(d) 50
(e) none of the above

ANSWER: b

12.50 Pipeline fluid flows are indicated below. Determine the maximum flow from Node 1 to Node 5.

From Node	To Node	Fluid Flow
1	2	300
2	1	0
1	3	0
3	1	150
1	4	200
4	1	200
1	5	100
5	1	100
2	4	200
4	2	200
3	4	250
4	3	300
3	5	300
5	3	250
4	5	100
5	4	0

(a) 300
(b) 400
(c) 600
(d) 500
(e) none of the above

ANSWER: d

12.51 Find the shortest route from Node 1 to Node 5 using the shortest-route technique.

From Node	To Node	Distance
1	2	200
1	3	150
2	3	50
2	4	300
3	4	250
3	5	200
4	5	150

(a) 350
(b) 400
(c) 450
(d) 600
(e) none of the above

ANSWER: a

12.52 Find the shortest route from Node 1 to Node 5.

From Node	To Node	Distance
1	2	250
1	3	150
1	4	200
2	3	50
2	4	150
3	4	150
3	5	100
2	5	150

(a) 200
(b) 350
(c) 250
(d) 450
(e) none of the above

ANSWER: c

12.53 Find the shortest route from Node 1 to Node 6.

From Node	To Node	Distance

1	2	150
1	3	200
2	3	100
2	4	200
2	5	50
3	4	350
3	5	300
4	6	100
5	6	100

(a) 300
(b) 450
(c) 550
(d) 650
(e) none of the above

ANSWER: a

12.54 Given the following traffic flows, in hundreds of cars per hour, what is the maximum traffic flow from City 1 to City 7?

	From City	To City	Flow

1	1	2	4
2	1	3	8
3	1	5	5
4	2	1	0
5	2	4	3
6	2	5	3
7	3	1	0
8	3	5	3
9	3	6	1
10	4	2	3
11	4	5	3
12	4	7	4
13	5	1	1
14	5	2	0
15	5	3	2
16	5	4	0
17	5	6	1
18	5	7	5
19	6	3	1
20	6	5	4
21	6	7	1
22	7	4	2
23	7	5	1
24	7	6	0

(a) 1200
(b) 1400
(c) 900
(d) 800
(e) none of the above

ANSWER: c

12.55 Solve the minimal-spanning tree problem defined below:

Branch	Start Node	End Node	Cost
1	1	3	5
2	1	2	1
3	2	4	3
4	2	5	4
5	3	4	6
6	4	6	2

(a) total cost = 13
(b) total cost = 15
(c) total cost = 17
(d) total cost = 11
(e) none of the above

ANSWER: b

12.56 Find the shortest route from Node 1 to Node 6.

	From Node	To Node	Distance
1	1	2	100
2	1	4	215
3	2	3	70
4	2	4	200
5	2	5	110
6	3	4	320
7	4	5	200
8	4	6	200
9	5	6	200

(a) total distance = 350
(b) total distance = 410
(c) total distance = 270
(d) total distance = 520
(e) none of the above

ANSWER: b

12.57 Given the following traffic flows, in hundreds of cars per hour, what is the maximum traffic flow from Town 1 to Town 7?

	From Town	To Town	Flow
1	1	2	4
2	1	3	7
3	1	5	9
4	2	1	0
5	2	4	3
6	2	5	5
7	3	1	1
8	3	5	3
9	3	6	4
10	4	2	3
11	4	5	1
12	4	7	0
13	5	1	1
14	5	2	0
15	5	3	3
16	5	4	0
17	5	6	5
18	5	7	1
19	6	3	1
20	6	5	6
21	6	7	3
22	7	4	5
23	7	5	2
24	7	6	0

(a) max flow = 4 units
(b) max flow = 6 units
(c) max flow = 3 units
(d) max flow = 9 units
(e) none of the above

ANSWER: a

12.58 Find the shortest route from Node 6 to Node 1.

	From Node	To Node	Distance
1	1	2	150
2	1	3	200
3	2	3	100
4	2	4	200
5	2	5	50
6	3	4	350
7	3	5	300
8	4	6	100
9	5	6	100

(a) branches 9, 7, and 2
(b) branches 8, 6, and 2
(c) branches 8, 6, 7, and 1
(d) branches 9, 5, and 1
(e) none of the above

ANSWER: d

12.59 Given the pipeline fluid flows indicated below, determine the maximum flow from Node 1 to Node 5.

	From Node	To Node	Fluid Flow
1	1	2	300
2	2	1	0
3	1	3	0
4	3	1	150
5	1	4	200
6	4	1	200
7	1	5	100
8	5	1	100
9	2	4	200
10	4	2	200
11	3	4	250
12	4	3	300
13	3	5	300
14	5	3	250
15	4	5	100
16	5	4	0

(a) 250
(b) 300
(c) 350
(d) 450
(e) none of the above

ANSWER: e

12.60 Find the least amount of cable that will allow Jack's Cable Company to connect the following nodes (houses).

From Node	To Node	Distance
1	2	250
1	3	150
1	4	400
2	3	50
2	4	100
3	4	200

(a) 250
(b) 400
(c) 350
(d) 300
(e) none of the above

ANSWER: d

12.61 Given the following nodes and distances, determine the minimum length of cable necessary to connect all six nodes.

	From Node	To Node	Distance
1	1	2	150
2	1	3	200
3	2	3	100
4	2	4	200
5	2	5	50
6	3	4	350
7	3	5	300
8	4	6	100
9	5	6	100

(a) 200
(b) 300
(c) 400
(d) 500
(e) none of the above

ANSWER: d

12.62 Given the following nodes and distances, determine the minimal length of cable necessary to connect all nodes, using Node 2 as the starting point.

	From	To	Distance
1	1	2	200
2	1	3	300
3	1	5	400
4	2	3	300
5	2	4	400
6	3	4	200
7	3	5	200
8	4	5	100
9	4	6	300
10	5	6	400

(a) 1200
(b) 1100
(c) 900
(d) 700
(e) none of the above

ANSWER: b

12.63 Find the shortest route from Node 1 to each of the other nodes in the transportation network represented below.

Route from Node	Distance
1 to 2	50
1 to 3	100
2 to 3	75
2 to 4	60
3 to 4	80
3 to 5	70
4 to 5	65
4 to 6	200
5 to 6	150

ANSWER:

Node	Shortest Route	Distance
2	1-2	50
3	1-3	100
4	1-2-4	110
5	1-3-5	170
6	1-2-4-6	310

12.64 As part of the planning for a major office development project, it is necessary to install telephone line to the buildings. Information about the project is given below. The distances are provided in hundreds of feet. Which offices should be connected so that total wiring costs (i.e., total distance) are minimized? What is the total length of this?

Building	Distances (100s ft)
1 to 2	4
1 to 4	3
2 to 3	2
2 to 4	4
3 to 5	1
3 to 6	5
4 to 5	3
4 to 7	3
5 to 7	2
6 to 7	6

ANSWER: One solution is to connect 1-4, 2-3, 3-6, 3-5, 4-5, 5-7. Total length = 16.

12.65 Given a network with the following distances:

From Node	To Node	Distance
1	2	4
1	3	1
2	3	2
2	4	3
3	4	6
3	5	4
3	6	2
4	5	7
5	6	5

(a) Determine which nodes should be connected to get the minimum distance from Nodes 1 through 7.
(b) Determine the minimum distance.

ANSWER:

(a) Connect 1-3, 2-3, 2-4, 3-5, 3-6

(b) Minimum distance = 12

12.66 The west-to-east air traffic system passing through the United States can handle aircraft flows with capacities in hundreds of planes per hour as shown. What is the peak air traffic load (From City 1 to City 5) in aircraft per hour that this system can handle?

From	To 1	To 2	To 3	To 4	To 5
City 1	-	2	-	4	-
City 2	1	-	2	3	3
City 3	2	2	-	5	2
City 4	-	-	-	-	3
City 5	-	2	2	1	-

ANSWER: 500 aircraft per hour.

12.67 Find the shortest route from Node 1 to each of the other nodes in the transportation network represented below.

Route From Node	Distance
1 to 2	50
1 to 3	100
2 to 3	75
2 to 5	60
3 to 4	80
3 to 5	70
3 to 6	65
4 to 6	200
5 to 6	150

ANSWER:

Node	Shortest Route	Distance
2	1-2	50
3	1-3	100
4	1-3-4	180
5	1-2-5	110
6	1-3-6	165

12.68 As part of the planning for a major office development project, it is necessary to install telephone lines to the buildings. Information about the project is given below. The distances are provided in hundreds of feet. Which offices should be connected so that total wiring costs (i.e., total distance) are minimized? What is the total length of this?

Buildings	Distances (100s ft)
1 to 2	4
1 to 3	3
1 to 4	2
2 to 4	4
3 to 5	1
3 to 6	5
4 to 5	3
4 to 7	3
5 to 7	2
6 to 7	6

ANSWER: Connect: 1-4, 4-5, 5-7, 3-6, 5-3, and either 4-2 or 1-2. Total length is 1700 feet.

12.69 Brantley College has decided to "wire" its campus. The first stage in this effort is to install the "backbone," i.e., to connect all the buildings. The table below gives the distances between the various buildings on campus in hundreds of feet. How should the buildings be connected to minimize the total length of cable? What length of cable is required?

Distances in Hundreds of Feet						
From	To					
	Building 1	Building 2	Building 3	Building 4	Building 5	Building 6
Building 1		3	7	5	5	4
Building 2			5	2	6	6
Building 3				5	4	4
Building 4					5	3
Building 5						4
Building 6						

ANSWER: Connect: 1-2, 2-4, 4-6, 3-5, 5-6. Total length is 1600 feet.

12.70 Given a network with the following distances:

From Node	To Node	Distance
1	2	4
1	4	1
2	3	2
2	4	3
3	4	6
3	5	4
3	6	2
4	5	7
4	7	5
5	6	5
5	7	8
6	7	4

(a) Determine which nodes should be connected to get the minimum distance flowing from Node 1 through Node 7.
(b) Determine the minimum distance.

ANSWER:

(a) Connect: 1-4, 2-4, 2-3, 3-6, 3-5, 6-7.

(b) Minimum distance = 16.

12.71 The east-to-west (City 5 to City 1) air traffic system passing through the U.S. can handle aircraft flows with capacities in hundreds of planes per hour as shown. What is the peak air traffic load in aircraft per hour from City 5 to City 1 that this system can handle?

From	To City 1	City 2	City 3	City 4	City 5
City 1	-	1	2		-
City 2	2	-	2		2
City 3		2	-		2
City 4	4	3	5	-	1
City 5	-	3	2	3	-

ANSWER: 500 aircraft per hour.

SHORT ANSWER/ESSAY

12.72 List three different network models that can be used to optimize a variety of problems.

ANSWER: minimal-spanning technique, maximal-flow technique, shortest-route technique

12.73 Briefly describe the minimal-spanning technique.

ANSWER: determines the path through a network that connects all the points while minimizing the total distance

12.74 Briefly describe the maximal-flow technique.

ANSWER: determines the maximal flow of any quantity or substance through a network

12.75 Briefly describe the minimal shortest-route technique.

ANSWER: determines the shortest route through a network

CHAPTER 13
Project Management

TRUE/FALSE

13.1 PERT and CPM are quantitative analysis tools designed to schedule and control large projects.

ANSWER: TRUE

13.2 PERT is a deterministic analysis tool allowing for precise times of activities within a project.

ANSWER: FALSE

13.3 PERT had its beginnings in a military department of the United States.

ANSWER: TRUE

13.4 CPM is a probabilistic analysis of managing a project.

ANSWER: FALSE

13.5 An event is a point in time that marks the beginning or ending of an activity.

ANSWER: TRUE

13.6 A network is a graphical display of a project that contains both activities and events.

ANSWER: TRUE

13.7 The optimistic time is the greatest amount of time that could be required to complete an activity.

ANSWER: FALSE

13.8 PERT is a network technique similar to CPM, but PERT allows for project crashing.

ANSWER: FALSE

13.9 The most likely completion time of an activity is used to represent that activity's time within a project.

ANSWER: FALSE

13.10 The expected completion time and variance of an activity is approximated by the normal distribution in a PERT analysis.

ANSWER: FALSE

13.11 PERT was developed for a project for which activity or task times were uncertain.

ANSWER: TRUE

13.12 CPM was developed for use in managing projects that are repeated and about which we have good information about activity or task completion times.

ANSWER: TRUE

13.13 With PERT, we are able to calculate the probability of finishing the project on a particular day.

ANSWER: TRUE

13.14 With CPM, we are able to calculate the probability of finishing the project on a particular day.

ANSWER: FALSE

13.15 A PERT or CPM network shows activities and activity sequences.

ANSWER: TRUE

13.16 One of the most difficult aspects of using PERT is defining the activities so that they have measurable/observable starts and finishes.

ANSWER: TRUE

13.17 Before drawing a PERT or CPM network, we must identify all activities and their predecessors.

ANSWER: TRUE

13.18 The three time estimates employed in PERT are optimistic time, average time, and pessimistic time.

ANSWER: FALSE

13.19 Given the variability of the activity completion time, the original critical path we identify in our PERT analysis may not always be the actual critical path as the project takes place.

ANSWER: TRUE

13.20 In PERT, the earliest start time for an activity is equal to the latest of the earliest finish times of all of its immediate predecessors.

ANSWER: TRUE

13.21 One of the limiting assumptions of PERT is that for any activity to start, all of its immediate predecessors must be complete.

ANSWER: TRUE

13.22 One of the most significant benefits of PERT is that it forces the project manager to sit down and plan the project in great detail – and thus come to an understanding of relationships between the activities.

ANSWER: TRUE

13.23 Slack is the time an activity can be delayed without impacting the completion time of the project.

ANSWER: TRUE

13.24 The variance of the project completion time is equal to the sum of the variances of all the activities.

ANSWER: FALSE

13.25 In PERT, we assume that the project completion time can be modeled by the normal distribution.

ANSWER: TRUE

13.26 One PERT/COST assumption is that money is spent at a constant rate over the time taken to complete an activity.

ANSWER: TRUE

13.27 A limitation of PERT/COST is the assumption that money is spent at a constant rate over the time taken to complete the project.

ANSWER: FALSE

13.28 In CPM, we assume that the cost to complete the task is a linear function of the time to complete the task.

ANSWER: TRUE

13.29 In CPM, crashing an activity that is not on the critical path increases the cost of the project.

ANSWER: TRUE

13.30 One of the drawbacks to using either CPM or PERT to manage an actual project is the amount of data that must be collected over the life of the project to implement either method.

ANSWER: TRUE

13.31 In PERT, the variance in completion time is equal to the variance of the most time consuming activity on the critical path.

ANSWER: FALSE

13.32 Given the assumptions in PERT, the probability that a project will be completed in less time than required by the activities on the critical path is approximately 50%.

ANSWER: TRUE

13.33 Gantt and PERT charts provide the same information, just in different formats.

ANSWER: FALSE

13.34 Gantt charts contain information about the time taken by each activity, but not about the sequential dependencies of the activities.

ANSWER: TRUE

MULTIPLE CHOICE

13.35 The critical path of a network is the

(a) shortest time path through the network.
(b) path with the fewest activities.
(c) path with the most activities.
(d) longest time path through the network.
(e) none of the above

ANSWER: d

13.36 In a PERT network, the earliest (activity) start time is the

(a) earliest time that an activity can be finished without delaying the entire project.
(b) latest time that an activity can be started without delaying the entire project.
(c) earliest time that an activity can start without violation of precedence requirements.
(d) latest time that an activity can be finished without delaying the entire project.
(e) none of the above

ANSWER: c

13.37 Slack time in a network is the

(a) time consuming job or task that is a key subpart of the total project.
(b) shortest amount of time that could be required to complete the activity.
(c) amount of time that you would expect it would take to complete the activity.
(d) amount of time that an activity can be delayed without delaying the entire project.
(e) none of the above

ANSWER: d

13.38 A network activity is a

(a) point in time that marks the beginning or ending of an activity.
(b) time consuming job that is a subpart of the total project.
(c) graphical display of a project.
(d) network technique that allows three time estimates for each activity in a project.
(e) the longest time path through the network.

ANSWER: b

13.39 Which of the following is not a concept associated with CPM?

(a) normal time
(b) probability
(c) normal cost
(d) crash cost
(e) deterministic network

ANSWER: b

13.40 PERT

(a) assumes we do not know ahead of time what activities must be completed.
(b) allows computation of the program's evaluation.
(c) is a network technique that uses three time estimates for each activity in a project.
(d) is a deterministic network technique that allows for project crashing.
(e) none of the above

ANSWER: c

13.41 CPM

(a) assumes we do not know ahead of time what activities must be completed.
(b) is opposite to that of PERT, as it does not consider the network activities.
(c) is a network technique that allows three time estimates for each activity in a project.
(d) is a deterministic network technique that allows for project crashing.
(e) none of the above

ANSWER: d

13.42 Managers use the network analysis of PERT and CPM to help them

(a) derive flexibility by identifying noncritical activities.
(b) replan, reschedule, and reallocate resources such as manpower and finances.
(c) plan, schedule, monitor, and control large and complex projects.
(d) all of the above

ANSWER: d

13.43 The expected time in PERT is

(a) a weighted average of the most optimistic time, most pessimistic time, and four times the most likely time.
(b) the modal time of a beta distribution.
(c) a simple average of the most optimistic, most likely, and most pessimistic times.
(d) the square root of the sum of the variances of the activities on the critical path.
(e) none of the above

ANSWER: a

13.44 Given an activity's optimistic, most likely, and pessimistic time estimates of 4, 5, and 12 days respectively, compute the PERT time for this activity.

(a) 5
(b) 6
(c) 7
(d) 12
(e) none of the above

ANSWER: b

13.45 Given an activity's optimistic, most likely, and pessimistic time estimates of 3, 3, and 9 days respectively, compute the PERT time for this activity.

(a) 3
(b) 4
(c) 5
(d) 9
(e) none of the above

ANSWER: b

13.46 Given an activity's optimistic, most likely, and pessimistic time estimates of 4, 8, and 18 days respectively, compute the PERT time for this activity.

(a) 4
(b) 8
(c) 9
(d) 18
(e) none of the above

ANSWER: c

13.47 Given an activity's optimistic, most likely, and pessimistic time estimates of 2, 10, and 20 days respectively, compute the PERT variance for this activity.

(a) 3
(b) 6
(c) 9
(d) 18
(e) none of the above

ANSWER: c

13.48 Given an activity's optimistic, most likely, and pessimistic time estimates of 4, 12, and 18 days respectively, compute the PERT variance for this activity.

(a) 2.33
(b) 5.44
(c) 8.00
(d) 64.00
(e) none of the above

ANSWER: b

13.49 Given an activity's optimistic, most likely, and pessimistic time estimates of 3, 5, and 15 days, respectively, compute the PERT standard deviation for this activity.

(a) 2
(b) 4
(c) 5
(d) 15
(e) none of the above

ANSWER: a

13.50 Given the following small project, the critical path is _______ days.

Activity	Immediate Predecessor	Time (days)
A	-	10
B	-	4
C	A, B	6

(a) 10
(b) 14
(c) 16
(d) 20
(e) none of the above

ANSWER: c

13.51 Given the following small project, the critical path is _______ days.

Activity	Immediate Predecessor	Time (days)
A	-	8
B	A	4
C	-	10

(a) 4
(b) 10
(c) 12
(d) 22
(e) none of the above

ANSWER: c

The following table provides information for questions 13.52 to 13.55.

Table 13-1		
The following represents a project with known activity times. All times are in weeks.		
Activity	Immediate Predecessor	Time
A	-	4
B	-	3
C	A	2
D	B	7
E	C, D	4
F	B	5

13.52 Using the data in Table 13-1, what is the minimum possible time required for completing the project?

(a) 8
(b) 14
(c) 25
(d) 10
(e) none of the above

ANSWER: b

13.53 Using the data in Table 13-1, what is the latest possible time that C may be started without delaying completion of the project?

(a) 0
(b) 4
(c) 8
(d) 10
(e) none of the above

ANSWER: c

13.54 According to Table 13-1, compute the slack time for activity D.

(a) 0
(b) 5
(c) 3
(d) 6
(e) none of the above

ANSWER: a

13.55 Using the data in Table 13-1, compute the latest finish time for activity E.

(a) 4
(b) 10
(c) 14
(d) 25
(e) none of the above

ANSWER: c

The following table provides information for questions 13.56 to 13.61.

Table 13-2				
The following represents a project with four activities. All times are in weeks.				
Activity	Immediate Predecessor	Optimistic Time	Most Likely Time	Pessimistic Time
A	-	2	8	14
B	-	8	8	8
C	A	6	9	18
D	B	5	11	17

13.56 According to the data in Table 13-2, what is the critical path?

(a) A, B
(b) A, C
(c) B, D
(d) A, B, C, D
(e) none of the above

ANSWER: c

13.57 According to the data in Table 13-2, what is the minimum expected completion time for the project?

(a) 18
(b) 19
(c) 37
(d) 11
(e) none of the above

ANSWER: b

13.58 According to Table 13-2, there are four activities in the project. Assume the normal distribution is appropriate to use to determine the probability of finishing by a particular time. If you wished to find the probability of finishing the project in 20 weeks or fewer, it would be necessary to find the variance and then the standard deviation to be used with the normal distribution. What variance would be used?

(a) 2
(b) 4
(c) 8
(d) 12
(e) none of the above

ANSWER: b

13.59 According to Table 13-2, there are four activities in the project. Assume the normal distribution is appropriate to use to determine the probability of finishing by a particular time. What is the probability that the project is finished in 16 weeks or fewer? (Round to two decimals.)

(a) 0.07
(b) 0.93
(c) 0.43
(d) 0.77
(e) none of the above

ANSWER: a

13.60 Consider a project that has an expected completion time of 60 weeks and a standard deviation of five weeks. What is the probability that the project is finished in 70 weeks or fewer? (Round to two decimals.)

(a) 0.98
(b) 0.48
(c) 0.50
(d) 0.02
(e) none of the above

ANSWER: a

13.61 Your company is considering submitting a bid on a major project. You determine that the expected completion time is 100 weeks and the standard deviation is 10 weeks. It is assumed that the normal distribution applies. You wish to set the due date for the project such that there is an 85 percent chance that the project will be finished by this time. What due date should be set?

(a) 108.0
(b) 110.4
(c) 89.6
(d) 85.0
(e) none of the above

ANSWER: b

The following table provides information for questions 13.62 to 13.64.

Table 13-3							
Activity	Immediate Predecessor	Optimistic	Most Likely	Pessimistic	Average	Standard Deviation	Variance
A	-	4	5	6	5	0.333	0.111
B	-	2	5	8	5	1.000	1.000
C	A	2	8	14	8	2.000	4.000
D	A	5	5	5	5	0.000	0.000
E	B, C	6	7	8	7	0.333	0.111

13.62 According to Table 13-3, there are five activities in a PERT project. Which activities are on the critical path?

(a) A,B,C,D,E
(b) A,C,E
(c) B,D
(d) A,B,C,D
(e) none of the above

ANSWER: b

13.63 According to Table 13-3, there are five activities in a PERT project. What is the variance of the critical path?

(a) 5.222
(b) 4.222
(c) 1.222
(d) 0
(e) none of the above

ANSWER: b

13.64 According to Table 13-3, there are five activities in a PERT project. If the normal distribution were used to find the probability of finishing this project in 24 weeks or fewer, what mean and variance would be used?

(a) 20 and 4.222
(b) 30 and 5.222
(c) 20 and 5.222
(d) 30 and 4.222
(e) none of the above

ANSWER: a

13.65 The critical path of a network is the

(a) path with the least variance.
(b) path with zero slack.
(c) path with the most activities.
(d) path with the largest variance.
(e) none of the above

ANSWER: b

13.66 In a PERT network, the latest (activity) start time is the

(a) earliest time that an activity can be finished without delaying the entire project.
(b) latest time that an activity can be started without delaying the entire project.
(c) earliest time that an activity can start without violation of precedence requirements.
(d) latest time that an activity can be finished without delaying the entire project.
(e) none of the above

ANSWER: b

13.67 Slack time in a network is the

(a) time consuming job or task that is a key subpart of the total project.
(b) shortest amount of time that could be required to complete the activity.
(c) amount of time that you would expect it would take to complete the activity.
(d) amount of time that an activity can be delayed without delaying the project.
(e) none of the above

ANSWER: d

13.68 PERT

(a) assumes we do not know ahead of time the specific amount of time an activity will require.
(b) allows time/cost trade-offs.
(c) is a probabilistic network technique that allows for project crashing.
(d) is a deterministic network technique that allows for project crashing.
(e) none of the above

ANSWER: a

13.69 In PERT,

(a) an activity may not start until all activities scheduled for an earlier time have finished.
(b) we can have no more than two activities taking place simultaneously.
(c) after the project has begun, it is possible for a path other than the original critical path to become critical.
(d) we assume that the time to complete an activity is described by the normal distribution.
(e) none of the above

ANSWER: c

13.70 In PERT,

(a) we assume that all activities are completed.
(b) an activity may not start until all activities scheduled for an earlier time have finished.
(c) we assume that all activities have definable start and end points.
(d) we assume that the time to complete an activity is described by the beta distribution.
(e) all of the above

ANSWER: b

13.71 In PERT, we assume that

(a) the times to complete individual activities are known with certainty.
(b) all activities are carried out by staff from our own organization.
(c) the total cost of a project is independent of the time to complete the project.
(d) the total time to complete all activities on the critical path is described by a normal distribution.
(e) none of the above

ANSWER: d

13.72 CPM

(a) assumes that we know ahead of time all activities that must be completed.
(b) assumes that we may obtain additional resources or move existing resources from one activity to another.
(c) is an important technique when we are planning a project similar to projects we have completed in the past.
(d) is a deterministic network technique that allows for time/cost trade-offs.
(e) all of the above

ANSWER: e

13.73 In contrast to CPM, PERT

(a) is a deterministic network model.
(b) requires all activities to be completed.
(c) assumes that activity costs are unknown.
(d) can identify activities that may, but do not necessarily, lie on the critical path.
(e) all of the above

ANSWER: d

13.74 The expected time in PERT is

(a) greater than the most likely time.
(b) equal to the most likely time.
(c) less than the most likely time.
(d) any of the above
(e) none of the above
ANSWER: d

13.75 Given an activity's optimistic, most likely, and pessimistic time estimates of 3, 7, and 11 days respectively, compute the expected time for this activity.

(a) 5
(b) 6
(c) 7
(d) 12
(e) none of the above

ANSWER: c

13.76 Given an activity's optimistic, most likely, and pessimistic time estimates of 3, 5, and 13 days respectively, compute the expected time for this activity.

(a) 3
(b) 4
(c) 5
(d) 6
(e) none of the above

ANSWER: d

13.77 Given an activity's optimistic, most likely, and pessimistic time estimates of 1, 9, and 17 days respectively, compute the PERT time for this activity.

(a) 4
(b) 8
(c) 9
(d) 18
(e) none of the above

ANSWER: c

13.78 Given an activity's optimistic, most likely, and pessimistic time estimates of 3, 6, and 9 days respectively, compute the PERT variance for this activity.

(a) 3
(b) 1
(c) 9
(d) 6
(e) none of the above

ANSWER: b

13.79 The project described by:

Activity	Immediate Predecessor	Time (days)
A	-	10
B	A	4
C	A	6
D	B, C	7
E	D	5

is best represented by which of the following networks?

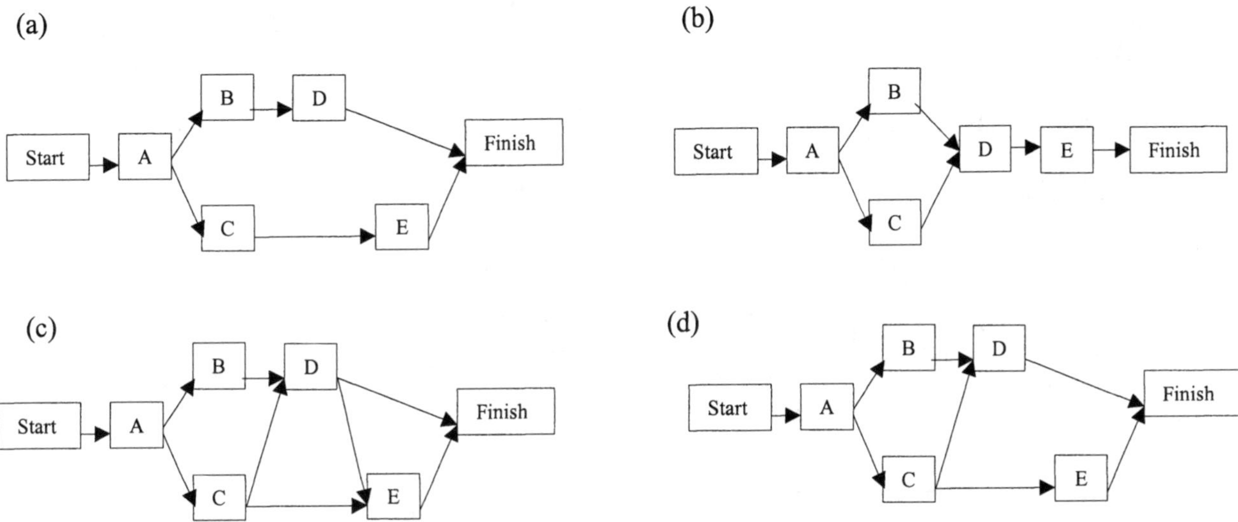

ANSWER: b

13.80 The project described by:

Activity	Immediate Predecessor	Time (days)
A	-	10
B	A	4
C	A	6
D	B, C	7
E	C	5

has a critical path of length of

(a) 21 days
(b) 14 days
(c) 23 days
(d) 32 days
(e) none of the above

ANSWER: c

13.81 The project described by:

Activity	Immediate Predecessor	Time (days)
A	-	6
B	A	2
C	-	8
D	B, C	5
E	D	7

has a critical path of length of

(a) 15 days
(b) 20 days
(c) 17 days
(d) 18 days
(e) none of the above

ANSWER: b

The following table provides information for questions 13.82 to 13.87.

Table 13-4		
The following represents a project with known activity times. All times are in weeks.		
Activity	Immediate Predecessor	Time
A	-	4
B	-	3
C	A	2
D	B	7
E	C, D	4
F	B	5
G	E, F	4

13.82 Using the data in Table 13-4, what is the minimum possible time required for completing the project?

(a) 8
(b) 12
(c) 18
(d) 10
(e) none of the above

ANSWER: c

13.83 Using the data in Table 13-4, what is the latest possible time that C may be started without delaying completion of the project?

(a) 0
(b) 4
(c) 8
(d) 10
(e) none of the above

ANSWER: c

13.84 Using the data in Table 13-4, compute the slack time for activity D.

(a) 0
(b) 5
(c) 3
(d) 6
(e) none of the above

ANSWER: a

13.85 Using the data in Table 13-4, compute the latest finish time for activity E.

(a) 4
(b) 10
(c) 14
(d) 25
(e) none of the above

ANSWER: c

13.86 Using the data in Table 13-4, determine the latest time activity A can be started without delaying the project completion.

(a) 4
(b) 3
(c) 8
(d) 6
(e) none of the above

ANSWER: a

13.87 Using the data in Table 13-4, determine the latest time activity A can be finished and not delay any activity?

(a) 4
(b) 0
(c) 8
(d) 5
(e) none of the above
ANSWER: c

13.88 Consider a project that has an expected completion time of 50 weeks and a standard deviation of 9 weeks. What is the probability that the project is finished in 57 weeks or fewer? (Round to two decimals.)

(a) 0.68
(b) 0.78
(c) 0.22
(d) 0.32
(e) none of the above

ANSWER: b

13.89 Your company is considering submitting a bid on a major project. You determine that the expected completion time is 150 weeks and the standard deviation is 10 weeks. It is assumed that the normal distribution applies. You wish to set the due date for the project such that there is a 95 percent chance that the project will be finished by this time. What due date should be set?

(a) 108.0
(b) 160.4
(c) 166.5
(d) 135.0
(e) none of the above

ANSWER: c

The following table provides information for questions 13.90 to 13.92.

Table 13-5						
Activity	Immediate Predecessor	Time	ES	EF	LS	LF
A	-	4	0	4	7	10
B	-	5	0	5	0	5
C	A	3	4	7	10	13
D	B	8	5	13	5	13
E	B	2	5	7	16	18
F	C, D	3	13	16	15	18
G	C, D	7	13	20	13	20
H	E, F	2	16	18	18	20

13.90 How long could activity E be delayed without delaying the completion of the project?

(a) 7
(b) 16
(c) 11
(d) 18
(e) none of the above

ANSWER: c

13.91 How long could activity F be delayed without delaying the project?

(a) 2
(b) 3
(c) 14
(d) 16
(e) none of the above

ANSWER: a

13.92 What is the minimum possible time required for completing the project?

(a) 14
(b) 18
(c) 17
(d) 20
(e) none of the above

ANSWER: d

The following table provides information for questions 13.93 to 13.95.

Table 13-6

Activity	Immediate Predecessor	Optimistic	Most Likely	Pessimistic	Average	σ	σ^2
A	-	2	3	4	3	0.333	0.111
B	-	2	5	8	5	1.000	1.000
C	A	1	2	9	3	1.330	1.780
D	A	5	5	5	5	0.000	0.000
E	B, C	6	7	8	7	0.333	0.111
F	B	12	12	12	12	0.000	0.000
G	D, E	1	5	9	6	1.333	1.780
H	G, F	1	4	8	4.167	1.167	1.362

13.93 Which activities are part of the critical path?

(a) A, B, E, G, H
(b) A, C, E, G, H
(c) A, D, G, H
(d) B, F, H
(e) none of the above

ANSWER: b

13.94 What is the variance of the critical path?

(a) 5.222
(b) 4.364
(c) 1.362
(d) 5.144
(e) none of the above

ANSWER: d

13.95 If the normal distribution were used to find the probability of finishing this project in 24 weeks or fewer, what mean and variance would be used?

(a) 20.833 and 5.144
(b) 22.167 and 5.144
(c) 23 and 5.222
(d) 20 and 4.222
(e) none of the above

ANSWER: b

The following figure (Fig 13-1) is to be used as data for problems 13.96 – 13.101.

Fig. 13-1

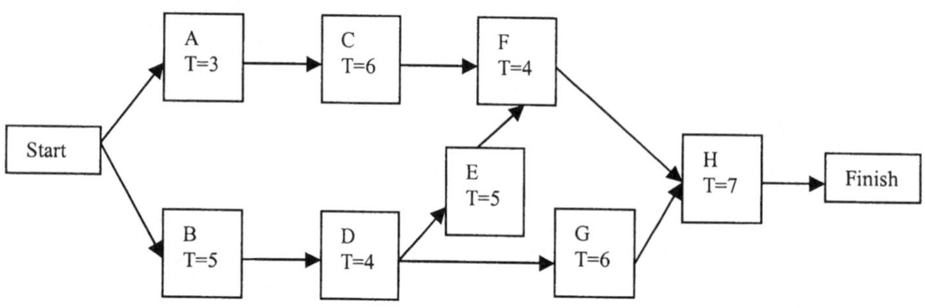

13.96 Given the network in Figure 13-1, the critical path is

(a) A,C,F,H
(b) B,D,E,F,H
(c) A,C,E,G,H
(d) B,D,G,E,F,H
(e) none of the above

ANSWER: b

13.97 Given the network in Figure 13-1, the time to complete those activities on the critical path is expected to be

(a) 20
(b) 22
(c) 25
(d) 26
(e) none of the above

ANSWER: c

13.98 Given the network shown in Figure 13-1, assume that completion of A is delayed by two days. What other activities are impacted?

(a) B
(b) D
(c) E
(d) C
(e) none of the above

ANSWER: d

13.99 Given the network shown in Figure 13-1, assume that completion of B is delayed by two days. What happens to the project?

(a) The critical path is extended by two days.
(b) The start of activity F is delayed by two days.
(c) The start of activity E is delayed by two days.
(d) all of the above
(e) none of the above

ANSWER: d

13.100 Given the network shown in Figure 13-1, assume that the completion of activity C is delayed by four days. What changes will take place?

(a) The critical path will change to: A, C, B, D, E, F, H.
(b) Activity F will be delayed by four days.
(c) Activity E will be delayed by four days.
(d) Activity G will be delayed by four days.
(e) none of the above

ANSWER: e

13.101 Given the network shown in Figure 13-1 and the following information, what is the variance of the critical path?

Activity	Expected time	Variance
A	3	2
B	5	3
C	6	3
D	4	1

E	4	1
F	4	2
G	6	2
H	7	2

(a) 16
(b) 7
(c) 9
(d) 8
(e) none of the above

ANSWER: c

PROBLEMS

13.102 Given:

Activity	Optimistic	Most Likely	Pessimistic
A	3	4	5
B	6	7	14
C	2	3	10
D	0.5	1	1.5
E	6	9	12
F	4	5	12
G	1	3	11

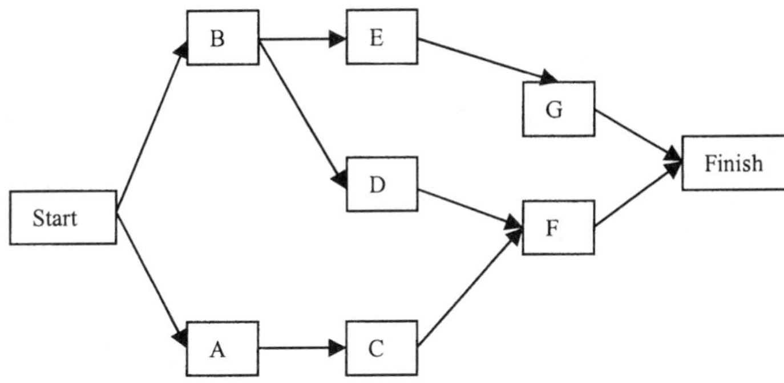

Determine:

(a) the critical path.
(b) the probability that the project will be completed in 22 weeks.

ANSWER:

(a) Critical path is B-E-G. Expected time is 21.
(b) Variance for critical path is 5.56, so standard deviation is 2.357. $P(X \leq 22) = 0.663$

13.103 A small software development project has five major activities. The times are estimated and provided in the table below.

Activity	Immediate Predecessor	a	m	b
A	–	2	5	8
B	–	3	6	9
C	A	4	7	10
D	B	2	5	14
E	C	3	3	3

(a) What is the expected completion time for this project?
(b) What variance would be used in finding probabilities of finishing by a certain time?

ANSWER:

(a) expected completion time = 15 (Activities A-C-E)
(b) variance = 1 + 1 + 0 = 2

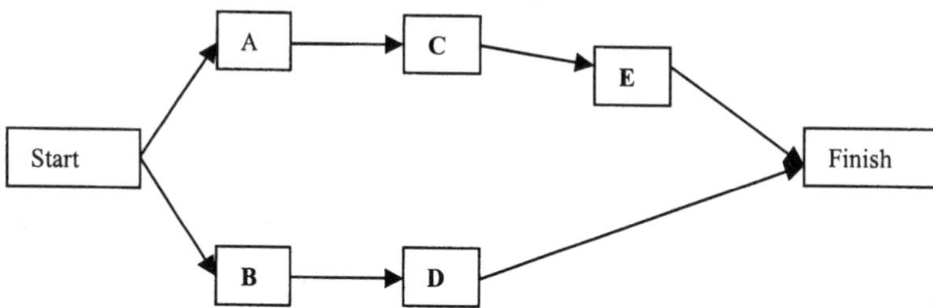

13.104 Development of a new deluxe version of a particular software product is being considered. The activities necessary for the completion of this are listed in the table below.

Activity	Normal Time	Crash Time	Normal Cost	Crash Cost	Immediate Predecessor
A	4	3	2000	2600	-
B	2	1	2200	2800	-
C	3	3	500	500	-
D	8	4	2300	2600	A
E	6	3	900	1200	B
F	3	2	3000	4200	C
G	4	2	1400	2000	D,E

(a) What is the project completion date?
(b) What is the total cost required for completing this project on normal time?
(c) If you wish to reduce the time required to complete this project by one week, which activity should be crashed, and how much will this increase the total cost?

ANSWER:

(a) Project completion time = 16 (Activities A-D-G)
(b) Total cost = $12,300
(c) Crash D one week at an additional cost of $75

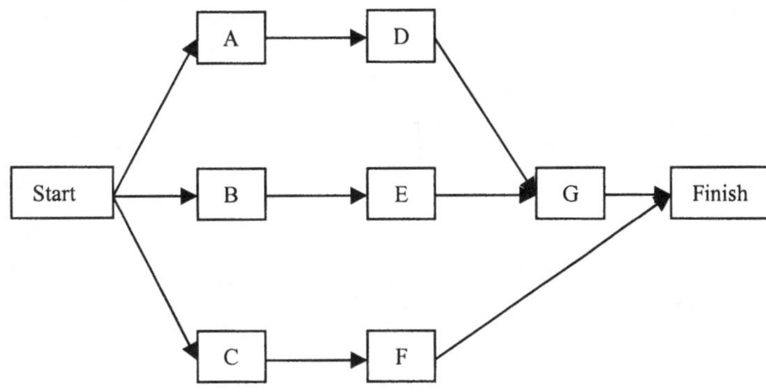

13.105 Draw the PERT network associated with the following activities.

	Immediate Predecessor
A	-
B	A
C	A
D	B
E	B
F	C, E
G	A, D
H	F
I	F
J	G, H, I

ANSWER:

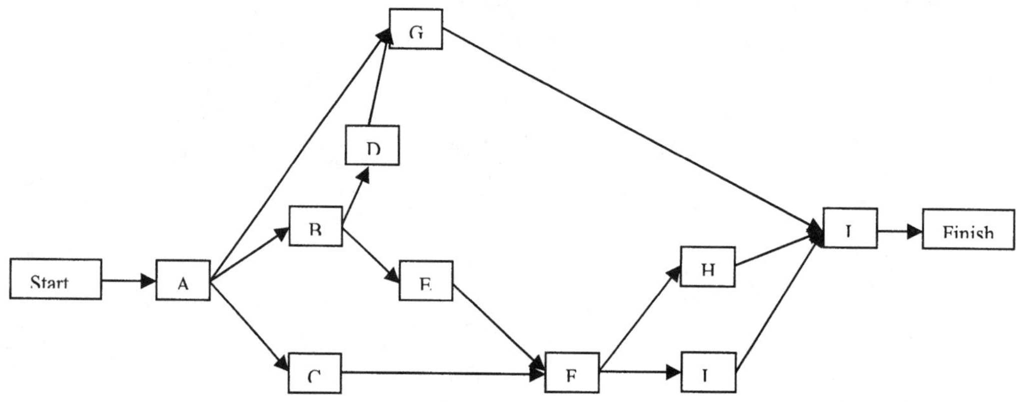

13.106 Given:

Activity	Optimistic	Most Likely	Pessimistic
A	3	4	5
B	6	7	14
C	2	3	10
D	6	9	12
E	4	5	12
F	1	3	11
G	1	2	9
H	2	5	8
I	1	4	7

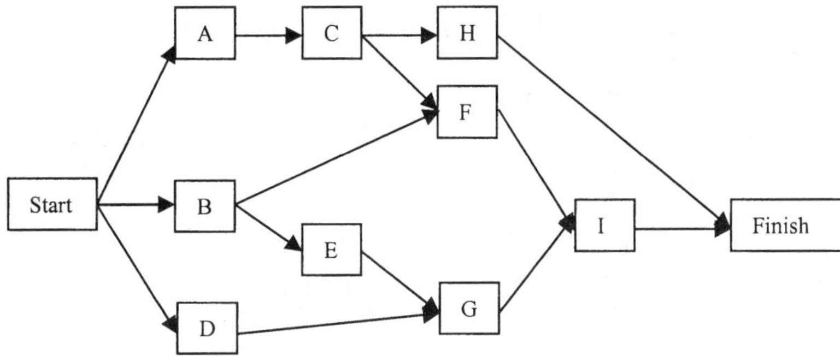

Determine:

(a) the critical path.
(b) the probability that the project will be completed in 22 weeks.

ANSWER:

(a) Critical path is B-E-G-I.
(b) Variance for critical path is 6.33; standard deviation is 2.51. $P(X \leq 22) = 0.65$

13.107 A small software development project has four major activities. The times are estimated and provided in the table below.

Activity	Immediate Predecessor	a	m	b
A	–	2	5	8
B	A	3	6	9
C	A	4	7	10
D	B	2	5	14
E	D	3	3	3
F	C	6	8	10
G	E, F	1	1	1
H	C	6	10	14
I	G, H	3	4	5

(a) What is the expected completion time for this project?
(b) What variance would be used in finding probabilities of finishing by a certain time?
ANSWER:

(a) expected completion time = 26 (Activities A-C-H-I)
(b) variance = 3.88

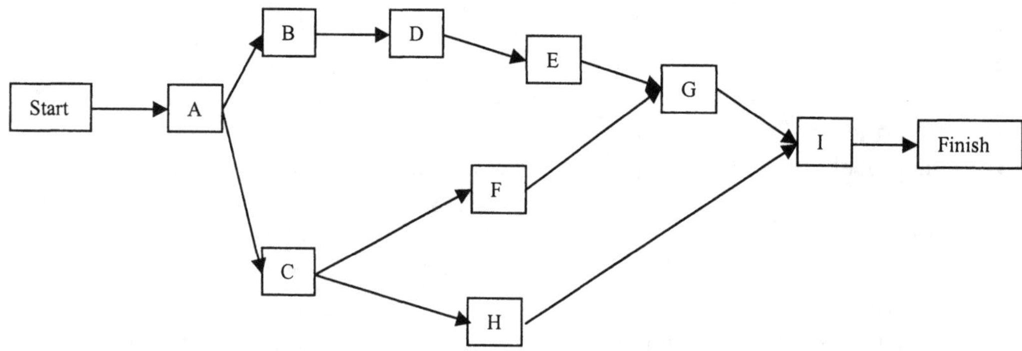

13.108 Development of a new deluxe version of a particular software product is being considered. The activities necessary for the completion of this are listed in the table below.

Activity	Normal Time	Crash Time	Normal Cost	Crash Cost	Immediate Predecessor
A	4	3	2,000	2,600	-
B	5	3	2,200	2,800	-
C	3	3	500	500	-
D	8	4	2,400	2,600	A
E	6	3	900	1,200	B
F	3	2	3,000	4,200	C
G	4	2	1,700	2,000	D,E

(a) If you wish to reduce the time required to complete this project by two weeks, which activity(ies) should be crashed, and how much will this increase the total cost?
(b) What would be the added cost if you wanted to complete the project in the minimum time possible?

ANSWER:

(a) Crash D one week at an additional cost of $50, and crash G one week at an additional cost of $150
(b) Crash D 4 weeks, G 2 weeks, E 3 weeks, A 1 week, and B 1 week, for a total additional cost of $1,700

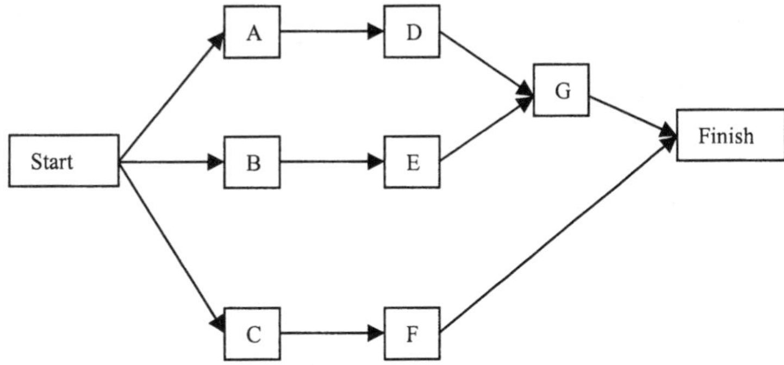

SHORT ANSWER/ESSAY

13.109 PERT is the acronym for what?

ANSWER: Program Evaluation and Review Technique

13.110 In a PERT analysis, how is the optimistic time defined?

ANSWER: the estimated time for an activity, should circumstances go as well as possible (should have a low probability of actual occurrence)

13.111 In a PERT analysis, how is the most likely time defined?

ANSWER: the best estimate of the time it takes to complete an activity

13.112 In PERT analysis, how is the pessimistic activity time defined?

ANSWER: the estimated time for an activity, based on unfavorable conditions (should have a low probability of actual occurrence)

13.113 In PERT/CPM, what is meant by the critical path?

ANSWER: the series of activities in a network that has zero slack or the longest time path through a network

CHAPTER 14
Waiting Lines and Queuing Theory Models

TRUE/FALSE

14.1 A goal of many waiting line problems is to help a firm find the ideal level of services that minimize the cost of waiting and the cost of providing the service.

ANSWER: TRUE

14.2 One difficulty in waiting line analysis is that it is sometimes difficult to place a value on customer waiting time.

ANSWER: TRUE

14.3 The goal of most waiting line problems is to identify the service level that minimizes service cost.

ANSWER: FALSE

14.4 Two characteristics of arrivals are the line length and queue discipline.

ANSWER: TRUE

14.5 Unlimited calling populations are assumed for most queuing models.

ANSWER: TRUE

14.6 An "infinite calling population" occurs when the likelihood of a new arrival does not depend on the number of past arrivals.

ANSWER: TRUE

14.7 On a practical note – if we were to study the waiting lines in a hair salon that had only five chairs for patrons waiting, we would have to use a finite queue waiting line model.

ANSWER: TRUE

14.8 If we are studying the arrival of automobiles at a highway toll station, we can assume an infinite calling population.

ANSWER: TRUE

14.9 When looking at the arrivals at the ticket counter of a movie theater, we can assume an unlimited queue.

ANSWER: TRUE

14.10 Arrivals are random when they are dependent on one another and can be predicted.

ANSWER: FALSE

14.11 On a practical note – if we are using waiting line analysis to study customers calling a telephone number for service, balking is probably not an issue.

ANSWER: FALSE

14.12 On a practical note– if we are using waiting line analysis to study cars passing through a single tollbooth, reneging is probably not an issue.

ANSWER: TRUE

14.13 On a practical note – we should probably view the checkout counters in a grocery store as a set of single channel systems.

ANSWER: TRUE

14.14 A bank with a single queue to move customers to several tellers is an example of a single-channel system.

ANSWER: FALSE

14.15 Service times often follow a Poisson distribution.

ANSWER: FALSE

14.16 An M | M | 2 model has Poisson arrivals exponential service times and two channels.

ANSWER: TRUE

14.17 In a single-channel, single-phase system, reducing the service time only reduces the total amount of time spent in the system, not the time spent in the queue.

ANSWER: FALSE

14.18 The wait time for a single-channel system is more than twice that for a two-channel system using two servers working at the same rate as the single server.

ANSWER: TRUE

14.19 Conducting an economic analysis is an important step in queuing analysis.

ANSWER: TRUE

14.20 Customers waiting time is an important factors in developing a queuing model.

ANSWER: FALSE

14.21 In the multichannel model (M/M/m), we must assume that the average service time for all channels is the same.

ANSWER: TRUE

14.22 If we compare a single-channel system with $\lambda = 15$, to a multichannel system (with three channels) with the service rate for the individual channel of $\lambda = 5$, we will find that the average wait time is less in the single-channel system.

ANSWER: FALSE

14.23 The multichannel system assures random arrivals that follow a normal distribution.

ANSWER: FALSE

14.24 Adding an additional service channel always reduces the average customer wait time and total expected cost.

ANSWER: FALSE

14.25 An automatic car wash is an example of a constant service time model.

ANSWER: TRUE

14.26 If we compare a single-channel system with exponential service rate (λ=5) to a constant service time model (λ=5), we will find that the average wait time in the constant service time model is less than the wait time in the probabilistic model.

ANSWER: TRUE

14.27 In a constant service time model, both the average queue length and average waiting time are halved.

ANSWER: TRUE

14.28 A hospital ward with only 30 beds could be modeled using a finite population model.

ANSWER: TRUE

14.29 A finite population model differs from an infinite population model because there is a random relationship between the length of the queue and the arrival rate.

ANSWER: FALSE

14.30 A transient state is the normal operating condition of the queuing system.

ANSWER: FALSE

14.31 A queue system is in a transient state before the steady state is reached.

ANSWER: TRUE

14.32 Little's Flow Equations are applicable for single-channel systems only.

ANSWER: FALSE

14.33 Little's Flow Equations are advantageous because if one characteristic of the operating system is known, the other characteristics can be easily found.

ANSWER: TRUE

14.34 Using a simulation model allows one to ignore the common assumptions required to use analytical models.

ANSWER: TRUE

14.35 If we are using a simulation queuing model, we still have to abide by the assumption of a Poisson arrival rate, and negative exponential service rate.

ANSWER: FALSE

MULTIPLE CHOICE

14.36 The most appropriate cost to be considered in making a waiting line decision is the

(a) expected service cost.
(b) expected waiting cost.
(c) total expected cost.
(d) expected balking cost.
(e) expected reneging cost.

ANSWER: c

14.37 Assume that we are using a waiting line model to analyze the number of service technicians required to maintain machines in a factory. Our goal should be to

(a) maximize productivity of the technicians.
(b) minimize the number of machines needing repair.
(c) minimize the downtime for individual machines.
(d) minimize the percent of idle time of the technicians.
(e) minimize the total cost (cost of maintenance plus cost of downtime).

ANSWER: e

14.38 Which of the following is usually the most difficult cost to determine?

(a) service cost
(b) facility cost
(c) calling cost
(d) waiting cost
(e) none of the above

ANSWER: d

14.39 In queuing problems, the size of the calling population is important because

(a) we have models only for problems with infinite calling populations.
(b) we have models only for problems with finite calling populations.
(c) the size of the calling population determines whether or not the arrival of one customer influences the probability of arrival of the next customer.
(d) we will have to consider the amount of space available for the queue.
(e) none of the above

ANSWER: c

14.40 Which of the following is not true about arrivals?

(a) Arrivals that are independent of each other are random.
(b) Random arrivals cannot be predicted exactly.
(c) The Poisson distribution is often used to represent arrival pattern.
(d) The exponential distribution is often used to represent arrival patterns.

ANSWER: d

14.41 An arrival in a queue that reneges is one who

(a) after joining the queue, becomes impatient and leaves.
(b) refuses to join the queue because it is too long.
(c) goes through the queue, but never returns.
(d) jumps from one queue to another, trying to get through as quickly as possible.
(e) none of the above

ANSWER: a

14.42 The customer who arrives at a bank, sees a long line, and leaves to return another time is

(a) balking.
(b) cropping.
(c) reneging.
(d) blithering.
(e) none of the above

ANSWER: a

14.43 The behavior of jumping from one queue to another trying to get through as quickly as possible is called

(a) balking.
(b) reneging.
(c) cropping.
(d) blithering.
(e) none of the above

ANSWER: e

14.44 The term queue *discipline* describes the

(a) degree to which members of the queue renege.
(b) sequence in which members of the queue arrived.
(c) degree to which members of the queue are orderly and quiet.
(d) sequence in which members of the queue are serviced.
(e) all of the above

ANSWER: d

14.45 A vendor selling newspapers on a street corner is an example of a

(a) single-channel, multiphase system.
(b) single-channel, single-phase system.
(c) multichannel, multiphase system.
(d) multichannel, single-phase system.
(e) none of the above

ANSWER: b

14.46 Lines at banks where customers wait for a teller window are usually representative of a

(a) single-channel, multiphase system.
(b) single-channel, single-phase system.
(c) multichannel, multiphase system.
(d) multichannel, single-phase system.
(e) none of the above

ANSWER: d

14.47 On arriving at a convention, if a person must first line up to register at a table, then proceed to a table to gather information, then pay at another single table, this is an example of a

(a) single-channel, multiphase system.
(b) single-channel, single-phase system.
(c) multichannel, multiphase system.
(d) multichannel, single-phase system.
(e) none of the above

ANSWER: a

14.48 A single automatic car wash with one bay and a cycle time of 2.5 minutes is what type of model?

(a) M | M | 1
(b) M | M | 2
(c) M | D | 1
(d) M | D | 2
(e) none of the above

ANSWER: c

14.49 Which of the following is not an assumption in common queuing mathematical models?

(a) Arrivals come from an infinite, or very large, population.
(b) Arrivals are Poisson distributed.
(c) Arrivals are treated on a first-in, first-out basis and do not balk or renege.
(d) Service rates follow the normal distribution.
(e) The average service rate is faster than the average arrival rate.

ANSWER: d

14.50 The *utilization factor* is defined as the

(a) percent of time the system is idle.
(b) average percent of time the customers wait in line.
(c) average time the service system is open.
(d) percent of time that a single customer is in the system.
(e) none of the above

ANSWER: e

14.51 A suburban specialty restaurant has developed a single drive-thru window. Customers order, pay, and pick up their food at the same window. Arrivals follow a Poisson distribution, while service times follow an exponential distribution. If the average number of arrivals is 6 per hour and the service rate is 2 every 15 minutes, what is the average number of customers in the system?

(a) 0.50
(b) 4.00
(c) 2.25
(d) 3.00
(e) none of the above

ANSWER: d

14.52 A suburban specialty restaurant has developed a single drive-thru window. Customers order, pay, and pick up their food at the same window. Arrivals follow a Poisson distribution while service times follow an exponential distribution. If the average number of arrivals is 6 per hour and the service rate is 2 every 15 minutes, what is the average number of customers waiting in line behind the person being served?

(a) 0.50
(b) 0.75
(c) 2.25
(d) 3.00
(e) none of the above

ANSWER: c

14.53 A suburban specialty restaurant has developed a single drive-thru window. Customers order, pay, and pick up their food at the same window. Arrivals follow a Poisson distribution while service times follow an exponential distribution. If the average number of arrivals is 6 per hour and the service rate is 2 every 15 minutes, what proportion of the time is the server busy?

(a) 0.25
(b) 0.50
(c) 0.75
(d) 2.25
(e) 3.00

ANSWER: c

14.54 A suburban specialty restaurant has developed a single drive-thru window. Customers order, pay, and pick up their food at the same window. Arrivals follow a Poisson distribution while service times follow an exponential distribution. If the average number of arrivals is 6 per hour and the service rate is 2 every 15 minutes, how much time will elapse from the time a customer enters the line until he/she leaves the restaurant?

(a) 0.25
(b) 0.50
(c) 0.75
(d) 2.25
(e) 3.00

ANSWER: b

14.55 Customers enter the waiting line at a cafeteria on a first-come, first-served basis. The arrival rate follows a Poisson distribution, while service times follow an exponential distribution. If the average number of arrivals is four per minute and the average service rate of a single server is seven per minute, what is the average number of customers in the system?

(a) 0.43
(b) 1.67
(c) 0.57
(d) 1.33
(e) none of the above
ANSWER: d

14.56 Customers enter the waiting line at a cafeteria on a first-come, first-served basis. The arrival rate follows a Poisson distribution, while service times follow an exponential distribution. If the average number of arrivals is four per minute and the average service rate of a single server is seven per minute, what is the average number of customers waiting in line behind the person being served?

(a) 0.76
(b) 0.19
(c) 1.33
(d) 1.67
(e) none of the above
ANSWER: a

14.57 Customers enter the waiting line to pay for food as they leave a cafeteria on a first-come, first-served basis. The arrival rate follows a Poisson distribution, while service times follow an exponential distribution. If the average number of arrivals is four per minute and the average service rate of a single server is seven per minute, what proportion of the time is the server busy?

(a) 0.43
(b) 0.57
(c) 0.75
(d) 0.25
(e) 0.33

ANSWER: b

14.58 Customers enter the waiting line to pay for food as they leave a cafeteria on a first-come, first-served basis. The arrival rate follows a Poisson distribution, while service times follow an exponential distribution. If the average number of arrivals is four per minute and the average service rate of a single server is seven per minute, on average, how much time will elapse from the time a customer enters the line until he/she leaves the cafeteria?

(a) 0.67 minutes
(b) 0.50 minutes
(c) 0.75 minutes
(d) 0.33 minutes
(e) 1.33minutes

ANSWER: d

14.59 At a local fast-food joint, cars arrive randomly at a rate of 12 every 30 minutes. The fast food joint takes an average of 2 minutes to serve each arrival. The utilization factor for this system is

(a) 0.467.
(b) 0.547.
(c) 0.800.
(d) 0.133.
(e) none of the above

ANSWER: c

14.60 At a local fast food joint, cars arrive randomly at a rate of 12 every 30 minutes. Service times are random (exponential) and average 2 minutes per arrival. The average time in the queue for each arrival is

(a) 2 minutes.
(b) 4 minutes.
(c) 6 minutes.
(d) 8 minutes.
(e) 10 minutes.

ANSWER: d

14.61 If the arrival rate and service times are kept constant and the system is changed from a single-channel to a two-channel system, then the average time an arrival will spend being serviced (W) is

(a) increased by 50 percent.
(b) reduced by 50 percent.
(c) exactly doubled.
(d) the same.
(e) none of the above

ANSWER: d

14.62 Customers arrive at the local gas station at the rate of 40 per hour. Due to unfortunate circumstances, there is only one pump available. What service rate is necessary to keep the average wait time less than 5 minutes?

(a) $\cong$ 45 per hour
(b) $\cong$ 47 per hour
(c) $\cong$ 49 per hour
(d) $\cong$ 50 per hour
(e) none of the above

ANSWER: d

14.63 Which of the following is the correct equation for total cost?

(a) mCs + λWCw
(b) mCw + λWCs
(c) mCs + λWqCw
(d) $mC_w + \lambda W_q C_s$
(e) None of the above

ANSWER: c

14.64 For a local hardware store, the total service cost is $10 per hour per employee and the waiting cost is $8 per hour per customer. Customers arrive at a rate of 20 per hour. On average a customer waits a total of 6 minutes. If a single clerk is employed, what is the total service cost?

(a) $26.00
(b) $106.00
(c) $16.00
(d) $10.60
(e) none of the above

ANSWER: a

14.65 For a local hardware store, the total service cost is $10 per hour per employee and the waiting cost is $8 per hour per customer. Customers arrive at a rate of 20 per hour. On average, a customer waits a total of 6 minutes. How many clerks should the hardware store employ?

(a) one
(b) two
(c) three
(d) four
(e) five

ANSWER: a

14.66 A post office has a single line for customers waiting for the next available postal clerk. There are two postal clerks who work at the same rate. The arrival rate of customers follows a Poisson distribution, while the service time follows an exponential distribution. The average arrival rate is three per minute and the average service rate is two per minute for each of the two clerks. What is the average length of the line?

(a) 3.429
(b) 1.929
(c) 1.143
(d) 0.643
(e) none of the above

ANSWER: b

14.67 A post office has a single line for customers waiting for the next available postal clerk. There are two postal clerks who work at the same rate. The arrival rate of customers follows a Poisson distribution, while the service time follows an exponential distribution. The average arrival rate is three per minute and the average service rate is two per minute for each of the two clerks. How long does the average person spend waiting for a clerk?

(a) 3.429
(b) 1.929
(c) 1.143
(d) 0.643
(e) none of the above
ANSWER: d

14.68 A post office has a single line for customers waiting for the next available postal clerk. There are two postal clerks who work at the same rate. The arrival rate of customers follows a Poisson distribution, while the service time follows an exponential distribution. The average arrival rate is three per minute and the average service rate is two per minute for each of the two clerks. What proportion of time are both clerks idle?

(a) 0.643
(b) 0.250
(c) 0.750
(d) 0.143
(e) none of the above
ANSWER: b

Table 14-1	
M/M/2	
Mean Arrival Rate:	9 occurrences per minute
Mean Service Rate:	7 occurrences per minute
Number of Servers:	2
Queue Statistics:	
Mean Number of Units in the System:	2.191
Mean Number of Units in the Queue:	0.905
Mean Time in the System:	14.609 minutes
Mean Time in the Queue:	6.037 minutes
Service Facility Utilization Factor:	0.643
Probability of No Units in System:	0.217

14.69 According to the information provided in Table 14-1, on average, how many units are in the line?

(a) 0.643
(b) 2.191
(c) 2.307
(d) 0.217
(e) 0.905

ANSWER: e

14.70 According to the information provided in Table 14-1, what proportion of time is at least one server busy?

(a) 0.643
(b) 0.905
(c) 0.783
(d) 0.091
(e) none of the above

ANSWER: c

14.71 Using the information provided in Table 14-1 and counting each person being served and the people in line, on average, how many people would be in this system?

(a) 0.905
(b) 2.191
(c) 6.037
(d) 14.609
(e) none of the above

ANSWER: b

14.72 According to the information provided in Table 14-1, what is the average time spent by a person in this system?

(a) 0.905 minutes
(b) 2.191 minutes
(c) 6.037 minutes
(d) 14.609 minutes
(e) none of the above

ANSWER: d

14.73 According to the information provided in Table 14-1, what percentage of the total available service time is being used?

(a) 90.5%
(b) 21.7%
(c) 64.3%
(d) It could be any of the above, depending on other factors.
(e) none of the above

ANSWER: c

14.74 Cars arrive at a local JLUBE franchise at the rate of 1 every 12 minutes. Service times are exponentially distributed with an average of 15 minutes. Jack Burns, the JLUBE owner, has decided to open a second work bay, i.e., make the shop into a two-channel system. Under this new scheme, the average customer will wait in line

(a) $\cong$ 9.6 minutes.
(b) $\cong$ 2.5 minutes.
(c) $\cong$ 24.6 minutes.
(d) $\cong$ 2.1 minutes.
(e) none of the above

ANSWER: a

14.75 Cars arrive at a local JLUBE franchise at the rate of 1 every 12 minutes. Service times are exponentially distributed with an average of 15 minutes. Jack Burns, the JLUBE owner, has decided to open a second work bay, i.e., make the shop into a two-channel system. Under this new scheme, the total time an average customer spends in the system will be

(a) $\cong$ 37 minutes.
(b) $\cong$ 2.1 minutes.
(c) $\cong$ 9.6 minutes.
(d) $\cong$ 24.6 minutes.

ANSWER: d

Table 14-2	
M/M/2	
Mean Arrival Rate:	5 occurrences per minute
Mean Service Rate:	3 occurrences per minute
Number of Servers:	2
Queue Statistics:	
Mean Number of Units in the System:	5.455
Mean Number of Units in the Queue:	3.788
Mean Time in the System:	1.091 minutes
Mean Time in the Queue:	0.758 minutes
Service Facility Utilization Factor:	0.833
Probability of No Units in System:	0.091

14.76 According to the information provided in Table 14-2, which presents a queuing problem solution, on average, how many units are in the line?

(a) 5.455
(b) 3.788
(c) 1.091
(d) 0.758
(e) 0.833

ANSWER: b

14.77 According to the information provided in Table 14-2, which presents a queuing problem solution, what proportion of time is at least one server busy?

(a) 0.833
(b) 0.758
(c) 0.091
(d) 0.909
(e) none of the above

ANSWER: d

14.78 According to the information provided in Table 14-2, which presents a queuing problem solution, there are two servers in this system. Counting each person being served and the people in line, on average, how many people would be in this system?

(a) 5.455
(b) 3.788
(c) 9.243
(d) 10.900
(e) none of the above

ANSWER: a

Table 14-3	
M/M/3:	
Mean Arrival Rate:	4 occurrences per hour
Mean Service Rate:	2 occurrences per hour
Number of Servers:	3
Queue Statistics:	
Mean Number of Units in the System:	2.889
Mean Number of Units in the Queue:	0.889
Mean Time in the System:	0.722 minutes
Mean Time in the Queue:	0.222 minutes
Service Facility Utilization Factor:	0.667
Probability of No Units in System:	0.111

14.79 According to the information provided in Table 14-3, which presents a queuing problem solution, what proportion of time is the system totally empty?

(a) 0.111
(b) 0.333
(c) 0.889
(d) 0.667
(e) none of the above

ANSWER: a

14.80 According to the information provided in Table 14-3, which presents a queuing problem solution, on average, how long does each customer spend waiting in line?

(a) 0.333 minutes
(b) 0.889 minutes
(c) 0.222 minutes
(d) 0.722 minutes
(e) 0.111 minutes

ANSWER: c

14.81 According to the information provided in Table 14-3, which presents a queuing problem solution what is the utilization rate of the service facility?

(a) 0.111
(b) 0.889
(c) 0.222
(d) 0.722
(e) 0.667

ANSWER: e

14.82 If the arrival rate and service times are kept constant and the system is changed from a two-channel system to a single-channel system, then the average time an arrival will spend in the waiting line is

(a) decreased.
(b) increased.
(c) exactly doubled.
(d) the same as before.
(e) It could be any of the above, depending on other parameters of the problem.

ANSWER: b

14.83 If everything else remains constant, including the mean arrival rate and service rate, except that the service time becomes constant instead of exponential,

(a) the average queue length will be halved.
(b) the average waiting time will be doubled.
(c) the average queue length will be doubled.
(d) There is not enough information to know what will happened to the queue length and waiting time.
(d) none of the above

ANSWER: a

14.84 At an automatic car wash, cars arrive randomly at a rate of 7 cars every 30 minutes. The car wash takes exactly 4 minutes (this is constant). On average, what would the length of the line be?

(a) 8.171
(b) 7.467
(c) 6.533
(d) 0.467
(e) none of the above

ANSWER: c

14.85 At an automatic car wash, cars arrive randomly at a rate of 7 every 30 minutes. The car wash takes exactly 4 minutes (this is constant). On average, how long would each car spend at the car wash?

(a) 28 minutes
(b) 32 minutes
(c) 17 minutes
(d) 24 minutes
(e) none of the above

ANSWER: b

14.86 At an automatic car wash, cars arrive randomly at a rate of 7 every 30 minutes. The car wash takes exactly 4 minutes (this is constant). On average, how long would each driver have to wait before receiving service?

(a) 28 minutes
(b) 32 minutes
(c) 17 minutes
(d) 24 minutes
(e) none of the above

ANSWER: a

14.87 At an automatic car wash, cars arrive randomly at a rate of 7 every 30 minutes. The car wash takes exactly 4 minutes (this is constant). On average, how many customers would be at the car wash (waiting in line or being serviced)?

(a) 8.171
(b) 7.467
(c) 6.533
(d) 0.467
(e) none of the above

ANSWER: b

14.88 At an automatic car wash, cars arrive randomly at a rate of 7 every 30 minutes. The car wash takes exactly 4 minutes (this is constant). The utilization factor for this system is

(a) 0.467.
(b) 0.533.
(c) 1.000.
(d) 0.933.
(e) none of the above

ANSWER: d

14.89 At a local fast food joint, cars arrive randomly at a rate of 12 every 30 minutes. The fast food joint takes exactly 2 minutes (this is constant). The average total time in the system is

(a) 5.4 minutes.
(b) 6.0 minutes.
(c) 8.0 minutes.
(d) 2.5 minutes.
(e) none of the above

ANSWER: b

Table 14-4	
M/D/1	
Mean Arrival Rate:	3 occurrences per minute
Constant Service Rate:	4 occurrences per minute
Queue Statistics:	
Mean Number of Units in the System:	1.875
Mean Number of Units in the Queue:	1.125
Mean Time in the System:	0.625 minutes
Mean Time in the Queue:	0.375 minutes
Service Facility Utilization Factor:	0.750
Probability of No Units in System:	0.250

14.90 According to the information provided in Table 14-4, which presents a queuing problem solution for a queuing problem with a constant service rate, on average, how much time is spent waiting in line?

(a) 1.875 minutes
(b) 1.125 minutes
(c) 0.625 minutes
(d) 0.375 minutes
(e) none of the above

ANSWER: d

14.91 According to the information provided in Table 14-4, which presents a queuing problem solution for a queuing problem with a constant service rate, on average, how many customers are in the system?

(a) 1.875
(b) 1.125
(c) 0.625
(d) 0.375
(e) none of the above

ANSWER: a

14.92 According to the information provided in Table 14-4, which presents a queuing problem solution for a queuing problem with a constant service rate, on average, how many customers arrive per time period?

(a) 3
(b) 4
(c) 1.875
(d) 1.125
(e) none of the above

ANSWER: a

14.93 According to Table 14-4, which presents a queuing problem with a constant service rate, on average, how many minutes does a customer spend in the service facility?

(a) 0.375 minutes
(b) 4 minutes
(c) 0.625 minutes
(d) 0.25 minutes
(e) none of the above

ANSWER: c

Table 14-5	
M/D/1	
Mean Arrival Rate:	5 occurrences per minute
Constant Service Rate:	7 occurrences per minute
Queue Statistics:	
Mean Number of Units in the System:	1.607
Mean Number of Units in the Queue:	0.893
Mean Time in the System:	0.321 minutes
Mean Time in the Queue:	0.179 minutes
Service Facility Utilization Factor:	0.714

14.94 According to the information provided in Table 14-5, which presents the solution for a queuing problem with a constant service rate, on average, how much time is spent waiting in line?

(a) 1.607 minutes
(b) 0.714 minutes
(c) 0.179 minutes
(d) 0.893 minutes
(e) none of the above

ANSWER: c

14.95 According to the information provided in Table 14-5, which presents the solution for a queuing problem with a constant service rate, on average, how many customers are in the system?

(a) 0.893
(b) 0.714
(c) 1.607
(d) 0.375
(e) none of the above

ANSWER: c

14.96 According to the information provided in Table 14-5, which presents a queuing problem solution for a queuing problem with a constant service rate, on average, how many customers arrive per time period?

(a) 5
(b) 7
(c) 1.607
(d) 0.893
(e) none of the above

ANSWER: a

14.97 According to the information provided in Table 14-5, which presents the solution for a queuing problem with a constant service rate, on average, how many minutes does a customer spend in the system?

(a) 0.893 minutes
(b) 0.321 minutes
(c) 0.714 minutes
(d) 1.607 minutes
(e) none of the above

ANSWER: b

14.98 According to the information provided in Table 14-5, which presents the solution for a queuing problem with a constant service rate, what percentage of available service time is actually used?

(a) 0.217
(b) 0.643
(c) 0.321
(d) 0.179
(e) none of the above

ANSWER: e

14.99 According to the information provided in Table 14-5, which presents the solution for a queuing problem with a constant service rate, the probability that the server is idle is

(a) 0.217.
(b) 0.643.
(c) 0.286.
(d) 0.714.
(e) none of the above

ANSWER: c

14.100 The school of business has 3 fax machines. The toner in each machine needs to be changed after about 5 hours of use. There is one unit secretary who is responsible for the fax machine maintenance. It takes him 15 minutes to replace the toner cartridge. What is the probability the system is empty?

(a) 1.1500
(b) 1.1658
(c) .8578
(d) .8696
(e) none of the above

ANSWER: c

14.101 The school of business has 3 fax machines. The toner in each machine needs to be changed after about 5 hours of use. There is one unit secretary who is responsible for the fax machine maintenance. It takes him 15 minutes to replace the toner cartridge. What is the average number of fax machines in the queue?

(a) 1.1658 fax machines
(b) 2.9904 fax machines
(c) .1563 fax machines
(d) .0142 fax machines
(e) none of the above

ANSWER: d

14.102 The school of business has 3 fax machines. The toner in each machine needs to be changed after about 5 hours of use. There is one unit secretary who is responsible for the fax machine maintenance. It takes him 15 minutes to replace the toner cartridge. What is the average number of fax machines in the system?

(a) .0142 fax machines
(b) .1563 fax machines
(c) .0249 fax machines
(d) .2749 fax machines
(e) none of the above

ANSWER: b

14.103 The school of business has 3 fax machines. The toner in each machine needs to be changed after about 5 hours of use. There is one unit secretary who is responsible for the fax machine maintenance. It takes him 15 minutes to replace the toner cartridge. What is the average waiting time in the queue?

(a) .0142 hours
(b) .1563 hours
(c) .0249 hours
(d) .2749 hours
(e) none of the above

ANSWER: c

14.104 The school of business has 3 fax machines. The toner in each machine needs to be changed after about 5 hours of use. There is one unit secretary who is responsible for the fax machine maintenance. It takes him 15 minutes to replace the toner cartridge. What is the average time spent in the system?

a) .0142 hours
b) .1563 hours
c) .0249 hours
d) .2749 hours
e) none of the above

ANSWER: d

14.105 The school of business has 3 fax machines. The toner in each machine needs to be changed after about 5 hours of use. There is one unit secretary who is responsible for the fax machine maintenance. It takes him 15 minutes to replace the toner cartridge. What is the probability that 2 fax machines need toner at the same time?

a) .8576
b) .1286
c) .0129
d) .1415
e) none of the above

ANSWER: c

PROBLEMS

14.106 A new shopping mall is considering setting up an information desk manned by one employee. Based upon information obtained from similar information desks, it is believed that people will arrive at the desk at the rate of 15 per hour. It takes an average of two minutes to answer a question. It is assumed that arrivals are Poisson and answer times are exponentially distributed.

(a) Find the probability that the employee is idle.
(b) Find the proportion of time that the employee is busy.
(c) Find the average number of people receiving and waiting to receive information.
(d) Find the average number of people waiting in line to get information.
(e) Find the average time a person seeking information spends at the desk.
(f) Find the expected time a person spends waiting in line to have his question answered.

ANSWER:

(a) $P_o = 0.50$
(b) $\rho = 0.50$
(c) $L = 1$
(d) $L_q = 0.50$
(e) $W = 0.0667$ hours
(f) $W_q = 0.0333$ hours

14.107 Sam the Vet is running a rabies vaccination clinic for dogs at the local grade school. Sam can vaccinate a dog every 3 minutes. It is estimated that the dogs will arrive independently and randomly throughout the day at a rate of 1 dog every 6 minutes, according to a Poisson distribution. Also assume that Sam's vaccinating times are exponentially distributed. Find the:

(a) probability that Sam is idle.
(b) proportion of time that Sam is busy.
(c) average number of dogs receiving or waiting to be vaccinated.
(d) average number of dogs waiting to be vaccinated.
(e) average time a dog waits before getting vaccinated.
(f) average amount (mean) of time a dog spends between waiting in line and getting vaccinated.

ANSWER:

(a) $P_o = 0.5$
(b) $\rho = 0.5$
(c) $L = 1$
(d) $L_q = 0.5$
(e) $W_q = 0.05$ hours
(f) $W = 0.1$ hours

14.108 Sam the Vet is running a rabies vaccination clinic for dogs at the local grade school. Sam can vaccinate a dog every 3 minutes. It is estimated that the dogs will arrive independently and randomly throughout the day at a rate of 1 dog every 4 minutes, according to a Poisson distribution. Also assume that Sam's vaccinating times are exponentially distributed. Find the:

(a) probability that Sam is idle.
(b) proportion of time that Sam is busy.
(c) average number of dogs receiving or waiting to be vaccinated.
(d) average number of dogs waiting to be vaccinated.
(e) average time a dog waits before getting vaccinated.
(f) average amount (mean) of time a dog spends between waiting in line and getting vaccinated.

ANSWER:

(a) $P_o = 0.25$
(b) $\rho = 0.75$
(c) $L = 3$
(d) $L_q = 2.25$
(e) $W_q = 0.15$ hours
(f) $W = 0.2$ hours

14.109 A dry cleaner has a single drive-thru window for customers. The arrival rate of cars follows a Poisson distribution, while the service time follows an exponential distribution. The average arrival rate is 20 per hour and the average service time is two minutes.

(a) What is the average number of cars in the line?
(b) What is the average time spent waiting to get to the service window?
(c) What percentage of time is the dry cleaner's drive-thru window idle?
(d) What is the probability there are more than 2 cars at the drive-thru window?

ANSWER:

(a) $L_q = 1.333$
(b) $Wq = 0.0667$ hours (4 minutes)
(c) $P_o = 0.333$
(d) $P_{n>k} = 0.2963$

14.110 A dry cleaner has a single drive-thru window for customers. The arrival rate of cars follows a Poisson distribution, while the service time follows an exponential distribution. The average arrival rate is 20 per hour and the average service time is two minutes.
If the dry cleaner wants to accommodate all of the waiting cars at least 95 percent of the time, how many car-lengths should they make the driveway leading to the window?

ANSWER:

They should make the driveway approximately 6 car-lengths long. Probability of having more than 7 cars in the system is 0.039.

14.111 Sam the Vet is running a rabies vaccination clinic for dogs at the local grade school. Sam can vaccinate a dog every 3 minutes. It is estimated that the dogs will arrive independently and randomly throughout the day at a rate of 1 dog every 6 minutes, according to a Poisson distribution. Also assume that Sam's vaccinating times are exponentially distributed.
Sam would like to have each waiting dog placed in a holding pen. If Sam wants to be certain he has enough cages to accommodate all dogs at least 90 percent of the time, how many cages should he prepare?

ANSWER:

He needs to prepare 2 cages. The probability of having more than 3 dogs in the system is 6.25 percent while the probability of having more than 2 dogs in the system is 12.5 percent.

14.112 A new shopping mall is considering setting up an information desk operated by two employees. Based on information obtained from similar information desks, it is believed that people will arrive at the desk at the rate of 20 per hour. It takes an average of 4 minutes to answer a question. It is assumed that arrivals are Poisson and answer times are exponentially distributed.

(a) Find the proportion of the time that the employees are busy.
(b) Find the average number of people waiting in line to get some information.
(c) Find the expected time a person spends just waiting in line to have his question answered.

ANSWER:

(a) $\rho = 0.667$
(b) $L_q = 1.0667$
(c) $W_q = 0.0533$ hours

14.113 Cars arrive at a parking lot entrance at the rate of 20 per hour. The average time to get a ticket and proceed to a parking space is two minutes. There are two lot attendants at the current time. The Poisson and exponential distribution appear to be relevant in this situation.

(a) What is the probability that an approaching auto must wait?
(b) What is the average waiting time?
(c) What is the average number of autos waiting to enter the garage?

ANSWER:

(a) Po = 0.50
(b) $W_q = 0.25$ minutes
(c) $L_q = 0.0833$ autos

14.114 Bank Boston has a branch at Bryant College. The branch is busiest at the beginning of the college year when freshmen and transfer students open accounts. This year, freshmen arrived at the office at a rate of 40 per day (8-hour day). On average, it takes the Bank Boston staff person about ten minutes to process each account application. The bank is considering having one or two tellers. Each teller is paid $12 per hour and the cost of waiting in line is assumed to be $8 per hour.

(a) What is the total daily waiting cost for the single teller model?
(b) What is the total daily waiting cost for the two-teller model?
(c) What is the total daily service cost for the single teller model?
(d) What is the total daily service cost for the two-teller model?
(e) Which model is preferred?

ANSWER:

(a) Total wait cost = [(5 * .833 hours) (8)] * 8 hours/day = $266.56
(b) Total wait cost = [(5 * .035 hours) (8)] * 8 hours/day = $11.20
(c) Total service cost = (1 * $12) * 8 hours/day = $96
(d) Total service cost = (2 * $12) * 8 hours/day = $192
(e) Two channel model

14.115 At the start of football season, the ticket office gets busy the day before the first game. Customers arrive at the rate of four every ten minutes. A ticket seller can service a customer in four minutes. Traditionally, there are two ticket sellers working. The university is considering an automated ticket machine similar to the airlines' e-ticket system. The automated ticket machine can service a customer in 2 minutes.

(a) What is the average length of the queue for the in-person model?
(b) What is the average length of the queue for the automated system model?
(c) What is the average time in the system for the in-person model?
(d) What is the average time in the system for the automated system model?
(e) Assume the ticket sellers earn $8 per hour and the machine costs $20 per hour (amortized over 5 years). The wait time is only $4 per hour because students are patient. What is the total cost of each model?

ANSWER:

(a) Lq = 2.844
(b) Lq = 1.6
(c) W = 0.1852 hours or 11.11 minutes
(d) W = 0.1 hours or 6 minutes
(e) Total cost (in-person) = (2 * $8/hour) + (24/hour * .1852 hours) ($4/hour) = $33.78
Total cost (automated) = (1 * $20/hour) + (24/hour * .1 hour) ($4/hour) = $29.60

14.116 A company has 6 computers and one technician to run an automated manufacturing facility. Each of these computers runs an average of 90 minutes without requiring any attention from the technician. Each time the technician is required to adjust a computer, an average of 15 minutes (following an exponential distribution) is required to fix the problem.

(a) On average, how many computers are waiting for service?
(b) On average, how long is a computer out of service?
(c) What is the average waiting time for service?

ANSWER:

The model here is M/M/1 with Finite Source (N=6) and $\lambda = 0.67$/hour and $\mu = 4$/hour
(a) $L_q = 0.862$
(b) W = .54 hours or 32.5 minutes
(c) $W_q = .29$ hours or 17.5 minutes

SHORT ANSWER/ESSAY

14.117 With regard to queue theory, define what is meant by balking.

ANSWER: the situation when arriving customers choose to not enter the queue

14.118 With regard to queue theory, define what is meant by reneging.

ANSWER: the situation when customers in a queue choose to leave the queue before getting service

14.119 What is meant by a single-channel queuing system?

ANSWER: one service facility system fed by one queue

14.120 What is meant by a multichannel queuing system?

ANSWER: more than one service facility system all fed by the same queue

14.121 What is meant by a single-phase system?

ANSWER: Arrivals leave the system after receiving service at only one station.

14.122 What is meant by a multiphase system?

ANSWER: Service is provided at more than one station, one after the other.

CHAPTER 15
Simulation Modeling

TRUE/FALSE

15.1 Simulation of a business or process is generally performed by building a mathematical model to represent the process or system.

ANSWER: TRUE

15.2 Simulation models are designed to generate optimal solutions, which can then be applied to real-world situations.

ANSWER: FALSE

15.3 A major advantage of using simulation techniques is to be able to study the interactive effect of individual components/variables.

ANSWER: TRUE

15.4 One advantage of simulation is that we can investigate the performance of a system without actually designing the system.

ANSWER: FALSE

15.5 One of the major advantages of simulation is "time compression," i.e., the ability to study in a relatively short period, activities that would, in reality, take place over a period of days, months, or even years.

ANSWER: TRUE

15.6 Simulation can sometimes predict problems with a system before they actually happen.

ANSWER: TRUE

15.7 One of the advantages to simulation is that it will usually give us very precise answers to extremely complex problems.

ANSWER: FALSE

15.8 One of the limitations of analytical models is that they typically consider the system only in steady state or "on average."

ANSWER: TRUE

15.9 Most simulations are done to identify minimum cost alternatives.

ANSWER: FALSE

15.10 Simulation models may contain both deterministic and probabilistic variables.

ANSWER: TRUE

15.11 Analytical models are preferable to simulation models in that the analytical model gives more precise results.

ANSWER: FALSE

15.12 Simulation models are limited to using standard probability distributions such as Poisson, exponential, normal, etc.

ANSWER: FALSE

15.13 The Monte Carlo simulation is used with variables that are probabilistic.

ANSWER: TRUE

15.14 When using a random number generator, one should never start in the middle of the table of random numbers.

ANSWER: FALSE

15.15 If we are using a Monte Carlo simulation model, we should expect the model to produce the same results for each set of random numbers used.

ANSWER: FALSE

15.16 Monte Carlo simulation requires that we run the simulation dozens of times with the same set of random numbers to see how the solutions differ as a function of the random numbers used.

ANSWER: FALSE

15.17 The wider the variation among results produced by using different sets of random numbers, the longer we need to run the simulation to obtain reliable results.

ANSWER: TRUE

15.18 Deterministic simulation models are based on the assumption that the product demand follows an exponential distribution and reorder lead time follow a Poisson distribution.

ANSWER: FALSE

15.19 Simulation models are useful for economic order quantity problems with probabilistic demand and lead time.

ANSWER: TRUE

15.20 A flow diagram is helpful in the logical coding procedures for programming a simulation process.

ANSWER: TRUE

15.21 If, in a simple queuing or waiting line problem, we wish to know the maximum likely waiting time, or the maximum likely length of the line, we must use a simulation model.

ANSWER: TRUE

15.22 If, for a simple queuing or waiting line problem, we compare the solution from an analytical model with that from a simulation, we will typically find them to be exactly the same.

ANSWER: FALSE

15.23 The advantage of simulation over queuing or waiting line models is that simulation allows us to relax our assumptions regarding arrival and service distributions.

ANSWER: TRUE

15.24 Simulation models can be classified into two categories: fixed time increment models and future event increment models.

ANSWER: FALSE

15.25 In fixed time increment models, the status of the system is updated at specified time intervals.

ANSWER: TRUE

15.26 Simulation of maintenance problems can help management analyze various staffing strategies based on machine downtime and labor cost.

ANSWER: TRUE

15.27 It is not possible to simulate preventive maintenance policies because of the uncertainty of the future.

ANSWER: FALSE

15.28 Operational gaming involves a single player competing with the computer simulated game.

ANSWER: FALSE

15.29 There are three categories of simulation models: Monte Carlo, operational gaming, and system simulation.

ANSWER: TRUE

15.30 Verification relates to building the right model.

ANSWER: FALSE

15.31 Validation relates to building the right model.

ANSWER: TRUE

15.32 Special purpose simulation languages are more advantageous to use than general purpose languages in simulation models.

ANSWER: TRUE

15.33 For most modern simulation languages, the only probability distributions provided are the Normal, Poisson, and Negative Exponential.

ANSWER: FALSE

MULTIPLE CHOICE

15.34 The following is not an advantage of simulation:

(a) It allows for the study of *what-if* questions.
(b) Each simulation model is unique.
(c) It allows the study of interaction of components or variables to determine which are important.
(d) It allows time compression.
(e) none of the above

ANSWER: b

15.35 Simulation can be effectively used in many

(a) inventory problems.
(b) transportation problems.
(c) maintenance policy problems.
(d) all of the above

ANSWER: d

15.36 The following is not a characteristic of Monte Carlo simulation:

(a) It uses random numbers.
(b) It uses random sampling of a probability distribution.
(c) It evaluates system responses to various policies.
(d) It deals with the dynamics of large organizational systems.
(e) none of the above

ANSWER: d

15.37 In assigning random numbers in a Monte Carlo simulation,

(a) it is important to use a normal distribution for all variables simulated.
(b) it is important to develop a cumulative probability distribution.
(c) it is not important to assign probabilities to an exact range of random number intervals.
(d) all of the above

ANSWER: b

Table 15-1		
A new young mother has opened a cloth diaper service. She is interested in simulating the number of diapers required for a one-year-old. She hopes to use this data to show the cost effectiveness of cloth diapers. The table below shows the number of diapers demanded daily and the probabilities associated with each level of demand.		
Daily Demand	Probability	Interval of Random Numbers
5	0.30	01-30
6	0.50	31-80
7	0.05	81-85
8	0.15	86-00
Random numbers for arrivals: 14, 74, 27, 03		

15.38 According to Table 15-1, if the random number 40 were generated for a particular day, what would the simulated demand be for that day?

(a) 5
(b) 6
(c) 7
(d) 20
(e) none of the above

ANSWER: b

15.39 According to Table 15-1, if the random number 96 were generated for a particular day, what would the simulated demand be for that day?

(a) 5
(b) 6
(c) 7
(d) 8
(e) none of the above

ANSWER: d

15.40 According to Table 15-1, what is the cumulative probability that demand is less than or equal to 7?

(a) 0.85
(b) 0.95
(c) 0.80
(d) 0.15
(e) none of the above

ANSWER: a

Table 15-2		
A pharmacy is considering hiring another pharmacist to better serve customers. To help analyze this situation, records are kept to determine how many customers will arrive in any 10-minute interval. Based on 100 ten-minute intervals, the following probability distribution has been developed and random numbers assigned to each event.		
Number of Arrivals	Probability	Interval of Random Numbers
6	0.2	01-20
7	0.3	21-50
8	0.3	51-80
9	0.1	81-90
10	0.1	91-00

15.41 According to Table 15-2, the number of arrivals in any 10-minute period is between 6 and 10, inclusive. Suppose the next three random numbers were 18, 89, and 67, and these were used to simulate arrivals in the next three 10-minute intervals. How many customers would have arrived during this 30-minute time period?

(a) 22
(b) 23
(c) 24
(d) 25
(e) none of the above

ANSWER: b

15.42 According to Table 15-2, the number of arrivals in any 10-minute period is between 6 and 10, inclusive. Suppose the next three random numbers were 20, 50, and 79, and these were used to simulate arrivals in the next three 10-minute intervals. How many customers would have arrived during this 30-minute time period?

(a) 18
(b) 19
(c) 20
(d) 21
(e) none of the above

ANSWER: d

15.43 According to Table 15-2, the number of arrivals in any 10-minute period is between 6 and 10 inclusive. Suppose the next 3 random numbers were 02, 81, and 18. These numbers are used to simulate arrivals into the pharmacy. What would the average number of arrivals per 10-minute period be based on this set of occurrences?

(a) 6
(b) 7
(c) 8
(d) 9
(e) none of the above

ANSWER: b

Table 15.3		
A pawn shop in Arlington, Texas, has a drive-through window to better serve customers. The following tables provide information about the time between arrivals and the service times required at the window on a particularly busy day of the week. All times are in minutes.		
Time Between Arrivals	Probability	Interval of Random Numbers
1	0.1	01-10
2	0.3	11-40
3	0.4	41-80
4	0.2	81-00
Service Time	Probability	Interval of Random Numbers
1	0.2	01-20
2	0.4	21-60
3	0.3	61-90
4	0.1	91-00
The first random number generated for arrivals is used to tell when the first customer arrives after opening.		

15.44 According to Table 15-3, the time between successive arrivals is 1, 2, 3, or 4 minutes. If the store opens at 8:00a.m. and random numbers are used to generate arrivals, what time would the first customer arrive if the first random number were 02?

(a) 8:01
(b) 8:02
(c) 8:03
(d) 8:04
(e) none of the above

ANSWER: a

15.45 According to Table 15-3, the time between successive arrivals is 1, 2, 3, or 4 minutes. The store opens at 8:00a.m. and random numbers are used to generate arrivals and service times. The first random number to generate an arrival is 39, while the first service time is generated by the random number 94. What time would the first customer finish transacting business?

(a) 8:03
(b) 8:04
(c) 8:05
(d) 8:06
(e) none of the above

ANSWER: d

15.46 According to Table 15-3, the time between successive arrivals is 1, 2, 3, or 4 minutes. The store opens at 8:00a.m. and random numbers are used to generate arrivals and service times. The first 3 random numbers to generate arrivals are 09, 89, and 26. What time does the third customer arrive?

(a) 8:07
(b) 8:08
(c) 8:09
(d) 8:10
(e) none of the above

ANSWER: a

15.47 According to Table 15-3, the time between successive arrivals is 1, 2, 3, or 4 minutes. The store opens at 8:00a.m. and random numbers are used to generate arrivals and service times. The first two random numbers for arrivals are 95 and 08. The first two random numbers for service times are 92 and 18. At what time does the second customer finish transacting business?

(a) 8:07
(b) 8:08
(c) 8:09
(d) 8:10
(e) none of the above

ANSWER: c

Table 15-4			
Variable Value		Probability	Cumulative Probability
0		0.08	0.08
1		0.23	0.31
2		0.32	0.63
3		0.28	0.91
4		0.09	1.00
Number of Runs	200		
Average Value	2.10		

15.48 According to Table 15-4, which presents a summary of the Monte Carlo output from a simulation of 200 runs, there are 5 possible values for the variable of concern. If this variable represents the number of machine breakdowns during a day, what is the probability that the number of breakdowns is 2 or fewer?

(a) 0.23
(b) 0.31
(c) 0.32
(d) 0.63
(e) none of the above

ANSWER: d

15.49 According to Table 15-4, which presents a summary of the Monte Carlo output from a simulation of 200 runs, there are 5 possible values for the variable of concern. If this variable represents the number of machine breakdowns during a day, what is the probability that the number of breakdowns is more than 4?

(a) 0
(b) 0.08
(c) 0.09
(d) 1.00
(e) none of the above

ANSWER: a

15.50 According to Table 15-4, which presents a summary of the Monte Carlo output from a simulation of 200 runs, there are 5 possible values for the variable of concern. If this variable represents the number of machine breakdowns during a day, based on this simulation run, what is the average number of breakdowns per day?

(a) 2.00
(b) 2.10
(c) 2.50
(d) 200
(e) none of the above
ANSWER: b

15.51 The use of simulation in competitive situations such as military games and business games is known as

(a) Monte Carlo methods.
(b) operational gaming.
(c) system simulation.
(d) all of the above

ANSWER: b

15.52 The use of simulation to examine corporate operations (industrial dynamics), national economies (econometric models), and urban governments is known as

(a) Monte Carlo methods.
(b) operational gaming.
(c) system simulation.
(d) all of the above
(e) none of the above

ANSWER: c

PROBLEMS

15.53 The number of cars arriving at a self-service gasoline station during the last 50 hours of operation are as follows:

# of Cars Arriving	Frequency
6	10
7	14
8	18
9	8

15.54 The following random numbers have been generated: 44, 30, 26, 09, 49, 52, 33, 89, 21, 37. Simulate 10 hours of arrivals at this station. What is the average number of arrivals during this period?

ANSWER:

# of Cars	Interval of Random Numbers
6	01–20
7	21–48
8	49–84
9	85–00

Arrivals: 7, 7, 7, 6, 8, 8, 7, 9, 7, 7 average number of arrivals = 7.3

15.55 The number of machine breakdowns in a day is 0, 1, or 2, with probabilities 0.6, 0.3, and 0.1, respectively. The following random numbers have been generated: 13, 10, 02, 18, 31, 19, 32, 85, 31, 94. Use these numbers to generate the number of breakdowns for 10 consecutive days. What proportion of these days had at least one breakdown?

ANSWER:

Breakdowns	Interval of Random Numbers
0	01–60
1	61–90
2	91–00

Breakdowns: 0, 0, 0, 0, 0, 0, 0, 1, 0, 2 proportion at least 1 breakdown = 2/10

15.56 A certain grocery store has noted the following figures with regard to the number of people who arrive at its three checkout stands ready to check out, and the time it takes to check out the individuals.

Arrivals/Min.	Frequency	Service Time in Min.	Frequency
0	0.3	1	0.1
1	0.5	2	0.3
2	0.2	3	0.4
		4	0.2

15.57 Simulate the utilization rate of the three checkout stands over four minutes using the following random numbers for arrivals: 07, 60, 49, and 95. Use the following random numbers for service: 77,76, 51, and 16. Note the results at the end of the four-minute period.

ANSWER:

t=	RN=	Arrival #	RN=	Service Time=
0	07	0		
1	60	1	77	3
2	49	1	76	3
3	95	2	51	3
			16	2

Note: the first customer arrives at minute 1 and exits at minute 4; the second customer enters at minute 2 and exits at minute 5. A third and fourth customer enter at minute 3. There is one server open, so customer four will wait for one minute until minute 4 when the first customer exits.

15.58 Average daily sales of a product are 8 units. The actual number of sales each day is either 7, 8, or 9, with probabilities 0.3, 0.4, and 0.3, respectively. The lead time for delivery of this averages 4 days, although the time may be 3, 4, or 5 days, with probabilities 0.2, 0.6, and 0.2. The company plans to place an order when the inventory level drops to 32 units (based on the average demand and average lead time). The following random numbers have been generated: 60, 87, 46, 63 (set 1) and 52, 78, 13, 06, 99, 98, 80, 09, 67, 89, 45 (set 2). Use set 1 of these to generate lead times and use set 2 to simulate daily demand. Simulate 2 ordering periods with this and determine how often the company runs out of stock before the shipment arrives.

ANSWER:	Interval of Random Numbers	Time	Interval of Random Numbers
7	01–30	3	01–20
8	31–70	4	21–80
9	71–00	5	81–00

First order: RN = 60 so lead time = 4 days.
Demand: day 1 8 (RN = 52)
day 2 9 (RN = 78)
day 3 7 (RN = 13)
day 4 7 (RN = 06)

Total demand during lead time = 31. Since the reorder point is 32, there is no stockout.

Second order: RN = 87 so lead time = 5
Demand: day 1 9 (RN = 99)
day 2 9 (RN = 98)
day 3 9 (RN = 80)
day 4 7 (RN = 09)
day 5 8 (RN = 67)

Total demand during lead time = 42. So, the company experienced a stockout during this time.

15.59 The time between arrivals at a drive-through window of a fast-food restaurant follows the distribution given below. The service time distribution is also given in the table below. Use the random numbers provided to simulate the activity of the first five arrivals. Assume that the window opens at 11:00a.m. and the first arrival after this is based on the first interarrival time generated.

Time Between Arrivals	Probability	Service Time	Probability
1	0.2	1	0.3
2	0.3	2	0.5
3	0.3	3	0.2
4	0.2		

Random numbers for arrivals: 14, 74, 27, 03
Random numbers for service times: 88, 32, 36, 24

What times does the fourth customer leave the system?

ANSWER:

Time between Arrivals	Prob.	Interval of Random Numbers	Service Time	Prob.	Interval of Random Numbers
1	0.2	01–20	1	0.3	01–30
2	0.3	21–50	2	0.5	31–80
3	0.3	51–80	3	0.2	81–00
4	0.2	81–00			

First arrival (RN=14) at 11:01. Service time 3 (RN=88). Leaves at 11:04.
Second arrival (RN=74) at 11:04 (3 minutes after 1st). Service time = 2 (RN=32). Leaves at 11:06.
Third arrival (RN=27) at 11:06. Service time = 2 (RN=36). Leaves at 11:08.
Fourth arrival (RN=03) at 11:07. Must wait 1 minute for service to start. Service time = 1 minute (RN=24). Leaves at 11:09.

15.60 Henry has a newspaper stand where he sells papers for $0.50 each. The papers cost him $0.30 each, giving him a 20-cent profit on each one he sells. From past experience, Henry knows that

20% of the time he sells 100 papers
20% of the time he sells 150 papers
30% of the time he sells 200 papers
30% of the time he sells 250 papers

Assuming that Henry believes the cost of a lost sale is 10 cents and any unsold papers cost him $0.30, simulate Henry's profit outlook over 5 days if he orders 175 papers for each of the 5 days. Use the following random numbers: 52, 06, 50, 88, 53.

ANSWER:

DAY	RN	DEMAND	UNSOLD	LOST	PROFIT
1	52	200	0	25	32.50
2	06	100	75	0	–2.50
3	50	200	0	25	32.50
4	88	250	0	75	27.50
5	53	200	0	25	32.50

Average profit = 24.50

15.61 A local computer store is running a sale on the first 99 flat panel monitors sold. There is an equally likely chance of 0–99 units being sold. Each monitor cost $250, and profit is $10 per monitor sold. That is, profit equals –$250 + $10X, where X = the number of monitors sold. The mean amount you would expect to sell is 49.5 units.

(a) Calculate the expected profit.
(b) Simulate the sale of 10 items, using the following double digit random numbers: 47, 77, 98, 11, 02, 18, 31, 20, 32, 90.
(c) Calculate the average profit in (b) above, and compare with the results of (a) above.

ANSWER:

a) expected value = -250 + 10(49.5) = $245
b) –250 + $10(47) = $220
–250 + $10(77) = $520
–250 + $10(98) = $730
–250 + $10(11) = –$140
–250 + $10(02) = –$230
–250 + $10(18) = –$ 70
–250 + $10(31) = $ 60
–250 + $10(20) = –$ 50
–250 + $10(32) = $ 70
–250 + $10(90) = $650

c) The average profit of these simulated sales is $176. If the sample size were larger, we would expect the two values to be closer.

SHORT ANSWER/ESSAY

15.62 Describe the basic concept of simulation models.

ANSWER: To build a mathematical model of a real-life system that attempts to mimic the reality of the real-life system

15.63 List three advantages of simulation techniques.

ANSWER: Simulations are flexible; can analyze large, complex real-world situations; can ask *what-if*?; can avoid tampering with the present system; can study the impact of individual variables on the modeled system, can simulate many time periods quickly; can incorporate any probabilistic distribution

15.64 List three disadvantages of simulation techniques.

ANSWER: Good models can be expensive; models do not generate optimal solutions; humans must generate conditions and constraint information for solutions

15.65 Explain what is meant by a Monte Carlo simulation?

ANSWER: the ability to experiment on the probabilistic elements of a simulation model through random sampling

15.66 Explain what is meant by operational gaming and give one example.

ANSWER: a simulation involving two or more competitors, military games, competing businesses, specific professional football strategies, etc.

15.67 Explain what is meant by systems simulations and give one example.

ANSWER: a large system simulation that allows users to test various policies and decisions to determine their effect on the operating environment, a business's sales expenditures, interest rates, wage rates, overhead costs, etc.

CHAPTER 16
Markov Analysis

TRUE/FALSE

16.1 The matrix of transition probabilities shows the likelihood that the system will change from one time period to the next.

ANSWER: TRUE

16.2 In the matrix of transition probabilities, $\mathbf{P}_{ij}$ is the conditional probability of being in state i in the future, given the current state j.

ANSWER: FALSE

16.3 The probabilities in any column of the matrix of transition probabilities will always sum to one.

ANSWER: FALSE

16.4 The vector of state probabilities for any period is equal to the vector of state probabilities for the preceding period multiplied by the matrix of transition probabilities.

ANSWER: TRUE

16.5 An equilibrium condition exists if the state probabilities for a future period are the same as the state probabilities for a previous period.

ANSWER: TRUE

16.6 Equilibrium state probabilities may be estimated by using Markov analysis for a large number of periods.

ANSWER: TRUE

16.7 The fundamental matrix is a partition of the matrix of transition.

ANSWER: TRUE

16.8 When absorbing states exist, the fundamental matrix is used to compute equilibrium conditions.

ANSWER: TRUE

16.9 For any absorbing state, the probability that a state will remain unchanged in the future is one.

ANSWER: TRUE

16.10 The four basic assumptions of Markov analysis are:

1. a limited or finite number of possible states.
2. the probability of changing states remains the same over time.
3. a future state is predictable from previous state and transition matrix.
4. the size and makeup of system are constant during analysis.

ANSWER: TRUE

16.11 In Markov analysis, states must be collectively exhaustive and mutually exclusive.

ANSWER: TRUE

16.12 $\pi(n+1) = n\pi P$

ANSWER: FALSE

16.13 In Markov analysis, the row elements of the transition matrix must sum to 1.

ANSWER: TRUE

16.14 In Markov analysis, if we know the present state vector and the transition matrix, we can determine previous states.

ANSWER: TRUE

16.15 Once a Markov process is in equilibrium, it stays in equilibrium.

ANSWER: TRUE

16.16 In Markov analysis, initial-state probability values determine equilibrium conditions.

ANSWER: FALSE

16.17 Markov analysis assumes that there are a limited number of states in the system.

ANSWER: TRUE

16.18 Markov analysis assumes that while a member of one state may move to a different state over time, the overall makeup of the system will remain the same.

ANSWER: TRUE

16.19 The vector of state probability gives the probability of being in a particular state at a particular point in time.

ANSWER: TRUE

16.20 The matrix of transition probabilities gives the probability of moving from one state to another.

ANSWER: TRUE

16.21 Markov analysis help us determine the likelihood of moving from state *i* to state *j*, but provides no information as to how we arrived in state *i*.

ANSWER: FALSE

16.22 A Markov process could be used as a model of how a disease progresses from one set of symptoms to another.

ANSWER: TRUE

16.23 One of the problems with using the Markov model to study population shifts is that we must assume that the reasons for moving from one state to another remain the same over time.

ANSWER: TRUE

MULTIPLE CHOICE

16.24 Markov analysis is a technique that deals with the probabilities of future occurrences by

(a) using the simplex solution method.
(b) analyzing presently known probabilities.
(c) statistical sampling.
(d) the minimal spanning tree.
(e) none of the above

ANSWER: b

16.25 Markov analysis might be effectively used for

(a) market share analysis.
(b) university enrollment predictions.
(c) machine breakdowns.
(d) all of the above

ANSWER: d

16.26 The following is an assumption of Markov analysis:

(a) There is a finite number of possible states.
(b) The probability of changing states remains the same.
(c) We can predict any future state from the previous state and the matrix of transition probabilities.
(d) The size and composition of the system remain constant.
(e) all of the above

ANSWER: e

16.27 In Markov analysis, the likelihood that any system will change from one period to the next is revealed by the

(a) cross-elasticities.
(b) fundamental matrix.
(c) matrix of transition probabilities.
(d) vector of state probabilities.
(e) state of technology.

ANSWER: c

16.28 Markov analysis assumes that conditions are both

(a) complementary and collectively exhaustive.
(b) collectively dependent and complementary.
(c) collectively dependent and mutually exclusive.
(d) collectively exhaustive and mutually exclusive.
(e) complementary and mutually exclusive.

ANSWER: d

16.29 Occasionally, a state is entered that will not allow going to any other state in the future. This is called

(a) status quo.
(b) stability dependency.
(c) market saturation.
(d) incidental mobility.
(e) an absorbing state.

ANSWER: e

16.30 A collection of all state probabilities for a given system at any given period of time is called the

(a) transition probabilities.
(b) vector of state probabilities.
(c) fundamental matrix.
(d) equilibrium condition.
(e) none of the above

ANSWER: b

16.31 In a matrix of transition probabilities (where i equals the row number and j equals the column number),

(a) each number represents the conditional probability of being in state *j* in the next period given that it is currently in the state of *i*.
(b) each number represents the probability that if something is in state *i*, it will go to state *j* in the next period.
(c) the number in row 3, column 3 represents the probability that something will remain in state 3 from one period to the next.
(d) the probabilities are usually determined empirically.
(e) all of the above

ANSWER: e

16.32 In a matrix of transition probabilities,

(a) the probabilities for any row will sum to one.
(b) the probabilities for any column will sum to one.
(c) the probabilities for any column are mutually exclusive and collectively exhaustive.
(d) none of the above

ANSWER: a

16.33 In Markov analysis, to find the vector of state probabilities for any period,

(a) one should find them empirically.
(b) subtract the product of the numbers on the primary diagonal from the product of the numbers on the secondary diagonal.
(c) find the product of the vector of state probabilities for the preceding period and the matrix of transition probabilities.
(d) find the product of the vectors of state probabilities for the two preceding periods.
(e) take the inverse of the fundamental matrix.

ANSWER: c

16.34 In the long run, in Markov analysis,

(a) all state probabilities will eventually become zeros or ones.
(b) the matrix of transition probabilities will change to an equilibrium state.
(c) generally, the vector of state probabilities, when multiplied by the matrix of transition probabilities, will yield the same vector of state probabilities.
(d) all of the above

ANSWER: c

16.35 To find the equilibrium state in Markov analysis,

(a) it is necessary to know both the vector of state probabilities and the matrix of transition probabilities.
(b) it is necessary only to know the matrix of transition probabilities.
(c) it is necessary only to know the vector of state probabilities for the initial period.
(d) one should develop a table of state probabilities over time and then determine the equilibrium conditions empirically.
(e) none of the above

ANSWER: b

16.36 In Markov analysis, the absorbing state

(a) refers to the condition whereby something in some state cannot go to any other state in the future.
(b) refers to the condition whereby something in some state cannot go to one particular other state in the future.
(c) means that, for some state, the probability of remaining in that state in the next period is zero.
(d) means that, for some state, the probability of leaving that state for the next period is one.

ANSWER: a

16.37 In Markov analysis, the fundamental matrix

(a) is necessary to find the equilibrium condition when there are absorbing states.
(b) can be found but requires, in part, partitioning of the matrix of transition probabilities.
(c) is equal to the inverse of the I minus B matrix.
(d) is multiplied by the A matrix in order to find the probabilities that amounts in non-absorbing states will end up in absorbing states.
(e) all of the above

ANSWER: e

16.38 If we want to use Markov analysis to study market shares for competitive businesses,

(a) it is an inappropriate study.
(b) simply replace the probabilities with market shares.
(c) it can only accommodate one new business each period.
(d) only constant changes in the matrix of transition probabilities can be handled in the simple model.
(e) none of the above

ANSWER: b

16.39 Where **P** is the matrix of transition probabilities, $\pi(4) =$

(a) $\pi(3)$ **P P P**.
(b) $\pi(3)$ **P P**.
(c) $\pi(2)$ **P P P**.
(d) $\pi(1)$ **P P P**.
(e) none of the above

ANSWER: d

16.40 The copy machine in an office is very unreliable. If it was working yesterday, there is an 80% chance it will work today. If it was not working yesterday, there is a 10% chance it will work today. What is the probability that it is not working today, if it was not working yesterday?

(a) 0.1
(b) 0.2
(c) 0.8
(d) 0.9
(e) none of the above

ANSWER: d

16.41 The copy machine in an office is very unreliable. If it was working yesterday, there is an 80% chance it will work today. If it was not working yesterday, there is a 10% chance it will work today. What is the probability it will not work today, if it was working yesterday?

(a) 0.1
(b) 0.2
(c) 0.8
(d) 0.9
(e) none of the above

ANSWER: b

16.42 The copy machine in an office is very unreliable. If it was working yesterday, there is an 80% chance it will work today. If it was not working yesterday, there is a 10% chance it will work today. If it is working today, what is the probability that it will be working 2 days from now?

(a) 0.16
(b) 0.64
(c) 0.66
(d) 0.80
(e) none of the above

ANSWER: c

16.43 The copy machine in an office is very unreliable. If it was working yesterday, there is an 80% chance it will work today. If it was not working yesterday, there is a 10% chance it will work today. If it is not working today, what is the probability that it will be working 2 days from now?

(a) 0.16
(b) 0.17
(c) 0.34
(d) 0.66
(e) none of the above

ANSWER: b

Table 16-1
The following data consists of a matrix of transition probabilities (**P**) of three competing companies, the initial market share π(1), and the equilibrium probability states. Assume that each state represents a company (Company 1, Company 2, Company 3, respectively) and the transition probabilities represent changes from one month to the next.
$\mathbf{P} = \begin{bmatrix} 0.1 & 0.6 & 0.3 \\ 0.7 & 0.1 & 0.2 \\ 0.2 & 0.2 & 0.6 \end{bmatrix}$ $\pi(1) = (0.3, 0.6, 0.1)$

16.44 Using the data in Table 16-1, determine Company 1's estimated market share in the next period.

(a) 0.10
(b) 0.20
(c) 0.42
(d) 0.47
(e) none of the above

ANSWER: d

16.45 Using the data in Table 16-1, determine Company 2's estimated market share in the next period.

(a) 0.26
(b) 0.27
(c) 0.28
(d) 0.29
(e) none of the above

ANSWER: a

16.46 Using the data in Table 16-1, and assuming the transition probabilities do not change, in the long run what market share would Company 2 expect to reach? (Rounded to two places.)

(a) 0.30
(b) 0.32
(c) 0.39
(d) 0.60
(e) none of the above

ANSWER: a

16.47 The weather is becoming important to you since you would like to go on a picnic today. If it was sunny yesterday, there is a 70% chance it will be sunny today. If it was raining yesterday, there is a 30% chance it will be sunny today. What is the probability it will be sunny today, if it was sunny yesterday?

(a) 0.1
(b) 0.2
(c) 0.7
(d) 0.8
(e) none of the above

ANSWER: c

16.48 The weather is becoming important to you since you would like to go on a picnic today. If it was sunny yesterday, there is a 70% chance it will be sunny today. If it was raining yesterday, there is a 30% chance it will be sunny today. What is the probability it will be sunny today, if it was raining yesterday?

(a) 0.1
(b) 0.3
(c) 0.7
(d) 0.8
(e) none of the above

ANSWER: b

16.49 The weather is becoming important to you since you would like to go on a picnic today. If it was sunny yesterday, there is a 70% chance it will be sunny today. If it was raining yesterday, there is a 30% chance it will be sunny today. If the probability that it was raining yesterday is 0.25, what is the probability that it will rain today?

(a) 0.1
(b) 0.3
(c) 0.4
(d) 0.7
(e) none of the above

ANSWER: c

16.50 The weather is becoming important to you since you would like to go on a picnic today. If it was sunny yesterday, there is a 65% chance it will be sunny today. If it was raining yesterday, there is a 30% chance it will be sunny today. If the probability that it was raining yesterday is 0.4, what is the probability that it will be sunny today?

(a) 0.650
(b) 0.390
(c) 0.510
(d) 0.490
(e) none of the above

ANSWER: c

Table 16-2
The following data consists of a matrix of transition probabilities (**P**) of three competing retailers, the initial market share $\pi(1)$, and the equilibrium probability states. Assume that each state represents a retailer (Retailer 1, Retailer 2, Retailer 3, respectively) and the transition probabilities represent changes from one month to the next.
$\mathbf{P} = \begin{bmatrix} 0.3 & 0.6 & 0.1 \\ 0.7 & 0.2 & 0.1 \\ 0.4 & 0.3 & 0.3 \end{bmatrix}$ $\pi(1) = (0.3, 0.6, 0.1)$

16.51 Using the data given in Table 16-2, find the market shares for the three retailers in month 2.

(a) $\pi(2) = (0.09, 0.42, 0.49)$
(b) $\pi(2) = (0.55, 0.33, 0.12)$
(c) $\pi(2) = (0.18, 0.12, 0.70)$
(d) $\pi(2) = (0.55, 0.12, 0.33)$
(e) none of the above

ANSWER: b

The following data is to be used for problems 16.52 – 16.55:

> Cuthbert Wylinghauser is a scheduler of transportation for the state of Delirium. This state contains three cities: Chaos (C_1), Frenzy (C_2), and Tremor (C_3). A transition matrix, indicating the probability that a resident in one city will travel to another, is given below. Cuthbert's job is to schedule the required number of seats, one to each person making the trip (transition), on a daily basis.
>
> Transition matrix: $$\begin{array}{c} \\ C \\ F \\ T \end{array}\begin{array}{c} \begin{array}{ccc} C & F & T \end{array} \\ \begin{bmatrix} .8 & .1 & .1 \\ .1 & .7 & .2 \\ .2 & .2 & .6 \end{bmatrix} \end{array}$$ $\pi(1) = [100,100,100]$

16.52 How many seats should Cuthbert schedule for travel from Chaos to Tremor for tomorrow?

(a) 80
(b) 70
(c) 20
(d) 60
(e) none of the above

ANSWER: e

16.53 Tomorrow evening, how many people can we expect to find in each city?

(a) Chaos = 90, Frenzy = 110, Tremor = 100
(b) Chaos = 110, Frenzy = 100, Tremor = 90
(c) Chaos = 80, Frenzy = 90, Tremor = 130
(d) Chaos = 100, Frenzy = 130, Tremor = 70
(e) none of the above

ANSWER: b

16.54 Find the equilibrium population for Frenzy (round to the nearest whole person).

(a) 126
(b) 95
(c) 79
(d) 100
(e) none of the above

ANSWER: b

16.55 What is the equilibrium population of Chaos (rounded to the nearest whole person)?

(a) 79
(b) 95
(c) 126
(d) 100
(e) none of the above

ANSWER: c

PROBLEMS

16.56 A certain utility firm has noticed that a residential customer's bill for one month is dependent on the previous month's bill. The observations are summarized in the following transition matrix.

This month's bill change over previous months		Next Month's Change		
		Increase	Same	Decrease
	Increase	0.1	0.2	0.7
	Same	0.3	0.4	0.3
	Decrease	0.5	0.3	0.2

The utility company would like to know the long-run probability that a customer's bill will increase, the probability the bill will stay the same, and the probability the bill will decrease.

ANSWER: probability of increase = 39/124
probability of no change = 37/124
probability of decrease = 12/31

16.57 A certain firm has noticed that employees' salaries from year to year can be modeled by Markov analysis. The matrix of transition probabilities follows.

	Salary in Next Year			
Salary in Current Year	Remains Unchanged	Receives Raise	Quits	Fired
Remains Unchanged	0.2	0.4	0.3	0.1
Receives Raise	0.5	0.3	0.0	0.2

(a) Set up the matrix of transition probabilities in the form: I 0
A B

(b) Determine the fundamental matrix for this problem.
(c) What is the probability that an employee who has received a raise will eventually quit?
(d) What is the probability that an employee who has received a raise will eventually be fired?

ANSWER: a

			Salary in Next Year	
Current Year	Employee Quits	Employee is Fired	Remains Unchanged	Receives Raise
Quits	1	0	0	0
Fired	0	1	0	0
Unchanged	0.3	0.1	0.2	0.4
Raise	0	0.2	0.5	0.3

(b) fundamental matrix: $\begin{bmatrix} 0.583 & 0.417 \\ 0.417 & 0.583 \end{bmatrix}$

(c) 0.417
(d) 0.583

16.58 The vector of state probabilities for period n is (0.3, 0.7).

The accompanying matrix of transition probabilities is: $\begin{bmatrix} 0.8 & 0.2 \\ 0.1 & 0.9 \end{bmatrix}$

Calculate the vector of state probabilities for period n+1.

ANSWER: (0.31 0.69)

16.59 Given the following matrix of transition probabilities, find the equilibrium state.

$$\begin{bmatrix} 0.8 & 0.2 \\ 0.4 & 0.6 \end{bmatrix}$$

ANSWER: (2/3 1/3)

16.60 Given the following vector of state probabilities and the accompanying matrix of transition probabilities, find the next period vector of state probabilities.

$$(0.2 \quad 0.3 \quad 0.5) \qquad \begin{bmatrix} 0.6 & 0.2 & 0.2 \\ 0.1 & 0.7 & 0.2 \\ 0.2 & 0.3 & 0.5 \end{bmatrix}$$

ANSWER: (0.25 0.4 0.35)

16.61 There is a 20% chance that any current client of company A will switch to company B this year. There is a 40% chance that any client of company B will switch to company A this year. If these probabilities are stable over the years, and if company A has 400 clients and company B has 300 clients,

(a) how many clients will each company have next year?
(b) how many clients will each company have in two years?

ANSWER: (a) Company A will have 440; Company B will have 260.
(b) Company A will have 456; Company B will have 244.

16.62 Over any given month, Hammond Market loses 10% of its customers to Otro Plaza and 20% to Tres Place. Otro Plaza loses 5% to Hammond and 10% to Tres Place. Tres Place loses 5% of its customers to each of the two competitors. At the present time, Hammond Market has 40% of the market, while the others have 30% each.

(a) Next month, what will the market shares be for the three firms?
(b) In two months, what will the market shares be for the three firms?

ANSWER: (a) Hammond 31%, Otro Plaza 31%, Tres Place 38%
(b) Hammond 25.15%, Otro Plaza 31.35%, Tres Place 43.5%

16.63 The fax machine in an office is very unreliable. If it was working yesterday, there is an 90% chance it will work today. If it was not working yesterday, there is a 5% chance it will work today.

(a) What is the probability that it is not working today, if it was not working yesterday?
(b) If it was working yesterday, what is the probability that it is working today?

ANSWER: (a) 0.95
(b) 0.90

16.64 There is a 30% chance that any current client of company A will switch to company B this year. There is a 20% chance that any client of company B will switch to company A this year. If these probabilities are stable over the years, and if company A has 1000 clients and company B has 1000 clients, in the long run (assuming the probabilities do not change), what will the market shares be?

ANSWER: 40% for A and 60% for B

16.65 Three fast food hamburger restaurants are competing for the college lunch crowd. Burger Bills has 40% of the market while Hungry Heifer and Salty Sams each have 30% of the market. Burger Bills loses 10 % of its customers to Hungry Heifer and 10% to Salty Sams each month. Hungry Heifer loses 5% of its customers to Burger Bills and 10% to Salty Sams each month. Salty Sams loses 10% of its customers to Burger Bills while 20% go to Hungry Heifer. What will the market shares be for the three businesses next month?

ANSWER: Burger Bills 36.5%
Hungry Heifer 35.5%
Salty Sams 28%

16.66 A firm currently has a 20% market share for its product, lint pickers. It has identified 2 plans to improve its market share. The transition matrices for both plans are listed below. Plan 1 costs $1 million and Plan 2 costs $1.5 million. The company's goal is to determine what its demand will be in the long-term.

Plan 1:	20% Share	40% Share	60% Share
20 Share	0.25	0.40	0.35
40 Share	0.20	0.35	0.45
60 Share	0.10	0.50	0.40

Plan 2:	20% Share	40% Share	60% Share
20 Share	0.30	0.30	0.40
40 Share	0.10	0.50	0.40
60 Share	0.20	0.30	0.50

A single percentage point of market share translates into an annual demand of 1,000 units per year. Also, each percentage point of market share means $100,000 of profit for the firm. Choose the plan that maximizes the firm's net income.

Answer: Plan 1 has the highest net income. Average market share in plan 1 is 44.91139 and for plan 2 it is 45.27778. The additional income of plan 2 is not enough to compensate for the marginal increase in cost.

SHORT ANSWER/ESSAY

16.67 What does the matrix of transition probabilities show with respect to a system being studied?

ANSWER: shows the likelihood of change from one state to another

16.68 Define what is meant by a state probability.

ANSWER: the probability of an event occurring at a point in time

16.69 Describe the situation of the existence of an equilibrium condition in a Markov analysis.

ANSWER: state probabilities do not change after a large number of periods, or if $\pi = \pi \mathbf{P}$

16.70 Given the following matrix of transition probabilities, write three equations that, when solved, will give the equilibrium state values.

$$\mathbf{P} = \begin{bmatrix} a & b \\ c & d \end{bmatrix}$$

ANSWER: $\pi_1 + \pi_2 = 1$ $(1-a)\ \pi_1 = c\ \pi_2$ $(1-d)\ \pi_2 = b\ \pi_1$

CHAPTER 17
Statistical Quality Control

TRUE/FALSE

17.1 Poor quality can be very expensive for the producing firm.

ANSWER: TRUE

17.2 Statistical process control uses regression and other forecasting tools to help control processes.

ANSWER: FALSE

17.3 One popular definition of quality is "Quality is the fitness for use."

ANSWER: TRUE

17.4 Control charts make it difficult to accurately compare new data with past performance.

ANSWER: FALSE

17.5 It is impossible to develop a process that has zero variability.

ANSWER: TRUE

17.6 If all of the control points on a control chart lie between the UCL and the LCL, the process is always in control.

ANSWER: FALSE

17.7 Assignable variations in a process are also called natural variations.

ANSWER: FALSE

17.8 An x-bar chart would be appropriate to monitor the number of defects by a production lot.

ANSWER: FALSE

17.9 The central limit theorem provides the statistical foundation for control charts.

ANSWER: TRUE

17.10 If we are tracking quality of performance for a class of students, we should plot the individual grades on an x-bar chart, and the pass/fail result on a p-chart.

ANSWER: TRUE

17.11 If a point on the control chart falls outside the upper control limits, we are 99.7% sure that the process has changed.

ANSWER: TRUE

17.12 A p-chart could be used to monitor the average weight of cereal boxes.

ANSWER: FALSE

17.13 If we are attempting to control the diameter of bowling bowls, we will find a p-chart to be quite helpful.

ANSWER: FALSE

17.14 A c-chart would be appropriate to monitor the number of weld defects on the steel plates of a ship's hull.

ANSWER: TRUE

MULTIPLE CHOICE

17.15 Which of the following is not a popular definition of quality?

(a) Quality is defined as a competitively priced product that surpasses customer needs.
(b) Quality is the degree to which a product conforms to design or specification.
(c) Quality is fitness for use.
(d) Even though quality cannot be defined, you know what it is.

ANSWER: a

17.16 Variations that need not occur in production processes are referred to as

(a) assignable variations.
(b) control variations.
(c) natural variations.
(d) process variations.
(e) none of the above

ANSWER: a

17.17 Variations that usually occur in a process are called

(a) process variations.
(b) natural variations.
(c) control variations.
(d) assignable variations.
(e) none of the above

ANSWER: b

17.18 A company believes a process monitored by an x-bar chart to be in control when the most recent control point exceeded the UCL value by 20%. The company should

(a) believe that a random bad luck chance occurred and proceed.
(b) suspect that an assignable cause of variation now exists and can be found.
(c) ignore the control point completely, as it is simply an outlier.
(d) wait for the next four samples to be taken to see if a trend develops.
(e) all of the above

ANSWER: b

17.19 Bags of pretzels are sampled to ensure proper weight. The overall average for the samples is 9 ounces. Each sample contains 25 bags. The standard deviation is estimated to be 2 ounces. The upper control chart limit (for 95.5% confidence) for the average would be

(a) 9.4.
(b) 8.6.
(c) 9.8.
(d) 8.2.
(e) none.

ANSWER: c

17.20 The inspection of cans of juice involves sampling some cans and weighing them. The overall average for the samples is 39 ounces. Each sample contains 36 cans. The standard deviation is estimated to be 2 ounces. The 99.7% lower control chart limit for the average would be

(a) 37.67.
(b) 38.00.
(c) 39.33.
(d) 40.00.
(e) none.

ANSWER: b

17.21 $\bar{x}$-charts indicate changes in

(a) variation.
(b) central tendency.
(c) natural variations.
(d) numbers of defects.
(e) none of the above

ANSWER: b

17.22 The normal distribution forms the basis for which of the following charts?

(a) c-chart
(b) $\bar{x}$-chart
(c) R-chart
(d) all of the above
(e) none of the above

ANSWER: b

17.23 The $\bar{x}$-chart would be useful when we

(a) took a number of measurements and computed the average.
(b) took a number of measurements and computed the ranges.
(c) found the fraction of the production lot defective.
(d) found the number of defective items in a production lot.
(e) none of the above

ANSWER: a

17.24 The R-chart would be useful when we

(a) took a number of measurements and computed the average.
(b) took a number of measurements and computed the ranges.
(c) found the fraction of the production lot defective.
(d) found the number of defective items in a production lot.
(e) none of the above

ANSWER: b

17.25 R-charts measure changes in

(a) central tendency.
(b) degree of variation.
(c) number of defects per production lot.
(d) natural variations.
(e) none of the above

ANSWER: b

Table 17-1			
(For use in problems 17.26 - 17.33			
Sample Size n	Mean Factor A_2	Upper Range D_4	Lower Range D_3
2	1.880	3.628	0
3	1.023	2.574	0
4	0.729	2.282	0
5	0.577	2.114	0
6	0.483	2.004	0
7	0.419	1.924	0.076
8	0.373	1.864	0.136
9	0.337	1.816	0.184
10	0.308	1.777	0.223
12	0.266	1.716	0.284

17.26 Bags of chocolate candy are sampled to ensure proper weight. The overall average for the samples is 36 ounces. Each sample contains eight bags. The average range is 1.3 ounces. The upper control chart limit for the average would be

(a) 36.3730
(b) 36.4849
(c) 35.6270
(d) 35.5150
(e) none of the above

ANSWER: b

17.27 Bags of chocolate candy are sampled to ensure proper weight. The overall average for the samples is 36 ounces. Each sample contains eight bags. The average range is 1.3 ounces. The lower control chart limit for the average would be

(a) 36.3730
(b) 36.4849
(c) 35.6270
(d) 35.5150
(e) none of the above

ANSWER: d

17.28 To guarantee that cans of soup are properly filled, some cans are sampled and the amounts measured. The overall average for the samples is 12 ounces. Each sample contains 10 cans. The average range is 0.4 ounces. The upper control chart limit for the average would be

(a) 12.1232.
(b) 11.8768.
(c) 13.2.
(d) 12.308.
(e) none of the above

ANSWER: a

17.29 To guarantee that cans of soda are properly filled, some cans are sampled and the amounts measured. The overall average for the samples is 12 ounces. Each sample contains 10 cans. The average range is 0.4 ounces. The lower control chart limit for the average would be

(a) 12.1232.
(b) 11.8768.
(c) 13.2.
(d) 12.308.
(e) none of the above

ANSWER: b

17.30 Bags of tea are sampled to ensure proper weight. The overall average for the samples is 8 ounces. Each sample contains 10 bags. The average range is 0.1 ounces. What is the lower limit of the average chart?

(a) 7.9692
(b) 8.0308
(c) 7.9076
(d) 8.0924
(e) none of the above

ANSWER: a

17.31 The Pristine Paint Company produces paint in gallon cans. They have found that in more than 10 samples of 8 cans each, the average gallon can contains 1.1 gallons of paint. The average range found over these samples is 0.15 gallons. What is the upper control limit for the averages in this process?

(a) 1.100
(b) 1.150
(c) 1.268
(d) 1.156
(e) none of the above

ANSWER: d

17.32 The average range of a process for packaging cereal is 1.1 ounces. If the sample size is 10, find the upper control chart limit for the range chart.

(a) 0.245
(b) 1.955
(c) 1.777
(d) 0.223
(e) none of the above

ANSWER: b

17.33 The average range of a process for packaging cereal is 1.1 ounces. If the sample size is 10, find the lower control chart limit for the range chart.

(a) 0.245
(b) 1.955
(c) 1.777
(d) 0.223
(e) none of the above

ANSWER: a

17.34 The binomial distribution forms the basis for which of the following charts?

(a) c-chart
(b) $\bar{x}$ -chart
(c) p-chart
(d) all of the above
(e) none of the above

ANSWER: c

17.35 The p-chart would be useful when we

(a) took a number of measurements and computed the average.
(b) took a number of measurements and computed the ranges.
(c) found the fraction of the production lot defective.
(d) found the number of defective items in a production lot.
(e) none of the above
ANSWER: c

17.36 Defects in computer hard-drives will usually render the entire computer worthless. For a particular model, the percent defective in the past has been 1%. If a sample size of 400 is taken, what would the 95.5% lower control chart limit be?

(a) 0.0001
(b) 0.0000
(c) 0.0010
(d) 0.0955
(e) ANSWER: a

17.37 A quality control program is being developed for batteries. The percent defective for these in the past has been 2%. If a sample size of 100 is taken, what would the 99.7% upper control chart limit be?

(a) 0.0000
(b) 0.0420
(c) 0.0620
(d) 0.0480

ANSWER: c

17.38 Defects in marble countertops usually require the whole top to be reconstructed. In one kitchen shop, the percent defective in the past has been one percent. If a sample size of 30 is taken, what should be the 95.5 percent upper control limit be?

(a) 0.030
(b) 0.000
(c) 0.046
(d) 0.064
(e) none of the above

ANSWER: c

17.39 Defects in the finish of new, custom, automobiles usually require the whole body to be repainted. In one "custom" shop, the percentage of defective finishes has been 2 percent. If a sample size of 10 is taken, what should be the 99.7 percent upper control limit be?

(a) 0.1328
(b) 0.1085
(c) 0.0443
(d) 0.1528
(e) none of the above

ANSWER: d

Given the sample results (100 units in each sample), in Table 17.2 for questions 17.40 – 17.41.

Table 17.2

Sample Number	Number of Errors	Fraction Defective
1	0	0.00
2	9	0.09
3	6	0.06
4	7	0.07
5	2	0.02
6	7	0.07
7	7	0.07
8	5	0.05
9	4	0.04
10	5	0.05

17.40 Find the 95.5% lower limit of the appropriate p-chart.

(a) 0.0076
(b) 0.0964
(c) 0.2014
(d) 0.1397
(e) none of the above

ANSWER: a

17.41 Find the 99.7% upper limit of the appropriate chart.

(a) 0.1560
(b) 0.0964
(c) 0.1186
(d) 0.520
(e) none of the above

ANSWER: c

17.42 The c-chart is be useful when we

(a) take a number of measurements and compute the average.
(b) take a number of measurements and compute the ranges.
(c) find the fraction of the production lot defective.
(d) find the number of defective items in a production lot.
(e) none of the above

ANSWER: d

17.43 A company has been receiving complaints about the attitude of some sales clerks. Over a 10-day period, the total number of complaints was 360. The company wishes to develop a control chart for the number of complaints. What would the upper control limit on the number of complaints per day be for a 3 sigma (99.7%) control chart?

(a) 18
(b) 36
(c) 42
(d) 54
(e) none of the above

ANSWER: d

17.44 A company has been receiving complaints about the attitude of some sales clerks. Over a 10-day period, the total number of complaints was 360. The company wishes to develop a control chart for the number of complaints. What would the lower control limit on the number of complaints per day be for a 3 sigma (99.7%) control chart?

(a) 0
(b) 18
(c) 36
(d) 54
(e) none of the above

ANSWER: b

17.45 A company has been receiving complaints about the quality of some of its merchandise. Over a 15-day period, the total number of complaints was 255. The company wishes to use a control chart for the number of complaints. During the current 15-day period, it appears that there will be approximately 34 complaints. The company should

(a) assume that the process is under control, and simply move on.
(b) assume that the high complaint rate was simply a natural variation and keep going as they are.
(c) immediately begin seeking the cause of this variation.
(d) assume that the variation is due to inappropriate data logging.
(e) none of the above

ANSWER: c

PROBLEMS

17.46 A company is producing cylindrical blocks for a children's toy. The average diameter of a block is 2.3 inches. Nine blocks are inspected and the diameters are measured. The standard deviation is estimated to be 0.01 inches. What are the 95.5% upper and lower control limits for the x-bar chart?

ANSWER: LCL=2.29 UCL=2.31

The following table is needed to answer questions 17.47 – 17.49

Table 17-3			
Sample Size N	Mean Factor A_2	Upper Range D_4	Lower Range D_3
2	1.880	3.628	0
3	1.023	2.574	0
4	0.729	2.282	0
5	0.577	2.114	0
6	0.483	2.004	0
7	0.419	1.924	0.076
8	0.373	1.864	0.136
9	0.337	1.816	0.184
10	0.308	1.777	0.223
12	0.266	1.716	0.284

17.47 A coffee company is attempting to make certain that all its packaged coffee beans contain the same amount of coffee bean by weight. Over the last few days, it has taken several samples. The overall average weight of the sampled packages is 16 ounces, with an average range of 3 ounces. Each sample was of four packages. What would be the 99.7 upper and lower control limits for an $\bar{x}$-chart?

ANSWER: LCL = 13.813 ounces UCL = 18.187 ounces

17.48 A coffee company is attempting to make certain that all its packaged coffee beans contain the same amount of coffee bean by weight. Over the last few days, it has taken several samples. The overall average weight of the sampled packages is 16 ounces, with an average range of 3 ounces. Each sample was of four packages. What would be the 99.7 upper and lower control limits for an R chart?

ANSWER: LCL = 6.846 ounces UCL = 0 ounces

17.49 At the Ezio Pasta Company, bags of macaroni are labeled "net weight 12.5 ounces." Each hour, nine bags are taken and weighed to check the process control. The standard deviation has been 0.25 ounces, and the average weight has been 12.5 ounces. The average range has been 0.3 ounces. A sample has just been taken with the following weights: 12.7, 12.4, 12.1, and 12.6. Is the process in or out of control?

ANSWER: The 99.7% control limits for an $\bar{x}$-chart are: LCL = 12.75, UCL = 12.25. The average of 12.45 is well within these limits. The 99.7% control limits for an R-chart are: LCL 0.055 ounces, UCL = 0.545 ounces. Therefore, since the range of this sample, 0.6 ounces, is outside the control limits for the range, we would conclude that the process is out of control.

The following table is needed to answer question 17.50

Table 17-4			
Sample Size n	Mean Factor A_2	Upper Range D_4	Lower Range D_3
2	1.880	3.628	0
3	1.023	2.574	0
4	0.729	2.282	0
5	0.577	2.114	0
6	0.483	2.004	0
7	0.419	1.924	0.076
8	0.373	1.864	0.136
9	0.337	1.816	0.184
10	0.308	1.777	0.223
12	0.266	1.716	0.284

17.50 A local children's boutique specializes in formal wear for young girls. It has recently hired a new seamstress. To assure the dresses have standard sizes, twenty samples of each 12 dresses that were labeled 3T were sampled. The average length from shoulder to hemline measured 21 inches with a range of 0.5 inches. A sample has just been taken with the following lengths: 21.25, 22.0, 21.5, 20.75, 21.25. Is the new seamstress performing at an acceptable quality level?

ANSWER: UCL = 21 + 0.5(0.266) = 21.133
LCL = 21 - 0.5(0.266) = 20.867
Range UCL = 1.716 * 0.5 = 0.858
LCL = 0.288 * 0.5 = 0.142

The new seamstress is not performing at an acceptable level.

17.51 A computer diskette manufacturer is concerned that some diskettes have bad sectors that would cause a diskette to hold less information than it was intended to hold. In the past, only 5% of these diskettes have had bad sectors. If the company wishes to set 99.7% control limits based on samples of size 500, what would these limits be?

ANSWER: LCL=0.0208 UCL=0.0792

17.52 A p-chart has been developed for a particular item. In the past, 4% of such items have been found to be defective. If a sample of 100 is taken, and 9 of these are found to be defective, should the process be considered out of control? Explain.

ANSWER: If 99.7% control limits are developed, they are as follows: LCL=0 (–.02) UCL=0.10. Since 9% is in this range, the process is not out of control.

17.53 A computer software manufacturer has a toll-free telephone number that customers may use if they have problems or questions about the software. In the past, the company has averaged four calls per hour on a particular product. If a 95.5% c-chart is developed for this, what would the limits be?
ANSWER: LCL=0 UCL=8

17.54 Leo Phan is the new business manager at PC Priced Right. He is concerned that his register is incorrectly ringing items. For those items sold during the last seven days, he has counted 8 that were incorrectly charged. What would be the 99.7% control limits on this process?

ANSWER: LCL = 0 (-0.5) UCL = 16.5

FILL-IN-THE-BLANKS

17.55 __________ refers to a quality emphasis that includes the supplier through to the customer.

ANSWER: TQM

17.56 When a process is out of control, ____________________ variations exist in the process.

ANSWER: assignable

17.57 __________ are graphs that show upper and lower limits for the process we want to control.

ANSWER: Control charts

17.58 When a process is in control, only ____________________ variations exist in the process.

ANSWER: natural

17.59 If the natural variations of a process are significant, we should ________________.

ANSWER: redesign the process

17.60 If the assignable variations of a process become significant, we should ______________.

ANSWER: adjust the process

17.61 Natural variation of a production process that follows a normal distribution is characterized by two parameters: ____________________ and ____________________.

ANSWER: mean (μ), standard deviation (σ)

17.62 A(n) ____________________ chart is appropriate to monitor the weight of chocolate candy bars.

ANSWER: x-bar

17.63 The two charts one might use to monitor test grades in a college course are ________, and _______.

ANSWER: $\bar{x}$-chart, R-chart

17.64 If we wish to monitor the average diameter of the hula hoops we are producing, the distribution we base our statistics on is the ________ distribution.

ANSWER: normal

17.65 A(n) __________________ chart is appropriate to monitor the percent defective of a production process.

ANSWER: p

17.66 A(n) __________________ chart is appropriate to monitor the number of needle sticks incurred inadvertently by nurses who are administering infectable medications.

ANSWER: c

17.67 A(n) __________________ chart is appropriate to monitor the percent of mortalities due to heart problems.

ANSWER: p

17.68 The chart one might use to monitor defects in producing carpet is a ________.

ANSWER: c-chart

17.69 If we wish to monitor the number of defects on a page in a printing process, the distribution we base our statistics on is the _______ distribution.

ANSWER: Poisson

MATCHING

17.70	R-chart	(a)	Count of attributes
17.71	p-chart	(b)	Average of variables
17.72	$\bar{x}$ -chart	(c)	Graphical presentation of process data
17.73	c-chart	(d)	Range of variables
17.74	Control chart	(e)	Fraction of attributes

ANSWERS: 17.70–d, 17.71–e, 17.72–b, 17.73–a, 17.74–c

17.75	$\bar{c} \pm 3\sqrt{c}$	(a)	Lower limit for an $\bar{x}$ -chart
17.76	$D_4\bar{R}$	(b)	Control limits for a c-chart
17.77	$\bar{x} + A_2\bar{R}$	(c)	Upper control limit for a p-chart
17.78	$\bar{p} + \sigma_{\bar{p}} 0$	(d)	Upper control limit for a Range chart
17.79	$\bar{x} - Z\sigma_{\bar{x}}$	(e)	Upper limit for an $\bar{x}$ -chart

ANSWERS: 17.75–b, 17.76–d, 17.77–e, 17.78–c, 17.79–a

MODULE 1
Analytic Hierarchy Process

TRUE/FALSE

M1.1 In multifactor decision making, individuals quantitatively and objectively consider the various factors in making their decisions.

ANSWER: FALSE

M1.2 Decision situations where we have difficulty in accurately determining various weighting factors are excellent candidates for the Analytic Hierarchy Process analysis.

ANSWER: TRUE

M1.3 An equivalent name for the Multifactor Evaluation Process (MFEP) is the Analytic Hierarchy Process (AHP).

ANSWER: FALSE

M1.4 When using the multifactor evaluation process, it is helpful if the importance weights for factors sum to 1.0.

ANSWER: TRUE

M1.5 In the multifactor evaluation process, we always select the alternative that has the highest total weighted evaluation.

ANSWER: TRUE

M1.6 In MFEP, the factor weights are summed and then multiplied by the total factor evaluation.

ANSWER: FALSE

M1.7 The consistency ratio (CR) is an indicator of the equality of factors.

ANSWER: FALSE

M1.8 λ is the average of the consistency ratios.

ANSWER: FALSE

M1.9 $CI = (\lambda - n) / (n - 1)$

ANSWER: TRUE

M1.10 If you can determine with confidence and accuracy the factor weights and factor evaluations, AHP is preferred.

ANSWER: FALSE

M1.11 AHP gives the factor weights and factor evaluations from which the final decision can be made.

ANSWER: TRUE

MULTIPLE CHOICE

M1.12 A decision-making technique in which individuals subjectively and intuitively consider the various factors in making their selection is known as

(a) multifactor decision making.
(b) the multifactor evaluation process.
(c) the analytic hierarchy process.
(d) pairwise comparison analysis.
(e) consistency ratio analysis.

ANSWER: a

M1.13 Mary states that the two factors critical to her having a successful vacation are golf course availability and good weather. If Mary insists that golf course availability is three times as important as the weather, what importance weights should be placed on golf course availability and good weather to be used for a multifactor evaluation process?

	Golf Weight	Weather Weight
(a)	0.80	0.20
(b)	0.20	0.80
(c)	0.75	0.25
(d)	0.25	0.75
(e)	none of the above	

ANSWER: c

M1.14 Given three alternatives and their total weighted evaluation, which action should be selected?

Alternative	Weighted Average
A	0.6
B	0.8
C	0.6

(a) Alternative A
(b) Alternative B
(c) Alternative C
(d) Alternative A or Alternative C
(e) none of the above

ANSWER: b

M1.15 Given the following key factors and their importance weights, determine a total weighted evaluation for A3.

Key Factor	Importance Weights	A1	A2	A3
K1	0.2	0.2	0.9	0.7
K2	0.7	0.8	0.5	0.4
K3	0.1	0.9	0.6	0.8

(a) 0.69
(b) 0.74
(c) 0.59
(d) 0.50
(e) none of the above

ANSWER: d

M1.16 Jason Rule has developed the following table to represent his research into the decision as to which college he would like to attend after graduation:

Table M1-1						
Factor	Weight	MSU	BC	PC	UNH	UM
Yearly cost	0.40	0.4	0.3	0.5	0.7	0.6
Location	0.10	0.7	0.3	0.4	0.3	0.2
Campus housing	0.10	0.3	0.5	0.3	0.3	0.4
Available courses	0.20	0.8	0.5	0.4	0.7	0.7
Expected social life	0.10	0.8	0.7	0.5	0.3	0.2
Availability of intramural sports	0.05	0.8	0.6	0.4	0.6	0.7
Student-owned auto policy	0.05	0.9	0.7	0.3	0.8	0.8
	1.00	0.59	0.44	0.44	0.58	0.54

Based on his weights and ratings of colleges, which college should he attend?

(a) MSU
(b) UM
(c) UNH
(d) PC
(e) none of the above

ANSWER: a

M1.17 Based on Table M1-1, what should be Jason's second choice?

(a) MSU
(b) BC
(c) PC
(d) UM
(e) none of the above

ANSWER: e

M1.18 Table M1-1 portrays Jason's initial evaluation of the colleges of interest. Jason has now decided that he should emphasize *Yearly Cost* somewhat less, and *Social life* somewhat more. His new ratings are: *Yearly Cost*: 0.30, and *Social Life*: 0.20. What will be his order of preference with these new weights?

(q) UM, MSU, BC, PC, UNH
(b) MSU, PC, UNH, BC, UM
(c) MSU, UNH, UM, BC, PC
(d) UNH, BC, UM, MSU, PC
(e) none of the above

ANSWER: c

M1.19 Table M1-1 portrays Jason's initial evaluation of the colleges of interest. Jason has now decided that (a) *Social Life* is more important than he first implied, and (b) that the student body at MSU is so large that he may feel lost – just a small fish in a big, big pond. He decides to change the weight for *Social Life* to 0.2, and change his rating of the *Social Life* at MSU to 0.4. He will compensate for the increase in the weight of *Social Life* by reducing the weight of *Yearly Cost*. Given these changes, what will be his second choice college?

(a) MSU
(b) PC
(c) UM
(d) UNH
(e) none of the above

ANSWER: d

M1.20 A pairwise comparison rating of 9 means that the two alternatives are

(a) equally preferred.
(b) moderately preferred.
(c) strongly preferred.
(d) very strongly preferred.
(e) extremely preferred.

ANSWER: e

M1.21 A pairwise comparison rating of 7 means that, relative to alternative 2, alternative 1 is

(a) equally preferred.
(b) moderately preferred.
(c) strongly preferred.
(d) very strongly preferred.
(e) extremely preferred.

ANSWER: d

M1.22 Which of the following matrices is not a correct pairwise comparison matrix?

A	A1	A2	A3
A1	1	4	7
A2	0.25	1	5
A3	0.1429	0.2	1

B	B1	B2	B3
B1	1	0.5	6
B2	2	1	5
B3	0.1667	0.2	1

C	C1	C2	C3
C1	1	0.333	0.2
C2	3	1	0.25
C3	5	4	1

D	D1	D2	D3
D1	1	5	2
D2	0.4	1	3
D3	0.5	0.3333	1

(a) A
(b) B
(c) C
(d) D
(e) all are correct pairwise comparison matrices

ANSWER: d

M1.23 Shown below is an incomplete pairwise comparison matrix for three alternatives. What comparison factor should A3 receive when compared to A2?

Factor	A1	A2	A3
A1	1	3	5
A2		1	7
A3		?	1

(a) 3
(b) 1/3
(c) 7
(d) 1/7
(e) none of the above

ANSWER: d

Table M1-2					
Factor	MSU	BC	PC	UNH	UM
MSU	1	7	8	8	9
BC		1	7	5	7
PC			1	6	9
UNH				1	8
UM					1

M1.24 Table M1-2 displays the result of the pairwise comparisons of the various schools in which Jason has an interest. The completed table is:

(a)

Factor	MSU	BC	PC	UNH	UM
MSU	1	7	8	8	9
BC	7	1	7	5	7
PC	8	7	1	6	9
UNH	8	5	6	1	8
UM	9	7	9	8	1

(b)

Factor	MSU	BC	PC	UNH	UM
MSU	1	7	8	8	9
BC	1/7	1	7	5	7
PC	1/8	1/7	1	6	9
UNH	1/8	1/5	1/6	1	8
UM	1/9	1/7	1/9	1/8	1

(c)

Factor	MSU	BC	PC	UNH	UM
MSU	1	7	8	8	9
BC	7	1	7	5	7
PC	8	9	1	6	9
UNH	5	6	7	1	8
UM	6	8	5	7	1

(d)

Factor	MSU	BC	PC	UNH	UM
MSU	1	7	8	8	9
BC	1/7	1	7	5	7
PC	1/8	1/8	1	6	9
UNH	1/9	1/7	1/6	1	8
UM	1/6	1/9	1/5	1/7	1

(e) none of the above

ANSWER: b

Table M1-3					
Factor	MSU	BC	PC	UNH	UM
MSU	1	5	7	3	8
BC	1/5	1	6	4	7
PC	1/7	1/6	1	9	5
UNH	1/3	1/4	1/9	1	7
UM	1/8	1/7	1/5	1/7	1

M1.25 The normalized matrix for Table M1-3 is:

(a)

Factor	MSU	BC	PC	UNH	UM
MSU	1	0.762	0.489	0.175	0.286
BC	0.111	1	0.419	0.233	0.250
PC	0.079	0.025	1	0.525	0.179
UNH	0.185	0.038	0.008	1	1
UM	0.069	0.022	0.014	0.008	0.036

(b)

Factor	MSU	BC	PC	UNH	UM
MSU	0.555	0.762	0.489	0.175	0.286
BC	0.111	0.152	0.419	0.063	0.372
PC	0.179	0.065	0.070	0.525	0.179
UNH	0.385	0.038	0.508	0.058	0.250
UM	0.069	0.022	0.014	0.008	0.036

(c)

Factor	MSU	BC	PC	UNH	UM
MSU	0.564	0.362	0.470	0.475	0.396
BC	0.152	0.152	0.419	0.233	0.250
PC	0.079	0.025	0.070	0.417	0.179
UNH	0.185	0.038	0.008	0.058	0.250
UM	0.069	0.022	0.014	0.008	0.036

(d)

Factor	MSU	BC	PC	UNH	UM
MSU	0.555	0.762	0.489	0.175	0.286
BC	0.111	0.152	0.419	0.233	0.250
PC	0.079	0.025	0.070	0.525	0.179
UNH	0.185	0.038	0.008	0.058	0.250
UM	0.069	0.022	0.014	0.008	0.036

(e) none of the above

ANSWER: d

Table M1-4					
Factor	MSU	BC	PC	UNH	UM
MSU	0.600	0.753	0.490	0.276	0.276
BC	0.120	0.151	0.420	0.165	0.241
PC	0.086	0.025	0.070	0.496	0.207
UNH	0.120	0.050	0.008	0.055	0.241
UM	0.075	0.022	0.012	0.008	0.034

M1.26 Given the normalized Table M1-4, the priorities of the colleges are:

(a)

MSU	0.095
BC	0.030
PC	0.479
UNH	0.219
UM	0.177

(b)

MSU	0.479
BC	0.219
PC	0.177
UNH	0.095
UM	0.030

(c)

MSU	0.095
BC	0.219
PC	0.030
UNH	0.479
UM	0.177

(d)

MSU	0.030
BC	0.479
PC	0.030
UNH	0.095
UM	0.219

(e) none of the above

ANSWER: b

M1.27 Shown below is a pairwise comparison matrix for coffee makers. What are the values of column one's normalized matrix?

	Brand 1	Brand 2	Brand 3
Brand 1	1	5	8
Brand 2		1	7
Brand 3			1

(a) 1.0000
0.2000
0.1250
(b) 0.7547
0.1509
0.0943
(c) 1.3250
6.6250
10.600
(d) 5.1982
3.8764
4.9721
(e) none of the above

ANSWER: b

M1.28 Shown below is a pairwise comparison matrix for coffee makers. What are the priorities for the three coffee maker brands?

	Brand 1	Brand 2	Brand 3
Brand 1	1	5	8
Brand 2		1	7
Brand 3			1

(a) 0.7547
0.1509
0.0943
(b) 0.5000
0.4375
0.0625
(c) 2.0094
0.7393
0.2511
(d) 0.6895
0.2504
0.06
(e) none of the above

ANSWER: d

M1.29 Determine the weighted sum vector for the indicated factor evaluation and its original pairwise comparison matrix.

	C1	C2	C3
Factor Evaluation	0.6267	0.2633	0.1100

	C1	C2	C3
C1	1	2	7
C2	0.5	1	2
C3	0.1429	0.5	1

(a) 0.7741
1.5717
5.0235

(b) 5.0235
1.5717
0.7741

(c) 1.9233
0.7967
0.3312

(d) 0.3312
0.7966
1.9233

(e) none of the above
ANSWER: c

M1.30 Determine the weighted sum vector for the indicated factor evaluation and its original pairwise comparison matrix.

	D1	D2	D3
Factor Evaluation	0.5443	0.1741	0.1148

	D1	D2	D3
D1	1	6	3
D2	0.1667	1	2
D3	0.3333	0.5	1

(a) 0.4467
0.6057
2.2669

(b) 1.9333
0.4944
0.3829

(c) 0.3779
0.0917
0.0912

(d) 2.5069
4.2082
0.7393

(e) none of the above

ANSWER: b

M1.31 Jason Rule is considering attending one of five different schools. Shown below are the priorities and the original pairwise comparison matrix.

Priorities Table:

MSU	0.40
BC	0.30
PC	0.20
UNH	0.07
UM	0.03

Pairwise Comparison Table:

Table M1-5					
Factor	MSU	BC	PC	UNH	UM
MSU	1	5	7	3	8
BC	1/5	1	6	4	7
PC	1/7	1/6	1	9	5
UNH	1/3	1/4	1/9	1	7
UM	1/8	1/7	1/5	1/7	1

The consistency vector is:

(a)

1.528598
3.871031
1.316178
1.494108
0.164312

(b)

1.316178
3.528598
0.494108
1.871031
0.164312

(c)

3.528598
1.871031
1.316178
0.494108
0.164312

(d)

1.316178
0.494108
0.164312
3.528598
1.871031

(e) none of the above

ANSWER: e

M1.32 In the Analytic Hierarchy Process, λ is

(a) the number of items or systems under consideration.
(b) equivalent to the CI.
(c) equivalent to the CR.
(d) equivalent to the RI.
(e) none of the above

ANSWER: e

M.1.33 Shown below is a consistency vector from an Analytic Hierarchy Process analysis.

Compute λ.

2.6895
2.5555
2.7985
2.6105

(a) Not enough information is given to compute λ
(b) 2.7985
(c) 2.6000
(d) 10.6540
(e) 2.6635

ANSWER: e

M 1.34 The consistency index is

(a) the average value of the consistency vector.
(b) CR/CI.
(c) RI/CR.
(d) $(\lambda - n)/(n - 1)$.
(e) none of the above

ANSWER: d

M 1.35 The consistency ratio is

(a) the average value of the consistency vector.
(b) CR/CI.
(c) RI/CI.
(d) $(\lambda - n)/(n - 1)$.
(e) none of the above

ANSWER: e

M 1.36 From an Analytic Hierarchy Process analysis, λ is computed to be 4.840, n = 3, RI = 0.58. Compute the consistency index.

(a) 0.92
(b) 1.5862
(c) 1.092
(d) 8.3448
(e) none of the above

ANSWER: a

M 1.37 From an Analytic Hierarchy Process analysis, λ is computed to be 4.123, n = 4, RI = 0.9. Compute the consistency index.

(a) 4.5811
(b) 1.0308
(c) 0.0456
(d) 0.0410
(e) none of the above

ANSWER: d

M 1.38 Given the following consistency vector--

7.369716
8.524687
7.446627
5.208015
5.459544

calculate the consistency index.

(a) 0.8502
(b) -0.0207
(c) 0.4504
(d) -0.7399
(e) none of the above

ANSWER: c

M 1.39 Higher values of the CR indicate

(a) the greater the level of consistency of the pairwise comparisons.
(b) an indication of low consistency of the pairwise comparisons.
(c) a moderate consistency of the pairwise comparisons.
(d) none of the above

ANSWER: b

M 1.40 From an Analytic Hierarchy Process analysis, λ is computed to be 4.840, n = 3, RI = 0.58. Compute the consistency ratio.

(a) 0.92
(b) 1.5862
(c) 1.092
(d) 8.3448
(e) none of the above

ANSWER: b

M 1.41 From an Analytic Hierarchy Process analysis, λ is computed to be 4.123, n = 4, RI = 0.9. Compute the consistency ratio.

(a) 4.5811
(b) 1.0308
(c) 0.0456
(d) 0.0410
(e) none of the above

ANSWER: c

M 1.42 Upon completion of an Analytic Hierarchy Process analysis, the CR = 0.047, thus

(a) the decision makers' answers are relatively consistent.
(b) the decision makers' should consider reevaluating their pairwise comparisons.
(c) no conclusion is available for this value of the CR.
(d) the decision maker has made near perfectly consistent pairwise comparisons.
(e) none of the above

ANSWER: a

M 1.43 Given a consistency index of 0.2070, and an n of 5, use the following table to calculate the consistency ratio.

n	2	3	4	5	6	7	8
RI	0.00	0.58	0.90	1.12	1.24	1.32	1.41

(a) 0.0414
(b) 0.1848
(c) 2.8019
(d) 0.2300
(e) none of the above

ANSWER: b

M 1.44 Upon completion of an Analytic Hierarchy Process analysis, the CR = 0.23, thus

(a) the decision makers' answers are relatively consistent.
(b) the decision makers' should consider reevaluating their pairwise comparisons.
(c) no conclusion is available for this value of the CR.
(d) the decision maker has made near perfectly consistent pairwise comparisons.
(e) none of the above

ANSWER: b

M1.45 The Analytic Hierarchy Process is preferred to a multifactor evaluation process when

(a) there is high confidence in determining factor weights without pairwise comparisons.
(b) there is low confidence in determining factor weights without pairwise comparisons.
(c) one desires a lesser level of computational analysis.
(d) none of the above

ANSWER: b

PROBLEMS

M1.30 In a four-factor analysis used in a multifactor evaluation process, it is desired to have the F_1 importance weight four times as much as the F_2 importance weight. The F_2 importance weight should be four times as much as the F_3 importance weight. The F_3 importance weight should be four times as much as the F_4 importance weight. Determine the appropriate importance weights of F_1, F_2, F_3, F_4 to be used in the multifactor evaluation process. (Hint: Consider numerator factors of 4.)

ANSWER: $F_1 + F_2 + F_3 + F_4 = 1$, $F_1 = 4 F_2$, $F_2 = 4F_3$, $F_3 = 4F_4$
therefore, Importance Weight (F_1) = 64/85
therefore, Importance Weight (F_2) = 16/85
therefore, Importance Weight (F_3) = 4/85
therefore, Importance Weight (F_4) = 1/85

M1.31 Two factors are considered essential to the selection of blue cheese for the Burgerhoff Restaurant — color and texture. The Burgerhoff insists that color is four times as important as is texture for food presentation purposes. The Burgerhoff is considering two brands of blue cheese. After tasting the two brands, color and texture ratings have been assigned as indicated. Use a multifactor evaluation process to determine which brand of cheese best suits the needs of the Burgerhoff.

Brand	Color	Texture
A	0.8	0.6
B	0.7	0.8

ANSWER: Importance Weight (Color) = 0.8
Importance Weight (Texture) = 0.2
Brand A: 0.8(0.8) + 0.2(0.6) = 0.76 <=======
Brand B: 0.8(0.7) + 0.2(0.8) = 0.72

M1.32 Given the following initial pairwise comparison matrix, determine the consistency ratio.

Factor	A	B	C
Item A	1	3	9
Item B	0.3333	1	8
Item C	0.1111	0.125	1

ANSWER:

Weighted Sum Vector	Consistency Vector	
2.0463	3.1978	λ=3.1094
0.9536	3.1174	CI=0.0547
0.1636	3.0129	CR=0.0943

M1.33 Construct an initial pairwise comparison matrix with the following information regarding an Ease of Use factor about three different commercial student information systems. System C, when compared to System A, is strongly preferred. When System C is compared to System B, System C is only moderately preferred. When compared to System A, System B is strongly preferred.

ANSWER:

Ease of Use	A	B	C
System A	1	0.2	0.2
System B	5	1	0.3333
System C	5	3	1

M1.34 Given the following initial pairwise comparison matrix, determine the consistency ratio.

Factor	A	B	C
Item A	1	6	9
Item B	0.1667	1	3
Item C	0.1111	0.3333	1

ANSWER:

Weighted Sum Vector	Consistency Vector	
2.3880	3.1240	λ=3.052
0.5027	3.0301	CI=0.0271
0.2100	3.0086	CR=0.0467

SHORT ANSWER/ESSAY

M1.35 Describe a multifactor evaluation process.

ANSWER: All important factors are given relative weights of importance. Each alternative is evaluated in terms of the weights.

M1.36 How is the consistency index computed?

ANSWER: $CI = (\lambda - n) / (n - 1)$

M1.37 Interpret the consistency ratio.

ANSWER: CR < 0.10 indicates general consistency among pairwise comparisons.

MODULE 2
Dynamic Programming

TRUE/FALSE

M2.1 Dynamic programming can be applied to a professional tennis player's serving strategy.

ANSWER: TRUE

M2.2 Each item in a knapsack problem will be a stage of the dynamic programming problem.

ANSWER: TRUE

M2.3 For knapsack problems, $s_{n-1} = a_n \times s_n + b_n \times d_n + c_n$ is a typical transformation expression.

ANSWER: TRUE

M2.4 The problem that NASA has in determining what types of cargo may be loaded on the space shuttle is an example of a knapsack problem.

ANSWER: TRUE

M2.5 Both dynamic programming and linear programming take a multi-stage approach to solving problems.

ANSWER: FALSE

M2.6 The second step in solving a dynamic programming problem is to solve the last stage of the problem for all conditions or states.

ANSWER: TRUE

M2.7 Subproblems in a dynamic programming problem are called stages.

ANSWER: TRUE

M2.8 In a shortest-route problem, the nodes represent the destinations.

ANSWER: TRUE

M2.9 In a shortest-route problem, the limit on the number of allowable decision variables from one node to another is the number of possible nodes to which one might yet travel.

ANSWER: TRUE

M2.10 Your local paper carrier could make use of the shortest-route technique.

ANSWER: FALSE

M2.11 Linear programming is typically applied to problems wherein one must make a decision at a specified point (or points) in time. Dynamic programming is typically applied to problems wherein one must make a sequence of decisions.

ANSWER: TRUE

M2.12 Dynamic programming can only be used to solve network-based problems.

ANSWER: FALSE

M2.13 In dynamic programming, the decision rules defining an optimal policy give optimal decisions for any entering condition at any stage.

ANSWER: TRUE

M2.14 In dynamic programming, there is a state variable defined for every stage.

ANSWER: TRUE

M2.15 A transformation changes the identities of the state variables.

ANSWER: FALSE

MULTIPLE CHOICE

M2.16 There are six cities (City 1 – City 6) serviced by a particular bus line. Limited routes are available, and the distance for each of these routes is presented in the table below.

From City	To City	Distance (100s miles)
1	2	8
1	3	4
2	4	12
2	5	8
3	4	8
3	5	14
4	6	6
5	6	4

If dynamic programming were used to solve for the minimum distance from City 1 to City 6, how many stages would there be?

(a) 6
(b) 5
(c) 4
(d) 3
(e) 2

ANSWER: d

M2.17 For the bus line problem of M2.16, what are the stages that provide the minimum distance?

(a) 1-2, 2-4, 4-6
(b) 1-2, 2-5, 5-6
(c) 1-3, 3-4, 4-6
(d) 1-3, 3-5, 5-6
(e) none of the above

ANSWER: c

M2.18 For the bus line problem of M2.16, what is minimum possible distance to travel from City 1 to City 6?

(a) 26
(b) 20
(c) 18
(d) 22
(e) none of the above

ANSWER: c

M2.19 There are three items (A, B, and C) that are to be shipped by air. The weights of these are 4, 5, and 3 tons, respectively, and the plane can carry 13 tons. The profits (in thousands of dollars) generated by these are 3 for A, 4 for B, and 2 for C. There are four units of each available for shipment. If this were to be solved as a dynamic programming problem, how many stages would there be?

(a) 1
(b) 2
(c) 3
(d) 4
(e) none of these

ANSWER: c

M2.20 There are three items (A, B, and C) that are to be shipped by air. The weights of these are 4, 5, and 3 tons, respectively. The profits (in thousands of dollars) generated by these are 3 for A, 4 for B, and 2 for C. There are four units of each available for shipment. Only 12 tons may be loaded on the plane. The maximum possible profit for this would be

(a) 7.
(b) 8.
(c) 9.
(d) 10.
(e) none of these

ANSWER: c

M2.21 There are three items (A, B, and C) that are to be shipped by air. The weights of these are 4, 5, and 3 tons, respectively. The profits (in thousands of dollars) generated by these are 6 for A, 7 for B, and 5 for C. A total of 14 tons may be carried by the plane. There are four units of each available for shipment. What is the maximum possible profit for this situation?

(a) 14
(b) 20
(c) 21
(d) 22
(e) none of these

ANSWER: d

M2.22 The following information describes a shortest-route problem with the distance in miles. How many stages will this dynamic problem have?

From	To	Distance		From	To	Distance
1	2	40		3	7	20
1	3	22		4	6	43
1	4	66		4	7	33
1	5	39		5	7	66
2	6	18		6	8	72
2	7	24		7	8	58
3	6	23				

(a) 8
(b) 4
(c) 3
(d) 2
(e) 1

ANSWER: c

The data below is a dynamic programming solution for a shortest route problem.

Table M2-1						
Stage 1	s_1	d_1	r_1	s_0	f_0	f_1
	6	6 – 7	12	7	0	12
	5	5 – 7	8	7	0	8
Stage 2	s_2	d_2	r_2	s_1	f_1	f_2
	4	4 – 6	5	6	12	17
	3	3 – 6	4	6	12	16
		3 – 5	13	5	8	21
	2	2 – 6	9	6	12	21
		2 – 5	4	5	8	12
Stage 3	s_3	d_3	r_3	s_2	f_2	f_3
	1	1 – 4	7	4	17	24
		1 – 3	7	3	16	23
		1 – 2	10	2	12	22

M2.23 Using the data in Table M2-1, determine the minimum distance from point 1 to point 7.

(a) 21
(b) 22
(c) 23
(d) 24
(e) 75

ANSWER: b

M2.24 Using the data in Table M2-1, determine the distance of stage 1 for the optimal route.

(a) 0
(b) 8
(c) 12
(d) 16
(e) 24

ANSWER: b

M2.25 Using the data in Table M2-1, determine the distance of stage 2 for the optimal route.

(a) 0
(b) 4
(c) 8
(d) 12
(e) 21

ANSWER: b

M2.26 Using the data in Table M2-1, determine the distance of stage 3 for the optimal route.

(a) 22
(b) 23
(c) 24
(d) 7
(e) 10

ANSWER: e

M2.27 Using the data in Table M2-1, determine the optimal arc of stage 1.

(a) 5
(b) 6
(c) 7
(d) 6 – 7
(e) 5 – 7

ANSWER: e

M2.28 Using the data in Table M2-1, determine the optimal arc of stage 2.

(a) 4 – 6
(b) 3 – 6
(c) 3 – 5
(d) 2 – 6
(e) 2 – 5

ANSWER: e

M2.29 What is the optimal arc of stage 3?

(a) 1
(b) 1 – 4
(c) 1 – 3
(d) 1 – 2
(e) none of the above

ANSWER: d

M2.30 What is the optimal travel path from point 1 to 7?

(a) 5, 7
(b) 6, 7
(c) 1, 2, 6, 7
(d) 1, 2, 5, 7
(e) 1, 3, 6, 7

ANSWER: d

Table M2-2						
Stage 1	s_1	d_1	r_1	s_0	f_0	f_1
	6	6 – 7	3	7	0	3
	5	5 – 7	12	7	0	12
Stage 2	s_2	d_2	r_2	s_1	f_1	f_2
	4	4 – 6	9	6	3	12
		4 – 5	5	5	12	17
	3	3 – 6	7	6	3	10
		3 – 5	13	5	12	25
	2	2 – 5	10	5	12	22
Stage 3	s_3	d_3	r_3	s_2	f_2	f_3
	1	1 – 4	2	4	12	14
		1 – 3	6	3	10	16
		1 – 2	3	2	22	25

M2.31 According to Table M2-2, which gives a solution to a shortest route problem solved with dynamic programming, which cities would be included in the best route?

(a) 1,2,3,4,5,6
(b) 1,4,6,7
(c) 1,2,5,6,7
(d) 6,7
(e) none of the above

ANSWER: b

M2.32 According to Table M2-2, which gives a solution to a shortest route problem solved with dynamic programming, the total distance from City 1 to City 7 is 14. What is the shortest distance from City 3 to City 7?

(a) 7
(b) 10
(c) 13
(d) 25
(e) none of these

ANSWER: b

M2.33 There are six cities (City 1– City 6) serviced by a particular airline. Limited routes are available, and the distances for each of these routes are presented in the table below.

From City	To City	Distance (100s miles)
1	2	4
1	3	2
2	4	6
2	5	4
3	4	4
3	5	7
4	6	3
5	6	2

M2.34 What is the minimum distance that must be traveled to get from City 1 to City 6?

(a) 9
(b) 10
(c) 11
(d) 12
(e) none of these

ANSWER: a

M2.35 A *stage* is a(n)

(a) alternative.
(b) policy.
(c) condition at the end of the problem.
(d) subproblem.
(e) none of the above

ANSWER: d

M2.36 A *transformation* describes

(a) the relationship between stages.
(b) the initial condition of the system.
(c) a stage.
(d) a state variable.
(e) none of the above

ANSWER: a

The following information is to be used for questions M2.37 - M2.40.

There are seven cities (City 1 -- City 7) served by Acme Trucking. Route availability is limited. The distances, in hundreds of miles, are given in the table below for each route.

From City	To City	Distance		From City	To City	Distance
1	2	5		3	5	9
1	3	7		4	5	8
2	3	4		4	6	12
2	4	6		5	6	10
2	5	9		5	7	15
3	4	6		6	7	8

M2.37 What is the minimum distance a load being moved from City 1 to City 7 must travel?

(a) 3000 miles
(b) 2900 miles
(c) 1500 miles
(d) 2700 miles
(e) none of the above

ANSWER: b

M2.38 What route should the truck from City 1 to City 7 take?

(a) 1-2, 2-5, 5-7
(b) 1-3, 3-4, 4-6, 6-7
(c) 1-2, 2-4, 4-5, 5-6, 6-7
(d) 1-3, 3-5, 5-6, 6-7
(e) none of the above

ANSWER: a

M2.39 If the truck were required to take the route from City 4 to City 5, what would be the shortest distance from City 1 to City 7?

(a) 2900 miles
(b) 3200 miles
(c) 3700 miles
(d) 3400 miles
(e) none of the above

ANSWER: d

M2.40 If the truck were required to take the route from City 4 to City 5, what would be the overall route?

(a) 1-3, 3-4, 4-5, 5-6, 6-7
(b) 1-2, 2-4, 4-5, 5-7
(c) 1-2, 2-3, 3-4, 4-5, 5-6, 6-7
(d) 1-3, 3-5, 5-6, 6-7
(e) none of the above

ANSWER: b

The following information is to be used for questions M2.41 – M2.42:

GATRA, the Greater Attleboro-Taunton Regional Transit Authority serves six cities (City 1 – City 6). While there are many restrictions (primarily roads on which they may not travel), they do have some choice of routes. The distances between cities, along permitted routes, are presented below.

From	To	Distance
1	2	3
1	3	4
2	3	7
2	4	12
2	5	28

From	To	Distance
3	4	8
3	5	22
4	5	12
4	6	15
5	6	2

M2.41 What is the minimum distance that must be traveled to get from City 1 to City 6?

(a) 26
(b) 9
(c) 11
(d) 3
(e) none of these

ANSWER: a

M2.42 What is the shortest route?

(a) 1-3, 3-5, 5-6
(b) 1-2, 2-3, 3-4, 4-5, 5-6
(c) 1-3, 3-4, 4-5, 5-6
(d) 1-2, 2-3, 3-5, 5-6
(e) none of the above

ANSWER: c

M2.43 There are four items (A, B, C, and D) that are to be shipped by truck. The weights of these are 3, 7, 4, and 5 tons, respectively, and the plane can carry 13 tons. The profits (in thousands of dollars) generated by these are 3 for A, 4 for B, 2 for C, and 5 for D. There are four units of each available for shipment. If this were to be solved as a dynamic programming problem, how many stages would there be?

(a) 1
(b) 2
(c) 3
(d) 4
(e) none of these

ANSWER: d

M2.44 There are four items (A, B, C, and D) that are to be shipped by truck. The weights of these are 3, 7, 4, and 5 tons, respectively, and the plane can carry 13 tons. The profits (in thousands of dollars) generated by these are 3 for A, 4 for B, 2 for C, and 5 for D. There are three units of each available for shipment. The maximum possible profit for this would be

(a) \$7
(b) \$11
(c) \$9
(d) \$10
(e) none of these

ANSWER: e

M2.45 The following information describes a shortest-route problem with the distance in miles. How many stages will this dynamic programming problem have?

Table M2-3

From	To	Distance in miles		From	To	Distance in miles
1	2	40		3	6	49
1	3	12		4	7	23
1	5	39		4	6	76
2	4	17		5	8	27
2	5	24		6	8	53
2	6	33		7	8	35
3	5	20				

(a) 8
(b) 4
(c) 3
(d) 2
(e) 1

ANSWER: b

M2.46 For the shortest route problem described in Table M2-3, what is the distance for the shortest route?

(a) 155 miles
(b) 66 miles
(c) 59 miles
(d) 114 miles
(e) none of the above

ANSWER: c

M2.47 For the shortest route problem described in Table M2-3, which arcs comprise the shortest route?

(a) 1-2, 2-6, 6-8
(b) 1-5, 5-8
(c) 1-2, 2-6, 6-8
(d) 1-3, 3-5, 5-8
(e) none of the above

ANSWER: d

Table M2-4						
From	To	Distance In miles		From	To	Distance In miles
1	2	40		3	6	31
1	3	68		4	7	57
1	5	41		4	6	4
2	4	63		5	8	53
2	5	56		6	8	27
2	6	47		7	8	45
3	5	60				

M2.48 For the shortest route problem described in Table M2-4, what is the length of the shortest route?

(a) 205 miles
(b) 94 miles
(c) 241 miles
(d) 108 miles
(e) none of the above

ANSWER: b

M2.49 For the shortest route problem described in Table M2-4, which arcs comprise the shortest route?

(a) 1-2, 2-6, 6-8
(b) 1-3, 3-5, 5-8
(c) 1-5, 5-8
(d) 1-2, 2-4, 4-7, 7-8
(e) none of the above

ANSWER: c

The data below is a dynamic programming solution for a shortest route problem.

Table M2-5						
Stage 1	s_1	d_1	r_1	s_0	f_0	f_1
	6	6 – 7	10	7	0	10
		5 – 7	7	7	0	7
Stage 2	s_2	d_2	r_2	s_1	f_1	f_2
	5	5 – 6	3	6	10	13
	4	4 – 6	5	6	10	15
		4 – 5	6	5	7	13
	3	3 – 5	9	5	7	16
	2	2 – 5	4	5	7	11
Stage 3	s_3	d_3	r_3	s_2	f_2	f_3
	3	3 – 4	4	4	13	17
	2	2 – 4	5	4	13	18
Stage 4	s_4	d_4	r_4	s_3	f_3	f_4
	1	1 – 3	7	3	16	23
		1 – 2	3	2	11	14

M2.50 Using the data in Table M2-5, determine the minimum distance from point 1 to point 7.

(a) 18
(b) 17
(c) 23
(d) 14
(e) none of the above

ANSWER: d

M2.51 Using the data in Table M2-5, determine the optimal distance of stage 1.

(a) 0
(b) 8
(c) 7
(d) 14
(e) none of the above

ANSWER: c

M2.52 Using the data in Table M2-5, determine the optimal distance of stage 2.

(a) 10
(b) 7
(c) 8
(d) 11
(e) none of the above

ANSWER: d

M2.53 Using the data in Table M2-5, determine the optimal distance of stage 3.

(a) 22
(b) 17
(c) 24
(d) 7
(e) none of the above

ANSWER: b

M2.54 Using the data in Table M2-5, determine the optimal arc of stage 1.

(a) 3 – 7
(b) 6 – 7
(c) 5 – 7
(d) 4 – 7
(e) none of the above

ANSWER: c

M2.55 Using the data in Table M2-5, determine the optimal arc of stage 2.

(a) 4 – 6
(b) 5 – 6
(c) 4 – 5
(d) 2 – 5
(e) none of the above

ANSWER: d

M2.56 Using the data in Table M2-5, determine the optimal arc of stage 4.

(a) 1 – 2
(b) 2 – 4
(c) 1 – 3
(d) 3 – 4
(e) none of the above

ANSWER: a

M2.57 Using the data in Table M2-5, determine the optimal travel path from point 1 to 7.

(a) 1 – 2, 2 – 4, 4 – 5, 5 – 7
(b) 1 – 2, 2 – 5, 5 – 7
(c) 1 – 3, 3 – 4, 4 – 5, 5 – 7
(d) 1 – 2, 2 – 4, 4 – 6, 6 – 7
(e) none of the above

ANSWER: b

There are six cities (City 1– City 6) serviced by a particular airline. Limited routes are available, and the distances for each of these routes are presented in the table below.

From City	To City	Distance (100s miles)
1	2	5
1	4	6
2	4	6
2	3	3
2	5	5
3	4	8
3	5	8
3	6	10
4	6	3
5	6	6

M2.58 What is the minimum distance that must be traveled to get from City 1 to City 6?

(a) 1100 miles
(b) 900 miles
(c) 1,300 miles
(d) 1,400 miles
(e) none of the above

ANSWER: b

M2.59 Which routes should be traveled?

(a) 1-2, 2-3, 3-5, 5-6
(b) 1-2, 2-3, 3-4, 4-6
(c) 1-2, 2-5, 5-6
(d) 1-4, 4-6
(e) none of the above

ANSWER: d

PROBLEMS

M2.60 Develop the shortest-route network for the problem below, and determine the minimum distance from node 1 to node 7.

From	To	Distance
1	2	4
1	3	3
2	4	6
2	5	7
3	4	4
3	5	5
4	6	6
5	6	4
6	7	3

ANSWER: Shortest distance 15. From 1 to 3 to 5 to 6 to 7.

M2.61 Develop the shortest-route network for the problem below, and determine the minimum distance from node 1 to node 8.

From	To	Distance
1	2	5
1	3	3
2	4	7
2	5	5
3	4	5
3	5	8
3	6	7
4	7	4
5	7	6
6	7	5
6	8	4
7	8	5

ANSWER: Shortest distance 14. From 1 to 3 to 6 to 8.

M2.62 There are four items (A, B, C, and D) that are to be shipped by air. The weights of these are 3, 4, 5, and 3 tons, respectively. The profits (in thousands of dollars) generated by these are 5 for A, 6 for B, 7 for C, and 6 for D. There are 2 units of A, 1 unit of B, 3 units of C, and 2 units of D available to be shipped. The maximum weight is 16 tons. Use dynamic programming to determine the maximum possible profits that may be generated.

ANSWER: Maximum profit 28. Carry 2 A, 1 B, and 2 D.

M2.63 The data below details the distances that a delivery service must travel. Use dynamic programming to solve for the shortest route from City 1 to City 8.

From	To	Distance (miles)
1	2	18
1	3	14
1	4	16
2	5	9
2	6	8
3	5	7
3	6	6

From	To	Distance (miles)
4	5	8
4	6	6
4	7	5
5	8	17
6	8	16
7	8	20

ANSWER: Path 1, 3, 6, 8 is optimal with a minimum distance of 36 miles.

M2.64 Hard D. Head has decided that he wants to climb one of the world's tallest mountains. He has mapped out a number of routes between various points on the mountain, and rated each route as to difficulty. His rating scale considers a 1 as being particularly easy, and a 10 as being almost impossible.

(a) Given the information below, identify the route that would provide the easiest climb.

(b) What would be the average rating of the route?

(c) What is wrong with this approach to Mr. Head's problem?

From Point	To Point	Rating
1	2	3
1	3	4
2	3	6
3	4	2
3	5	6
4	5	4
4	6	7
4	8	8
5	6	4

From Point	To Point	Rating
5	7	5
5	8	8
5	9	10
6	7	7
6	8	7
7	8	5
7	9	6
8	9	9

ANSWER:

(a) The route with the lowest overall rating is: 1-3, 3-5, 5-9. Total rating points are 20.

(b) The average rating is 6.67 per segment.

(c) The problem is that climb segment 5-9 is included in the route-a segment that is almost impossible by his rating. He would probably be better off choosing another route.

SHORT ANSWER/FILL IN THE BLANK

M2.65 What is meant by a decision variable in a shortest-route problem?

ANSWER: It serves as identification from one node to another on an arc.

M2.66 What is the decision criterion for a shortest route problem?

ANSWER: minimization of the total distance traveled

M2.67 What is the decision criterion for a knapsack problem?

ANSWER: maximizing profit or minimizing cost of carried cargo in a container with a limited weight or limited volume characteristic

M2.68 What are the four steps in dynamic programming?

ANSWER:

1. Divide the original problem into subproblems or stages.
2. Solve the last stage for all possible conditions or states.
3. Work backward from the last stage. Solve each intermediate stage.
4. Obtain the optimal solution by solving all states sequentially.

M2.69 What are the four elements defining each stage in a dynamic programming problem?

ANSWER:

1. input
2. decision
3. output
4. return

M2.70 Identify two types of problems that can be solved by dynamic programming.

ANSWER: shortest-route problem, knapsack problem

M2.71 Discuss, briefly, the role of the transformation function.

ANSWER: The transformation function defines the relationship between stages in the dynamic programming problem.

M2.72 Discuss, briefly, the difference between a decision variable and a state variable.

ANSWER: A decision variable is what we choose; a state variable is what results.

M2.73 In the shortest-route problem, circles represent ________, and arrows represent ______.

ANSWER: nodes or "locations,"; arcs or "paths between the locations"

MODULE 3
Distribution Theory and the Normal Distribution

TRUE/FALSE

M3.1 The binomial distribution can be used when there are a small number of states of nature and/or alternatives.

ANSWER: FALSE

M3.2 Cost volume analysis deals only with costs while break-even analysis deals with both costs and revenues.

ANSWER: FALSE

M3.3 σ describes the dispersion or spread of the normal distribution.

ANSWER: TRUE

M3.4 When computing Z for a break-even analysis: as σ increases, Z decreases.

ANSWER: TRUE

M3.5 In many business break-even analyses, the normal distribution can be used to estimate demand.

ANSWER: TRUE

M3.6 If a variable other than demand is random (price, fixed or variable cost, etc.) the problem of break-even analysis becomes much more complex.

ANSWER: TRUE

M3.7 Using EOL requires one to identify the loss per unit when sales are below the break-even point.

ANSWER: TRUE

M3.8 The unit normal loss integral can be used to compute EOL.

ANSWER: TRUE

M3.9 EVPI and minimum EOL are equivalent.

ANSWER: TRUE

M3.10 In determining the EOL with the normal distribution, as D increases, the unit normal loss integral, N(D), also increases.

ANSWER: FALSE

MULTIPLE CHOICE

M3.11 In many business decisions, there are numerous states of nature and/or alternatives. These problems are best handled by

(a) constructing a large decision table and using Excel.
(b) constructing a large decision tree.
(c) using the normal distribution.
(d) using the integral loss distribution.
(e) one of the above.

ANSWER: c

M3.12 The price/unit minus the variable cost/unit is

(a) loss/unit when sales are below the break-even point.
(b) the break-even point.
(c) the Z value.
(d) EOL.
(e) none of the above

ANSWER: e

M3.13 If fixed costs were to double unexpectedly, the break-even point would be

(a) unaffected.
(b) doubled.
(c) halved.
(d) increased by a factor of four.
(e) none of the above

ANSWER: b

M3.14 If the price/unit were doubled at the same time that the variable cost/unit doubled, the break-even point would be

(a) unaffected.
(b) doubled.
(c) halved.
(d) increased by a factor of four.
(e) none of the above

ANSWER: c

M3.15 If variable cost/unit falls, the fixed cost rises, and the selling price/unit remains constant, the break-even point

(a) stays the same.
(b) decreases.
(c) increases.
(d) none of the above
(e) unable to say without more information

ANSWER: e

M3.16 Loss/unit when sales are below the break-even point is equal to

(a) (total revenue - total cost)/number of units.
(b) selling price.
(c) price/unit minus variable cost per unit.
(d) EOL.
(e) none of the above

ANSWER: a

M3.17 If the break-even volume doubles, this suggests that

(a) variable cost has increased.
(b) fixed cost has increased.
(c) selling price has decreased.
(d) any one of (a), (b), or (c)
(e) none of the above

ANSWER: d

M3.18 If the fixed costs are $10,000 and the variable cost/unit is $10 and the break-even is 100 units, what is the selling price per unit?

(a) $200.
(b) $110.
(c) $59.
(d) none of the above
(e) unable to say without more information

ANSWER: b

M3.19 The Truck Toys Company manufactures traditional wooden toy trucks. It has determined its variable cost/unit to be \$1.50/truck. Fixed costs, however, are quite high because old equipment is used in the manufacturing process and costly packaging is needed to market the toy trucks. The fixed costs are estimated at \$11,000/month. The company sells their toy trucks at a price of \$7.75/each. How many toy trucks must be sold annually to break even?

(a) ≅ 1,760 toy trucks
(b) ≅ 5500 toy trucks
(c) ≅ 20,000 toy trucks
(d) ≅ 1,879 toy trucks
(e) none of the above

ANSWER: e

M3.20 Harry Sprague makes custom bowling balls. His fixed cost is \$255,000, variable cost is \$45.50, and selling price is \$55.50. To what value must he reduce his variable cost if he wants a break-even point of 10,000 units?

(a) \$39
(b) \$37
(c) \$35
(d) \$30
(e) none of the above

ANSWER: d

M3.21 When using the normal distribution to approximate demand, which of the following is <u>not</u> true:

(a) We assume demand is normally distributed.
(b) We assume demand is a random variable.
(c) We assume 50 percent of the time demand is less than the mean.
(d) We assume the fixed cost follows a normal distribution.
(e) All of the above are true.

ANSWER: d

M3.22 Demand is estimated to be 800 units. If Z is taken to be 1.5, when the estimated average demand is 400 units, determine σ for this data.

(a) 71,111
(b) −71,111
(c) 266
(d) −266
(e) none of the above

ANSWER: d

M3.23 Tony B. is attempting to start a landscaping business. He estimates that to break-even, he will need about 150 customers. He believes that he will lose approximately $500 per customer for each customer fewer than the 150. At the moment, he believes there is an 80% probability that he will be able to secure between 130 and 170 customers, and that there is a 50/50 chance that demand will be greater than 160 customers. What is the mean or expected number of sales?

(a) 130
(b) 150
(c) 160
(d) 170
(e) none of the above

ANSWER: c

M3.24 For volumes greater than the break-even point, the opportunity loss function is

(a) a function of K, the loss per unit.
(b) 0.
(c) dependent on how much the volume is greater than the break-even point.
(d) halved.
(e) none of the above

ANSWER: b

M3.25 The opportunity loss function gives us information about

(a) the variable costs we should expect to incur.
(b) cost and revenues as a function of demand.
(c) the number of products we should expect to sell.
(d) profits lost if demand is less than the break-even point.
(e) none of the above.

ANSWER: d

M3.26 Given the following opportunity loss function, determine the loss when 1,100 units are sold.
Opportunity loss = 3 (1,000 – X) for X ≤ 1,000, otherwise 0.

(a) 0
(b) -300
(c) 300
(d) 3
(e) 600

ANSWER: a

M3.27 Given the following opportunity loss function, determine the loss when 600 units are sold.

Opportunity loss = 2 (600 – X) for X ≤ 600, otherwise 0.

(a) 2
(b) 600
(c) 1,200
(d) 0
(e) 300

ANSWER: d

M3.28 Given the following opportunity loss function, determine the loss when 400 units are sold.

Opportunity loss = 3 (1,000 – X) for X ≤ 1,000, otherwise 0.

(a) 1,200
(b) 0
(c) 600
(d) 3
(e) 1,800

ANSWER: e

M3.29 To determine the EOL with the normal distribution,

(a) one must compute D.
(b) one must compute Z.
(c) one must use the standard normal table.
(d) all of the above
(e) none of the above

ANSWER: a

M3.30 If D = 1.00, then N(1.00) is approximately

(a) 0.69000.
(b) 1.00000.
(c) 0.08332.
(d) 0.35090.
(e) none of the above

ANSWER: c

M3.31 If D = 1.01, s = 900, K = 10, and the selling price is $11, the EOL is:

(a) ≅ 10,000
(b) ≅ 9,100
(c) ≅ 736
(d) ≅ 810
(e) none of the above

ANSWER: c

M3.32 Tony B. is attempting to start a landscaping business. He estimates that to break-even, he will need about 140 customers. He believes he will lose approximately $500 per customer for each customer fewer than the 140. At the moment, he believes that there is an 80% probability that he will be able to secure at least 130 customers and that there is a 50/50 chance that demand will be greater than 150 customers. He has several marketing research firms offering (for a price, of course) to conduct a survey that will provide additional information regarding the probability of demand. How much should he be willing to spend if he decides to have a survey made?

(a) ≅ $4,000
(b) ≅ $3,000
(c) ≅ $5,000
(d) ≅ $2,700
(e) none of the above

ANSWER: d

M3.33 The computed EOL will be the same as the computed

(a) EMV.
(b) unit normal loss.
(c) break-even point.
(d) EVPI.
(e) none of the above

ANSWER: d

PROBLEMS

M3.34 The IRU Company manufactures traditional wooden pencils. They have determined their variable cost/unit to be $0.012 /pencil. Fixed costs, however, are quite high because of old processing equipment and costly packaging. The fixed costs are estimated at $140,000 /month. IRU sells their pencils at a price of $13.248/gross. (There are 144 pencils in a gross). How many grosses of pencils must be sold annually to break even?

ANSWER: selling price/pencil = 13.248/144 = 0.092 $/pencil
break-even point = 140,000/(0.092-0.012) = 1,750,000 pencils/month = 145,833 gross/year

M3.35 Jack Spratt makes candlesticks. His fixed cost is $5,000, variable cost is $3.50, and selling price, $8.50. To what value must he reduce his variable cost if he wants a break-even point of 900 units?

ANSWER:

Variable cost = (900*8.50 – 5,000)/900 = $2.94

M3.36 The break-even point was determined to be 3,000 units/month. Next month begins an increased lease payment for the production facility. The overall effect will be to increase the fixed costs by 10%. How will the break-even point be affected?

ANSWER: break-even point(NEW) = break-even point(OLD) (1.1) = 3,300

M3.37 If the break-even point was estimated to be 500 units when fixed costs are estimated at $1,200/month, what would the EMV be if average demand is estimated at 750?

ANSWER: 500 = 1,200/(P – V), therefore (P – V) = 2.4 EMV = (2.4)(750) – (1,200) = 600

M3.38 Average demand is estimated at 1,200 units/month. It is believed there is a 20% chance for demand to be higher than 1,800. Determine the μ and σ of a normal distribution that estimates demand.

ANSWER: $\mu = 1200$, $\sigma = (1{,}800 - 1{,}200)/\ (0.84) = 714$

M3.39 Given the following opportunity loss function, determine the loss when ,7000 units are sold. Opportunity loss: 6(9,000 - X) for $X \leq 9{,}000$.

ANSWER:

OL = 6(9,000 – 7,000) = 12,000

M3.40 Determine N(D) for the following D values: 0.01, 0.21, 0.77, and 1.20.

ANSWER:

N(D) = 0.3940, 0.3027, 0.1267, 0.05610

M3.41 If D = 0.75, s = 500, K = 6, and the selling price/unit = 5, determine EOL.

ANSWER:

EOL = $K\sigma$ N(D) = 6 (500) N(0.75) = 6 (500)(0.1312) = 394

SHORT ANSWER/FILL IN THE BLANK

M3.42 Break-even analysis answers what common management question?

ANSWER: At what point do revenues equal costs?

M3.43 In decision-making, we use the normal distribution when there are ________.

ANSWER: several alternatives, and the distribution is bell-shaped

M3.44 In terms of fixed costs, variable cost/unit, and the selling price/unit, what is the break-even point?

ANSWER: break-even point = fixed cost / (selling price/unit – variable cost/unit)

M3.45 Complete this mathematical statement: P(loss) = ___________

ANSWER: P(demand < break-even)

M3.46 Complete this mathematical statement: _________ = P(demand > break-even).

ANSWER: P(profit)

M3.47 The mean of a distribution locates the _________ of the distribution.

ANSWER: center or expected value

M3.48 As σ increases, the spread of a distribution ________.

ANSWER: increases

M3.49 Briefly describe the opportunity loss function.

ANSWER: a function that relates opportunity loss in dollars to sales in units

M3.50 Expected opportunity loss has the same value as ________.

ANSWER: EVPI

MODULE 4
Game Theory

TRUE/FALSE

M4.1 Game theory is a way to consider the impact of games on business.

ANSWER: FALSE

M4.2 Game theory has been used to plan warfare strategies.

ANSWER: TRUE

M4.3 Game theory is not very useful during Union negotiations.

ANSWER: FALSE

M4.4 The cornerstone of game theory is Harsanui equilibrium and Harsanui bargaining problems.

ANSWER: FALSE

M4.5 Game models are classified by the number of players, the maximum payoffs, and the likelihood of each outcome.

ANSWER: FALSE

M4.6 In a zero-sum game, what one player gains is lost by the other.

ANSWER: TRUE

M4.7 In a competitive business market, one company's strategy might be to minimize its potential losses.

ANSWER: TRUE

M4.8 In a competitive business market, one company's strategy might be to maximize its minimum profits.

ANSWER: TRUE

M4.9 The minimax criterion is equivalent to maximizing one's minimum gains.

ANSWER: TRUE

M4.10 Minimizing one's maximum losses is identical to maximizing one's minimum gains.

ANSWER: TRUE

M4.11 The upper value of the game is selected as the minimum of the maximum numbers in a column.

ANSWER: TRUE

M4.12 The lower value of the game is selected as the maximum of the minimum numbers in a row.

ANSWER: TRUE

M4.13 If the upper value of the game is larger than the lower value of the game, a saddle point condition exists.

ANSWER: FALSE

M4.14 The value of a two-person pure strategy game is equal to the lower value of the game.

ANSWER: TRUE

M4.15 When there is no saddle point, the game is a mixed strategy game.

ANSWER: TRUE

M4.16 Dominance increases the size of games by allowing additional strategies to be considered.

ANSWER: FALSE

MULTIPLE CHOICE

M4.17 Game theory is the study of

(a) how optimal strategies are formulated in conflict.
(b) decisions and their consequences.
(c) pure probability.
(d) conditional probability.
(e) none of the above

ANSWER: a

M4.18 The saddle point in a payoff matrix is always the

(a) largest number in its column and the largest number in its row.
(b) largest number in its column and the smallest number in its row.
(c) smallest number in its column and the largest number in its row.
(d) smallest number in its column and the smallest number in its row.
(e) none of the above

ANSWER: b

M4.19 The minimax criterion is to

(a) minimize one's maximum losses.
(b) maximize one's maximum losses.
(c) maximize one's minimum gains.
(d) minimize one's minimum gains.
(e) both (a) and (c) are correct

ANSWER: e

M4.20 Consider the following two-person game. The payoff for X is given in the table. X will always play strategy

	Y_1	Y_2
X_1	4	6
X_2	1	–3

(a) X_1.
(b) X_2.
(c) Y_1.
(d) Y_2.
(e) not enough information given

ANSWER: a

M4.21 Consider the following two-person game, and determine the saddle point if it exists.

	Y_1	Y_2
X_1	4	6
X_2	2	–3

(a) –3
(b) 2
(c) 4
(d) 6
(e) there is no saddle point

ANSWER: c

M4.22 CleanClothes dry cleaners is opening a pick-up and delivery service. There is only one other dry cleaner that currently offers this service. To advertise, CleanClothes is considering either newspaper ads or attaching flyers to the doors of many local homes. The payoff for each of CleanClothes' potential strategies is given in the table below. What strategy will CleanClothes (X) play?

	Y_1 (newspaper ads)	Y_2 (flyers)
X_1 (newspaper ads)	52	37
X_2 (flyers)	26	18

(a) X_1
(b) X_2
(c) Y_1
(d) Y_2
(e) not enough information given

ANSWER: a

M4.23 CleanClothes dry cleaners is opening a pick-up and delivery service. There is only one other dry cleaner that currently offers this service. To advertise, CleanClothes is considering either newspaper ads or attaching flyers to the doors of many local homes. The payoff for each of CleanClothes' potential strategies is given in the table below. What strategy will the existing dry cleaners (Y) play?

	Y_1 (newspaper ads)	Y_2 (flyers)
X_1 (newspaper ads)	52	37
X_2 (flyers)	26	18

(a) X_1
(b) X_2
(c) Y_1
(d) Y_2
(e) not enough information given

ANSWER: d

M4.24 CleanClothes dry cleaners is opening a pick-up and delivery service. There is only one other dry cleaner that currently offers this service. To advertise, CleanClothes is considering either newspaper ads or attaching flyers to the doors of many local homes. The payoff for each of CleanClothes' potential strategies is given in the table below. What is the saddle point, if any, of this game?

	Y_1 (newspaper ads)	Y_2 (flyers)
X_1 (newspaper ads)	52	37
X_2 (flyers)	26	18

(a) 37
(b) 17
(c) 16
(d) 8
(e) there is no saddle point
ANSWER: a

M4.25 Bagles RUS is expanding into a high-growth suburban area. To promote business and lure customers from the competing Wer Bagel store, they are considering offering a free dozen bagels to the first 50 customers or radio advertisement. The payoff for Bagels RUS is given in the table below. What is Bagels RUS' (X) best strategy?

	Y_1	Y_2
X_1	3	6
X_2	2	–2

(a) X_1
(b) X_2
(c) Y_1
(d) Y_2
(e) none of the above

ANSWER: a

M4.26 Bagles RUS is expanding into a high-growth suburban area. To promote business and lure customers from the competing Wer Bagel store, they are considering offering a free dozen bagels to the first 50 customers or radio advertisement. The payoff for Bagels RUS is given in the table below. What is Wer Bagels' (Y) best strategy?

	Y_1	Y_2
X_1	3	6
X_2	2	-2

(a) X_1
(b) X_2
(c) Y_1
(d) Y_2
(e) none of the above

ANSWER: c

M4.27 Bagles RUS is expanding into a high-growth suburban area. To promote business and lure customers from the competing Wer Bagel store, they are considering offering a free dozen bagels to the first 50 customers or radio advertisement. The payoff for Bagels RUS is given in the table below. What is the saddle point, if any, for the bagel stores?

	Y_1	Y_2
X_1	3	6
X_2	2	-2

(a) 3
(b) 6
(c) 2
(d) -2
(e) there is no saddle point

ANSWER: a

M4.28 In a two-person, zero sum game,

(a) the sum of losses equals zero.
(b) the sum of gains equals zero.
(c) the sum of losses for one player must equal the sum of gains for the other player.
(d) none of the above

ANSWER: c

M4.29 The value of a mixed strategy game is

(a) the maximum outcome of the game.
(b) the minimum outcome of the game.
(c) the outcome of the game played once.
(d) the average outcome of the game played an infinite number of times.
(e) none of the above

ANSWER: d

M4.30 If it is known what percentage of the time each player plays each strategy, then the value of a two-person game can be computed

(a) from only the optimal strategy row.
(b) from only the optimal strategy column.
(c) from any column or row.
(d) except for a zero sum game.
(e) none of the above

ANSWER: c

M4.31 Considering the following two-person game, what percentage of the time should X play strategy X_2?

	Y_1	Y_2
X_1	6	3
X_2	2	8

(a) 1/3
(b) 2/3
(c) 4/9
(d) 5/9
(e) none of the above

ANSWER: a

M4.32 Considering the following two-person game, what percentage of the time should Y play strategy Y_1?

	Y_1	Y_2
X_1	6	3
X_2	2	8

(a) 1/3
(b) 2/3
(c) 4/9
(d) 5/9
(e) none of the above

ANSWER: d

M4.33 Considering the following two-person game, the value of the game (if played many times) is

	Y_1	Y_2
X_1	6	3
X_2	2	8

(a) 19.00.
(b) 4.75.
(c) 4.67.
(d) unable to be computed, as the α was not given.

ANSWER: c

M4.34 The value of the following game is 2.5. Therefore,

	Y_1	Y_2
X_1	3	2
X_2	−1	6

(a) X_1 will gain 2.5 points.
(b) X_2 will gain 2.5 points.
(c) X will gain 2.5 points.
(d) Y will gain 2.5 points.
(e) none of the above

ANSWER: c

M4.35 Given the following two-person game, which strategy can be eliminated by use of dominance?

	Y_1	Y_2
X_1	13	9
X_2	6	8
X_3	12	14

(a) X_1
(b) X_2
(c) X_3
(d) Y_1
(e) Y_2

ANSWER: b

PROBLEMS

M4.36 Given the following two-person game, what strategy should the players play?

	Y_1	Y_2
X_1	15	20
X_2	8	4

ANSWER: This is a pure strategy. X should play X_1 and Y should play Y_1.

M4.37 What is the value of the following two-person game?

	Y_1	Y_2
X_1	15	20
X_2	8	4

ANSWER: This is a pure strategy with value 15.

M4.38 Given the following two-person game, what strategy should the players play?

	Y_1	Y_2
X_1	6	2
X_2	–4	1

ANSWER: This is a pure strategy. X should play X_1 and Y should play Y_2.

M4.39 What is the value of the following two-person game?

	Y_1	Y_2
X_1	6	2
X_2	–4	7

ANSWER: The value is 3.33

M4.40 Given the following two-person game, what strategy should the players play?

	Y_1	Y_2
X_1	12	16
X_2	14	8

ANSWER: This is a mixed strategy. $12Q + 14(1 - Q) = 16Q + 8(1 - Q) ==> Q = 3/5$
$12P + 16(1 - P) = 14P + 8(1 - P) ==> P = 4/5$

M4.41 Given the following two-person game, what strategy should the players play?

	Y_1	Y_2
X_1	6	−2
X_2	−1	4

ANSWER: This is a mixed strategy. $6Q - (1 - Q) = -2Q + 4(1 - Q) ==> Q = 5/13$
$6P - 2(1 - P) = -P + 4(1 - P) ==> P = 6/13$

SHORT ANSWER/ESSAY

M4.42 List at least two game theory applications.

ANSWER: war, negotiations, business

M4.43 The cornerstone of modern game theory includes the concepts developed by this person.

ANSWER: John Nash

M4.44 Describe a two-person zero sum game.

ANSWER: a game of two contestants in which the sum of gains of one player equals the sum of losses of the other player

M4.45 What is meant by a mixed strategy game?

ANSWER: a game in which there is no saddle point

M4.46 What is meant by the value of a mixed strategy game?

ANSWER: the average or expected game outcome if the game is played an infinite number of times

M4.47 Explain the principle of dominance as used in game theory.

ANSWER: used to eliminate strategies that would not ever be played

MODULE 5
Mathematical Tools: Determinants and Matrices

TRUE/FALSE

M5.1 An $n \times m$ determinant is the same as an $n \times m$ matrix.

ANSWER: FALSE

M5.2 Determinants are useful in solving a set of simultaneous equations.

ANSWER: TRUE

M5.3 A determinant has a single numerical value.

ANSWER: TRUE

M5.4 An $n \times m$ matrix, when added to an $m \times n$ matrix ($n \neq m$), yields an $n \times n$ matrix.

ANSWER: FALSE

M5.5 The matrix multiplication (**AB**), where **A** and **B** are any matrix, is equal to the matrix multiplication (**BA**).

ANSWER: FALSE

M5.6 An $n \times m$ matrix, when multiplied by an $m \times n$ matrix, yields an $n \times n$ matrix.

ANSWER: TRUE

M5.7 An $n \times m$ matrix, when multiplied by an $m \times p$ matrix, yields an $n \times p$ matrix.

ANSWER: TRUE

M5.8 A cofactor of a matrix is the set of numbers that remains after a given row and column have been removed from a matrix.

ANSWER: TRUE

M5.9 An adjoint is the transpose of the matrix of cofactors.

ANSWER: TRUE

M5.10 $\mathbf{A}^{-1}\mathbf{A} = \mathbf{A}\,\mathbf{A}^{-1} = \mathbf{I}$

ANSWER: TRUE

M5.11 An $n \times m$ matrix multiplied by a $p \times m$ matrix yields an $n \times p$ matrix.

ANSWER: FALSE

M5.12 The subtraction of an $n \times m$ matrix from an $n \times m$ matrix yields an $n \times m$ matrix.

ANSWER: TRUE

M5.13 We can develop an $n \times m$ matrix by the addition of an $n \times m$ matrix and an $n \times p$ matrix, where $p < n$.

ANSWER: FALSE

M5.14 We can develop an $n \times m$ matrix by adding an $n \times p$ matrix and an $n \times r$ matrix where $p + r = m$.

ANSWER: FALSE

M5.15 We can always perform the matrix multiplication **AA**.

ANSWER: FALSE

M5.16 All matrices have the same number of rows as columns.

ANSWER: FALSE

M5.17 A matrix having only a single column with multiple rows, or a single row with multiple columns, is called a vector.

ANSWER: TRUE

M5.18 A matrix multiplied by its inverse is always equal to the identity matrix.

ANSWER: TRUE

M5.19 We can find only the inverse of square matrices.

ANSWER: TRUE

M5.20 An identity matrix has 1's in all positions of the matrix.

ANSWER: FALSE

M5.21 We cannot multiply an $n \times m$ matrix by a $1 \times m$ matrix.

ANSWER: TRUE

M5.22 We cannot multiply an $n \times m$ matrix by an $m \times 1$ matrix.

ANSWER: FALSE

M5.23 The value of the determinant of the following matrix is 7. $\begin{bmatrix} 2 & 3 \\ 1 & 5 \end{bmatrix}$

ANSWER: TRUE

M5.24 The value of the determinant of the following matrix is 7. $\begin{bmatrix} 3 & 5 \\ 2 & 6 \end{bmatrix}$

ANSWER: FALSE

M5.25 $\begin{bmatrix} 2 & 3 \\ 1 & 5 \end{bmatrix} \text{x} \begin{bmatrix} 3 & 5 \\ 2 & 6 \end{bmatrix} = \begin{bmatrix} 12 & 28 \\ 13 & 35 \end{bmatrix}$

ANSWER: TRUE

M5.26 $\begin{bmatrix} 2 & 3 \\ 1 & 5 \end{bmatrix} \text{x} \begin{bmatrix} 2 \\ 1 \end{bmatrix} = \begin{bmatrix} 7 & 7 \end{bmatrix}$

ANSWER: TRUE

M5.27 We cannot multiply a $1 \times m$ matrix by an $n \times m$ matrix.

ANSWER: TRUE

M5.28 We cannot multiply an $n \times 1$ matrix by an $n \times m$ matrix.

ANSWER: TRUE

M5.29 $\begin{bmatrix} 3 & 2 \end{bmatrix} \begin{bmatrix} 1 & 0 \\ 0 & 1 \end{bmatrix} \begin{bmatrix} 4 \\ 1 \end{bmatrix} = \begin{bmatrix} 14 \end{bmatrix}$

ANSWER: TRUE

M5.30 $\begin{bmatrix} 4 \\ 1 \end{bmatrix} \begin{bmatrix} 1 & 0 \\ 0 & 1 \end{bmatrix} \begin{bmatrix} 3 & 2 \end{bmatrix} = \begin{bmatrix} 14 \end{bmatrix}$

ANSWER: FALSE

M5.31 Matrices can be used by television station executives to describe the channel switching behavior of their eight o'clock TV news audience.

ANSWER: TRUE

M5.32 As a mathematical tool, determinants are of value in helping to solve a series of simultaneous equations.

ANSWER: TRUE

M5.33 A set of *simultaneous equations* can be solved through the use of determinants by setting up a proportion of two special determinants for each unknown variable.

ANSWER: TRUE

5.34 To create the transpose of a given matrix, we simply interchange the rows with the columns.

ANSWER: TRUE

MULTIPLE CHOICE

M5.35 A matrix is

(a) a determination of probability.
(b) a qualitative tool used to solve a set of simultaneous equations.
(c) an array of numbers.
(d) a single column of non-zero numbers.
(e) none of the above

ANSWER: c

M5.36 The value of the determinant $\begin{vmatrix} a & b \\ c & d \end{vmatrix}$ is

(a) ab – cd.
(b) ac – bd.
(c) ab + cd.
(d) ac + bd.
(e) ad – cb.

ANSWER: e

M5.37 The correct determinant value for the determinant $\begin{vmatrix} 8 & 6 \\ 3 & 4 \end{vmatrix}$ would be

(a) (8)(4)(3)(6).
(b) (8)(4) + (3)(6).
(c) (8)(4) – (3)(6).
(d) (8)(3) – (6)(4).
(e) (8)(6) – (3)(4).

ANSWER: c

M5.38 An $n \times m$ matrix, when added to an $n \times m$ matrix, yields

(a) an $n \times m$ matrix.
(b) an $m \times n$ matrix.
(c) a $2(n \times m)$ matrix.
(d) a $2n \times 2m$ matrix.
(e) none of the above

ANSWER: a

M5.39 An $n \times m$ matrix, when added to an $m \times n$ matrix, yields

(a) an $n \times m$ matrix.
(b) an $m \times n$ matrix.
(c) a $2(n \times m)$ matrix.
(d) a $2n \times 2m$ matrix.
(e) none of the above

ANSWER: e

M5.40 An $n \times m$ matrix, when multiplied by an $n \times m$ matrix, yields

(a) an $n \times m$ matrix.
(b) an $m \times n$ matrix.
(c) an $n^2 \times m^2$ matrix.
(d) an $(n \times m)^2$ matrix.
(e) none of the above

ANSWER: e

M5.41 An $n \times m$ matrix, when multiplied by an $m \times n$ matrix, yields

(a) an $n \times m$ matrix.
(b) an $m \times n$ matrix.
(c) an $n \times n$ matrix.
(d) an $n \times m \times n$ matrix.
(e) none of the above

ANSWER: c

M5.42 An $n \times n$ matrix, when multiplied by an $n \times n$ matrix, yields

(a) an $n \times n$ matrix.
(b) a $2n$ matrix.
(c) an $n^2 + n^2$ matrix.
(d) an $(n \times n)^2$ matrix.
(e) none of the above

ANSWER: a

M5.43 An $n \times m$ matrix, when multiplied by an $m \times p$ matrix, yields

(a) an $n \times m \times m \times p$ matrix.
(b) an $n \times m \times p$ matrix.
(c) an $n \times p$ matrix.
(d) a p matrix.
(e) none of the above

ANSWER: c

M5.44 Add the matrices $\begin{bmatrix} 2 & 3 \\ 1 & 4 \end{bmatrix}$ & $\begin{bmatrix} 6 & 1 \\ -1 & 2 \end{bmatrix}$

(a) cannot be added

(b) $\begin{bmatrix} 8 & 4 \\ 0 & 6 \end{bmatrix}$

(c) $\begin{bmatrix} 12 & -1 \\ 3 & 8 \end{bmatrix}$

(d) $\begin{bmatrix} 5 & 7 \\ 5 & 1 \end{bmatrix}$

(e) $\begin{bmatrix} 5 & 1 \\ 5 & 7 \end{bmatrix}$

ANSWER: b

M5.45 Element 1,1 of the inverse of the matrix $\begin{bmatrix} 3 & 5 \\ 4 & 7 \end{bmatrix}$ is

(a) –5.
(b) –4.
(c) 3.
(d) 7.
(e) none of the above

ANSWER: d

M5.46 Element 1,2 of the inverse of the matrix $\begin{bmatrix} 3 & 5 \\ 4 & 7 \end{bmatrix}$ is

(a) –5.
(b) –4.
(c) 3.
(d) 7.
(e) none of the above

ANSWER: a

M5.47 Element 2,1 of the inverse of the matrix $\begin{bmatrix} 3 & 5 \\ 4 & 7 \end{bmatrix}$ is

(a) –5.
(b) –4.
(c) 3.
(d) 7.
(e) none of the above

ANSWER: b

M5.48 Element 2,2 of the inverse of the matrix $\begin{bmatrix} 3 & 5 \\ 4 & 7 \end{bmatrix}$ is

(a) –5.
(b) –4.
(c) 3.
(d) 7.
(e) none of the above

ANSWER: c

M5.49 Element 1,1 of the inverse of the matrix $\begin{bmatrix} 6 & 5 \\ 5 & 4 \end{bmatrix}$ is

(a) –5.
(b) –4.
(c) 4.
(d) 5.
(e) none of the above

ANSWER: b

M5.50 Multiply matrix $\begin{bmatrix} 7 & 1 \\ -3 & 2 \end{bmatrix}$ by $\begin{bmatrix} 4 \\ 3 \end{bmatrix}$

(a) $\begin{bmatrix} 31 & -6 \end{bmatrix}$
(b) $\begin{bmatrix} 31 \\ -6 \end{bmatrix}$
(c) $\begin{bmatrix} -6 & 31 \end{bmatrix}$
(d) $\begin{bmatrix} -6 \\ 31 \end{bmatrix}$
(e) none of the above

ANSWER: b

M5.51 Multiply matrix $\begin{bmatrix} 7 & 1 & 0 \\ -3 & 0 & 2 \\ 1 & 3 & 1 \end{bmatrix}$ by $\begin{bmatrix} 6 & 0 & -1 \\ -2 & -1 & 0 \\ 0 & 1 & 0 \end{bmatrix}$.

(a) $\begin{bmatrix} 40 & -1 \\ -18 & 2 \\ 0 & -1 \end{bmatrix}$

(b) $\begin{bmatrix} 40 & -18 & 0 \\ -1 & 2 & -2 \\ -7 & 3 & -1 \end{bmatrix}$

(c) $\begin{bmatrix} 40 & -1 & -7 \\ -18 & 2 & 3 \\ 0 & -2 & -1 \end{bmatrix}$

(d) $\begin{bmatrix} 40 & 1 & 7 \\ 18 & 2 & 3 \\ 0 & 2 & 1 \end{bmatrix}$

(e) none of the above

ANSWER: c

M5.52 To solve the following set of simultaneous equations, the determinant solution for X would be

$$4X + 3Y = 7$$
$$2X - 2Y = 5$$

(a) $X = \begin{vmatrix} 7 & 3 \\ 5 & -2 \end{vmatrix} \div \begin{vmatrix} 4 & 3 \\ 2 & -2 \end{vmatrix}$

(b) $X = \begin{vmatrix} 4 & 3 \\ 2 & -2 \end{vmatrix} \div \begin{vmatrix} 4 & 7 \\ 2 & 5 \end{vmatrix}$

(c) $X = \begin{vmatrix} 4 & 3 \\ 2 & -2 \end{vmatrix} \div \begin{vmatrix} 7 & 3 \\ 5 & -2 \end{vmatrix}$

(d) $X = \begin{vmatrix} 4 & 7 \\ 2 & 5 \end{vmatrix} \div \begin{vmatrix} 4 & 3 \\ 2 & -2 \end{vmatrix}$

(e) none of the above

ANSWER: a

M5.53 To solve the following set of simultaneous equations, the determinant solution for Y would be

$$4X + 3Y = 7$$
$$2X - 2Y = 5$$

(a) $Y = \begin{vmatrix} 7 & 3 \\ 5 & -2 \end{vmatrix} \div \begin{vmatrix} 4 & 3 \\ 2 & -2 \end{vmatrix}$

(b) $Y = \begin{vmatrix} 4 & 3 \\ 2 & -2 \end{vmatrix} \div \begin{vmatrix} 4 & 7 \\ 2 & 5 \end{vmatrix}$

(c) $Y = \begin{vmatrix} 4 & 3 \\ 2 & -2 \end{vmatrix} \div \begin{vmatrix} 7 & 3 \\ 5 & -2 \end{vmatrix}$

(d) $Y = \begin{vmatrix} 4 & 7 \\ 2 & 5 \end{vmatrix} \div \begin{vmatrix} 4 & 3 \\ 2 & -2 \end{vmatrix}$

(e) none of the above

ANSWER: d

M5.54 The value of the determinant $\begin{vmatrix} 6 & 3 \\ 2 & 10 \end{vmatrix}$ is

(a) 60.
(b) 6.
(c) 54.
(d) 21.
(e) none of the above

ANSWER: c

M5.55 The value of the determinant $\begin{vmatrix} 4 & 5 \\ -2 & 8 \end{vmatrix}$ is

(a) 30.
(b) 42.
(c) 16.
(d) 20.
(e) none of the above

ANSWER: b

M5.56 The value of the determinant $\begin{vmatrix} 6 & 2 \\ 4 & 3 \end{vmatrix}$ is

(a) 6243.
(b) 24.
(c) 15.
(d) 10.
(e) none of the above

ANSWER: d

M5.57 The value of the determinant $\begin{vmatrix} 6 & 3 \\ 8 & 4 \end{vmatrix}$ is

(a) 21.
(b) 50.
(c) 0.
(d) 48.
(e) none of the above

ANSWER: c

M5.58 The value of the determinant $\begin{vmatrix} -6 & -2 \\ -4 & -8 \end{vmatrix}$ is

(a) –8.
(b) +8.
(c) –40.
(d) +40.
(e) none of the above

ANSWER: d

M5.59 The value of the determinant $\begin{vmatrix} 2 & 3 & 1 \\ 4 & 8 & 2 \\ 6 & 1 & 5 \end{vmatrix}$ is

(a) 128.
(b) 96.
(c) 8.
(d) 232.
(e) none of the above

ANSWER: c

M5.60 The value of the determinant $\begin{vmatrix} 2 & 3 & 1 \\ 3 & 4 & 1 \\ 1 & 2 & 5 \end{vmatrix}$ is

(a) 8.
(b) 7.
(c) 4.
(d) -4.
(e) none of the above

ANSWER: d

M5.61 The value of the determinant $\begin{vmatrix} 2 & 5 & 2 \\ 3 & 0 & 0 \\ 4 & 3 & 4 \end{vmatrix}$ is

(a) 2.
(b) 14.
(c) -42.
(d) 42.
(e) none of the above

ANSWER: c

M5.62 The value of the determinant $\begin{vmatrix} 4 & 2 & 0 \\ 4 & 0 & 3 \\ 0 & 6 & 1 \end{vmatrix}$ is

(a) not able to be determined.
(b) 0.
(c) 80.
(d) -80.
(e) none of the above

ANSWER: d

M5.63 An $n \times m$ matrix when added to a $p \times m$ matrix $(p < m)$, yields

(a) an $n \times m$ matrix.
(b) an $n \times p$ matrix.
(c) an $m \times p$ matrix.
(d) an $m \times m$ matrix.
(e) none of the above

ANSWER: e

M5.64 Add the matrices $\begin{bmatrix} 1 & 2 \\ 2 & 5 \\ 4 & 3 \end{bmatrix}$ & $\begin{bmatrix} 2 & 3 \\ 1 & 4 \end{bmatrix}$.

(a) $\begin{bmatrix} 3 & 5 \\ 3 & 9 \\ 4 & 3 \end{bmatrix}$

(b) $\begin{bmatrix} 1 & 2 \\ 4 & 8 \\ 5 & 7 \end{bmatrix}$

(c) $\begin{bmatrix} 3 & 5 \\ 3 & 9 \end{bmatrix}$

(d) $\begin{bmatrix} 4 & 8 \\ 5 & 7 \end{bmatrix}$

(e) none of the above

ANSWER: e

M5.65 $\begin{vmatrix} 1 & 3 \\ 5 & 4 \end{vmatrix} =$

(a) 11
(b) -11
(c) 15
(d) 4
(e) none of the above

ANSWER: b

M5.66 $\begin{bmatrix} 3 & 1 \\ 4 & 5 \end{bmatrix}\begin{bmatrix} 1 & 3 \\ 5 & 4 \end{bmatrix} =$

(a) $\begin{bmatrix} 13 & 8 \\ 32 & 29 \end{bmatrix}$

(b) $\begin{bmatrix} 32 & 29 \\ 13 & 8 \end{bmatrix}$

(c) $\begin{bmatrix} 13 & 32 \\ 8 & 29 \end{bmatrix}$

(d) $\begin{bmatrix} 8 & 13 \\ 29 & 32 \end{bmatrix}$

(e) none of the above

ANSWER: d

M5.67 $\begin{bmatrix} 5 & 7 \\ 6 & 4 \end{bmatrix}\begin{bmatrix} 1 & 5 \end{bmatrix} =$

(a) $\begin{bmatrix} 40 \\ 6 \end{bmatrix}$

(b) $\begin{bmatrix} 5 & 35 \\ 6 & 20 \end{bmatrix}$

(c) $\begin{bmatrix} 0 \end{bmatrix}$

(d) $\begin{bmatrix} 40 & 26 \end{bmatrix}$

(e) none of the above

ANSWER: e

M5.68 $\begin{bmatrix} 1 & 5 \end{bmatrix} \begin{bmatrix} 5 & 7 \\ 6 & 4 \end{bmatrix} =$

(a) $\begin{bmatrix} 35 & 27 \end{bmatrix}$

(b) $\begin{bmatrix} 35 \\ 27 \end{bmatrix}$

(c) $\begin{bmatrix} 5 & 35 \\ 6 & 20 \end{bmatrix}$

(d) $\begin{bmatrix} 20 & 6 \\ 35 & 5 \end{bmatrix}$

(e) none of the above

ANSWER: a

M5.69 $\begin{bmatrix} 3 & 4 \\ 6 & 7 \end{bmatrix}^{-1} =$

(a) $\begin{bmatrix} .333 & .250 \\ .167 & .143 \end{bmatrix}$

(b) $\begin{bmatrix} -2.333 & 1.333 \\ 2 & -1 \end{bmatrix}$

(c) $\begin{bmatrix} 1.333 & -2.333 \\ -1 & 2 \end{bmatrix}$

(d) $\begin{bmatrix} .167 & .143 \\ .250 & .333 \end{bmatrix}$

(e) none of the above

ANSWER: b

M5.70 $\begin{bmatrix} 3 & 5 & 2 \\ 1 & 7 & 6 \\ 5 & 3 & 1 \end{bmatrix} - \begin{bmatrix} 2 & 4 & 3 \\ 5 & 1 & 4 \\ 2 & 2 & 0 \end{bmatrix} =$

(a) $\begin{bmatrix} 1 & 0 & 0 \\ 0 & 1 & 0 \\ 0 & 0 & 1 \end{bmatrix}$

(b) $\begin{bmatrix} 5 & 9 & 5 \\ 6 & 8 & 10 \\ 7 & 5 & 1 \end{bmatrix}$

(c) $\begin{bmatrix} 1 & 1 & -1 \\ -4 & 6 & 2 \\ 3 & 1 & 1 \end{bmatrix}$

(d) $\begin{bmatrix} -1 & -1 & 1 \\ 4 & -6 & -2 \\ -3 & -1 & -1 \end{bmatrix}$

(e) none of the above

ANSWER: c

M5.71 Transpose $\begin{bmatrix} 1 & 7 & 3 \\ 5 & 2 & 8 \\ 4 & 9 & 0 \end{bmatrix} =$

(a) $\begin{bmatrix} 3 & 7 & 1 \\ 8 & 2 & 5 \\ 0 & 9 & 4 \end{bmatrix}$

(b) $\begin{bmatrix} 1 & 5 & 4 \\ 7 & 2 & 9 \\ 3 & 8 & 0 \end{bmatrix}$

(c) $\begin{bmatrix} 4 & 9 & 0 \\ 8 & 2 & 5 \\ 1 & 7 & 3 \end{bmatrix}$

(d) $\begin{bmatrix} 4 & 1 & 2 \\ 7 & 5 & 3 \\ 8 & 0 & 9 \end{bmatrix}$

(e) none of the above

ANSWER: b

M5.72 $\begin{vmatrix} 5 & 3 & 4 \\ 2 & 1 & 0 \\ 4 & 2 & 3 \end{vmatrix} =$

(a) 0
(b) 3
(c) -5
(d) -3
(e) none of the above

ANSWER: d

M5.73 $\begin{bmatrix} 3 & 3 & 3 \\ 2 & 2 & 2 \\ 1 & 1 & 1 \end{bmatrix}^{-1} =$

(a) $\begin{bmatrix} .333 & .333 & .333 \\ .5 & .5 & .5 \\ 1. & 1. & 1. \end{bmatrix}$

(b) $\begin{bmatrix} .333 & .5 & .1 \\ .5 & .333 & .5 \\ .1 & .5 & .333 \end{bmatrix}$

(c) $\begin{bmatrix} .333 & .5 & 1. \\ .333 & .5 & 1. \\ .333 & .5 & 1. \end{bmatrix}$

(d) $\begin{bmatrix} 1 & 0 & 0 \\ 0 & 1 & 0 \\ 0 & 0 & 1 \end{bmatrix}$

(e) none of the above

ANSWER: e

M5.74 $\begin{bmatrix} 2 & 3 & 7 \\ 4 & 2 & 1 \\ 5 & 6 & 8 \end{bmatrix}^{-1} =$

(a) $\begin{bmatrix} .270 & .486 & -.297 \\ -.730 & -.514 & .703 \\ .378 & .081 & -.216 \end{bmatrix}$

(b) $\begin{bmatrix} .197 & .310 & .089 \\ -.432 & -.477 & -.102 \\ .730 & .103 & .982 \end{bmatrix}$

(c) $\begin{bmatrix} .371 & -.204 & -.401 \\ .397 & .203 & .215 \\ .201 & -.403 & -.112 \end{bmatrix}$

(d) $\begin{bmatrix} .201 & -.403 & -.112 \\ .197 & -.432 & .103 \\ .317 & .215 & .379 \end{bmatrix}$

(e) none of the above

ANSWER: a

M5.75 Matrices and determinants are useful for

(a) Markov analysis.
(b) game theory.
(c) linear programming.
(d) all of the above
(e) none of the above

ANSWER: d

M5.76 Which of the following statements is *not* true about *Matrix(ces)*?

(a) A matrix is a display of numbers arranged in rows and columns.
(b) Matrices are usually enclosed in parentheses or brackets.
(c) Matrices are used as an effective means of presenting or summarizing business data.
(d) Matrices cannot be considered as a quantitative tool.
(e) none of the above

ANSWER: d

M5.77 Which of the following mathematical operations cannot be performed on Matrices?

(a) matrix addition, subtraction, and multiplication
(b) matrix inversion
(c) transposing a matrix
(d) multiple regression
(e) none of the above

ANSWER: d

M5.78 Which one of the following is *not* a step in computing a matrix of cofactors?

(a) selecting an element in the original matrix
(b) calculating the value of the determinant of the cofactor
(c) returning to step 1 and continue until all elements in the original matrix have been replaced by their cofactor values
(d) interchanging the rows with the columns
(e) none of the above

ANSWER: d

PROBLEMS

M5.79 Evaluate the determinant $\begin{vmatrix} 16 & 12 \\ 24 & 10 \end{vmatrix}$.

ANSWER: –128

M5.80 Evaluate the determinant $\begin{vmatrix} 4 & 6 & 2 \\ 8 & 3 & -1 \\ -2 & 2 & 5 \end{vmatrix}$.

ANSWER: –116

M5.81 Evaluate the determinant $\begin{vmatrix} 2 & 6 & 3 & 0 \\ 4 & -3 & -2 & 1 \\ -1 & 4 & -2 & -1 \\ 3 & 1 & 4 & 2 \end{vmatrix}$.

ANSWER: 126

M5.82 Add the matrices $\begin{bmatrix} 4 & 6 \\ 2 & 3 \end{bmatrix}$ & $\begin{bmatrix} 4 & 6 \\ 2 & 3 \end{bmatrix}$.

ANSWER: $\begin{bmatrix} 8 & 12 \\ 4 & 6 \end{bmatrix}$

M5.83 Multiply the matrix $\begin{bmatrix} a & b \\ c & d \end{bmatrix}$ by $\begin{bmatrix} a & b \\ c & d \end{bmatrix}$.

ANSWER: $\begin{bmatrix} aa + bc & ab + bd \\ ac + cd & bc + dd \end{bmatrix}$

M5.84 Multiply the matrix $\begin{bmatrix} 4 & 6 \\ 2 & 3 \end{bmatrix}$ by $\begin{bmatrix} 4 & 6 \\ 2 & 3 \end{bmatrix}$.

ANSWER: $\begin{bmatrix} 28 & 42 \\ 14 & 21 \end{bmatrix}$

M5.85 Determine the inverse of the matrix $\begin{bmatrix} 1 & 4 & 0 \\ 0 & 4 & 11 \\ 0 & 1 & 3 \end{bmatrix}$.

ANSWER: $\begin{bmatrix} 1 & -12 & 44 \\ 0 & 3 & -11 \\ 0 & -1 & 4 \end{bmatrix}$

M5.86 Evaluate the determinant $\begin{bmatrix} 1 & 7 & 9 & 5 & 7 & 4 \\ 2 & 4 & 5 & 4 & 4 & 0 \\ 7 & 2 & 9 & 1 & 2 & 5 \\ 3 & 6 & 5 & 9 & 6 & 2 \\ 1 & 7 & 9 & 5 & 7 & 4 \\ 3 & 7 & 4 & 1 & 7 & 6 \end{bmatrix}$.

ANSWER: 0. Note that row 1 and row 5 are the same, and columns 2 and 4 are the same.

M5.87 Evaluate the determinant $\begin{bmatrix} 1 & 7 & 9 \\ 2 & 4 & 5 \\ 7 & 2 & 9 \end{bmatrix}$.

ANSWER: -71

M5.88 Multiple matrix $\begin{bmatrix} 1 & 2 & 3 \end{bmatrix}$ by $\begin{bmatrix} 5 & 0 & 0 \\ 4 & 2 & 1 \\ 0 & 3 & 0 \end{bmatrix}$.

ANSWER: $\begin{bmatrix} 13 & 13 & 2 \end{bmatrix}$

M5.89 Find the inverse of $\begin{bmatrix} 1 & 2 & 4 \\ 2 & 3 & 1 \\ 3 & 1 & 5 \end{bmatrix}$.

ANSWER: $\begin{bmatrix} -0.500 & 0.215 & 0.357 \\ 0.250 & 0.250 & -0.250 \\ 0.250 & -0.179 & 0.360 \end{bmatrix}$

M5.90 Find the inverse of $\begin{bmatrix} 1 & 1 & 4 \\ 2 & 0 & 1 \\ 3 & 1 & 5 \end{bmatrix}$.

ANSWER: no inverse exists - determinant = 0

SHORT ANSWER/FILL IN THE BLANK

M5.91 Describe a matrix.

ANSWER: an array of numbers, of size $n \times m$, that has more than a single numerical value

M5.92 What size matrix is yielded when an $n \times m$ matrix is added to an $n \times m$ matrix?

ANSWER: $n \times m$

M5.93 What size matrix is yielded when an $n \times m$ matrix is multiplied by an $m \times n$ matrix?

ANSWER: $n \times n$

M5.94 What size matrix is yielded when an $n \times m$ matrix is multiplied by an $m \times p$ matrix?

ANSWER: $n \times p$

M5.95 What size matrix is yielded when an $n \times m$ matrix is multiplied by an $m \times p$ matrix, the result of which is multiplied by a $p \times r$ matrix?

ANSWER: $n \times r$

M5.96 What size matrix is yielded when an $n \times m$ matrix is multiplied by an $n \times p$ matrix?

ANSWER: an $n \times m$ matrix cannot be multiplied by an $n \times p$ matrix

M5.97 Define what a matrix transpose is.

ANSWER: a matrix's rows and columns are interchanged

M5.98 Why does the matrix $\begin{pmatrix} +4 & +8 \\ +3 & +6 \end{pmatrix}$ have no definable inverse?

ANSWER: the determinant = 0

M5.99 Describe the adjoint.

ANSWER: Adjoint is the transpose of the matrix of the cofactors.

MODULE 6
Calculus-Based Optimization

TRUE/FALSE

M6.1 The slope of a straight line is constant when measured at any point along the line.

ANSWER: TRUE

M6.2 The slope of a nonlinear function varies depending on the point along the line at which it is measured.

ANSWER: TRUE

M6.3 To determine the slope of a nonlinear function at a point, we must find the slope of a line tangent to the point.

ANSWER: TRUE

M6.4 The derivative of a constant is one.

ANSWER: FALSE

M6.5 The second derivative tells about the slope of the first derivative.

ANSWER: TRUE

M6.6 A zero value for the derivative of a nonlinear function always indicates the location of a maximum or minimum.

ANSWER: FALSE

M6.7 The first step in attempting to find a minimum or maximum of a nonlinear function is to take the derivative of the function, set it equal to zero, and solve for x.

ANSWER: TRUE

M6.8 At a minimum of a nonlinear function, the first derivative is equal to zero, and the second derivative is positive.

ANSWER: TRUE

M6.9 If, for a nonlinear function, the first derivative is equal to zero and the second derivative is equal to zero, we have both a maximum and a minimum occurring simultaneously.

ANSWER: FALSE

M6.10 We can find a point of inflection by simply setting the second derivative of the nonlinear function equal to zero and solving.

ANSWER: FALSE

M6.11 The EOQ model is obtained by taking the second derivative of the revenue function.

ANSWER: FALSE

M6.12 To maximize total revenues, one can set the derivative of the total revenue function equal to zero and solve.

ANSWER: TRUE

MULTIPLE CHOICE

M6.13 The derivative of $2x^2 + 2x + 7$ is

(a) $2x + 2$.
(b) $1x + 7$.
(c) $4x + 2$.
(d) $x^2 + 7$.
(e) none of the above

ANSWER: c

M6.14 The derivative of $5x^3 + 3x^2 + 7x + 9$ is

(a) $15X^2 + 6x + 7$.
(b) $6x^2 + 7x + 9$.
(c) $5x^2 + 3x + 7$.
(d) $3x^2 + 2x + 7$.
(e) none of the above

ANSWER: a

M6.15 The derivative of $19x^4 + 2x^3 + 5x^2 + 1x + 9$ is
(a) $19x^3 + 2x^2 + 5x + 1$.
(b) $4x^3 + 3x^2 + 2x + 1$.
(c) $12x^2 + 6x + 9$.
(d) $76x^3 + 6x^2 + 10x + 1$.
(e) none of the above

ANSWER: d

M6.16 The derivative of $\frac{3}{x^5}$ is

(a) $\frac{15}{x^6}$

(b) $-\frac{15}{x^6}$

(c) $\frac{3}{x^4}$

(d) $\frac{15}{x^4}$

(e) none of the above

ANSWER: b

M6.17 The second derivative of $7x^4 + 6x^3 + 5x + 3$ is

(a) $7x^3 + 6x^2 + 5$.
(b) $28x^3 + 18x^2 + 5x + 3$.
(c) $28x^3 + 18x^2 + 5$.
(d) $84x^2 + 36x$.
(e) none of the above

ANSWER: d

M6.18 The critical point for the function $y = 3x^2 + 5x + 2$ is at

(a) x = -5/6.
(b) x = 3/5.
(c) x = -3/2.
(d) there is no critical point
(e) none of the above

ANSWER: a

M6.19 The critical point for the function $y = 7x^2 - 7x + 4$ lies at

(a) x = -1.
(b) x = 1.
(c) x = -1/2.
(d) x = 1/2.
(e) none of the above
ANSWER: d

M6.20 Find the point at which the following function is a maximum: $\frac{x^3}{3} - 2x^2 + 3x + 6$.

(a) x = 3
(b) x = 1
(c) x = 0
(d) x = -3
(e) none of the above

ANSWER: b

M6.21 Find the point at which the following function is a minimum: $y = \frac{x^3}{3} - 2x^2 + 3x + 6$.

(a) x = 3
(b) x = 1
(c) x = 0
(d) x = -3
(e) none of the above

ANSWER: a

M6.22 Find the point at which the following function has an inflection point: $y = \frac{x^3}{3} - 2x^2 + 3x + 6$.

(a) 3
(b) 1
(c) 2
(d) 0
(e) none of the above

ANSWER: c

M6.23 Find the critical point for the function $y = X^3 + 60$. This point is a(n)

(a) maximum.
(b) minimum.
(c) inflection point.
(d) could be any of the above
(e) none of the above

ANSWER: c

M6.24 Profit for the Dew Drop Inn Country Diner is given by $p = -0.1q_2 + 1.80q + 100$, where p is profit and q is the number of customers. What number of customers maximizes profit?

(a) 100
(b) 900
(c) 300
(d) 9
(e) none of the above

ANSWER: d